GROW YOUR OWN PHYSIC GARDEN

GROW YOUR OWN PHYSIC GARDEN

Use the Power of Medicinal Plants Grounded in Science

Elaine Perry, Valerie Laws and Nicolette Perry

Dilston Physic Garden, Dilston, UK
Registered Charity No. 1120141

www.dilstonphysicgarden.com

Published by DPG Publishing
978-1-9163504-0-3

Cover image: Andrey Danilovich

Printed by CPI Antony Rowe Ltd, UK

To Ixtlilton and Patecatl, the Aztec gods of medicine and healing

CONTENTS

PROLOGUE

From Brains to Botanics:
Origins of a Physic Garden

We authors are two scientists, Elaine Perry (Neurochemist and Emeritus Professor, Newcastle University) and Nicolette Perry (Pharmacognosist PhD and Director of Dilston Physic Garden in Northumberland), and one writer (science and poetry), Valerie Laws (Dilston Physic Garden writer-in-residence).

Here is Elaine's perspective on how this book came to be written.

You could call it a brain wave, but not in the usual sense of the word. Dilston Physic Garden began with brains, human brains mostly.

Since the 1970s I have been doing research on what can go wrong with our brain chemicals. Not a plant in sight. But our team made groundbreaking discoveries in the field of Alzheimer's disease and contributed to the development of the drugs, few even today, that help with some of the symptoms.

But something was lacking: patients were only helped for a while. There was no 'wonder drug' to combat dementia. A new direction was needed. And here I confess that the idea of looking to the plant world for solutions came to me after a session of transcendental meditation. It's a technique that promotes relaxed awareness. Long ago, Pythagoras used to insist that his students meditate each morning before their scientific studies. Appropriately, then, I looked back in time for ideas.

As I searched through encyclopaedias of ancient herbal medicine, I was astonished to find that some plants were said to improve memory. The ancient Greeks told their students to wear garlands of rosemary during their exams to help their recall. The question of how to test this knowledge in our strictly scientific lab, where I had just been appointed a professor of neurochemical pathology, was answered by chance. University students enlisted for a summer research project; one was co-author Nicolette.

First results showed that extracts of traditional plants like sage and lemon balm worked on memory mechanisms in a test tube. We could hardly believe it! Only after repeated results did we dare to accept it was a breakthrough. Word spread, scientific papers were published, grants obtained, a new university research centre established … and I acquired an acre of land in the Northumbrian countryside to grow medicinal plants.

Dilston Physic Garden grew as if by chance. At first I worked alone, well-meaning friends insisting nothing would ever grow in such an exposed area. But it did, and wonderful people volunteered to help take the garden forward. So it opened to the public and became a charity for education.

And that is the crux of the matter. Education. Our physic garden's main mission is to spread and support the knowledge that plants can treat conditions and maintain health. Our approach is strictly scientific, assessing folklore remedies through modern lab work and human studies, just as it was in our university research, twenty years after that original breakthrough.

At the same time, the garden attracted inspired artists, sculptors and writers, like co-author Valerie Laws. Working with neuroscientists and pathologists, she became our writer-in-residence at Dilston.

Ancient knowledge is so easily lost and, with it, the chance to rediscover the healing power of plants and discover new medical drugs. Medicinal plant gardens are few and far between, and you may not find yourself near ones like ours in a wild and windy corner of Northumberland. So writing this book provides a new way of spreading the word. Uniquely, ours is a gardening book grounded in science. We tell you how herbs do their healing.

To answer the question of how one academic, accustomed to scientific writing, could create an authoritative, lively book, enjoyable for non-scientists, I recruited Nicolette and Valerie as co-authors. Dr Nicolette Perry, Director of Dilston Physic Garden education and a pharmacognosist (an expert in medicinal compounds of biological origin) has made the book state-of-the-art on plant chemistry and biology. Valerie Laws, one of whose signature poetry installations for the garden is included at the end of the book, has worked to make the text engaging and accessible.

We hope the book excites your interest and inspires enthusiasm for growing your own medicinal plants. It is in three parts: (1) know, (2) grow and (3) use the plants for your health and well-being. The 'know' chapters are about the science of medicinal plants (human and lab studies, as well as chemistry), and look at how medical herbalism compares to evidence-based medicine today and the untapped potential for medicinal plants in the future. The 'grow' chapters contain ideas on how to plan and grow your own physic garden, which of the many safe and effective plant species you can choose from and how to grow and maintain them. In the third 'use' section you will learn how to make safe remedies, how they can help care for the family and animals, and how you can enjoy them as fine food and drink, harmless herbal highs and incense.

This book will excite your interest – enjoy and step out of the pages to grow your own physic garden, even just a border bed or a window box. The more medicinal plants we keep known and grown, the greater the chance we will find new ways to maintain good health and treat currently incurable conditions.

INTRODUCTION

Plant Medicine: Ancient to Modern

'If you have a garden and a library, you have everything you need.'
Marcus Tullius Cicero

'Physic' is the old English word for medicine, what 'physicians' both practise and prescribe. So a physic garden grows plants to make medicines that aid well-being or cure.

For thousands of years, plants have been gathered for use as remedies, but to see how physic gardens came about we must first look back and see how medicines evolved and how medicines and plants are inextricably linked.

Herbal medicines throughout the ages

People used medicinal plants as far back as Palaeolithic times. Dental plaque on human teeth from the Middle East that are over 5,000 years old contains purple nut sedge (*Cyperus rotundus*), used nowadays to treat fevers and digestive disorders. Fossilised faeces from Brazil, thousands of years old, contains high concentrations of pollen from plants with medicinal, antiparasitic worm- and pain-killing properties. Bronze Age burial sites at Fan Foel in Wales show evidence of healing plants, such as meadowsweet, used today for fever and pain.

Traditional Chinese and Ayurvedic (Indian) plant remedies have developed independently of Western medicine. Ancient Chinese silk scrolls found at burial sites contain formulations made up of hundreds of medicinal plants and date back some 5,000 years. When searching for plants for our own physic garden, we can find Asian medicinal plants based on ancient practice.

Wild animals do it

We know that animals, both wild and domestic, self-medicate. They seek out bark and leaves that have no nutritional value, but which control infections and parasites and heal wounds and injuries. This remarkable gift, whether instinctive or learned, has its own jaw-breaking technical term – zoopharmacognosy. It's thought to be instinct, because many wild animals deliberately eat plants that have specific health benefits. When chimpanzees chew leaves of the bitter plant *Vernonia amygdalina* (bitter leaf), which have antiparasitic activity, their infections from parasites like *Plasmodium* (which causes malaria) diminish. African elephants chew leaves from a tree in the Boraginaceae family that appear to induce birth; Kenyan women accordingly brew a tea from the same leaves to induce childbirth. We wondered why our cat, Moth, kept eating horsetail until we discovered that it's good for the gut and his diarrhoea was disappearing. So, do we humans have similar instincts, or have we lost them, just as we have forgotten how to forage for food in the wild?

Written records on medicinal plants stretch back over 2,000 years. The writings of three ancient Greek practitioners of herbal medicine still illuminate our practice of plant medicine today.

HIPPOCRATES HIRACLIDÆ F. COVS.
Ex marmore antiquo.

Hippocrates Asclepiades, the father of medicine who extolled the virtues of plants.

Hippocrates (c. 460–377 BC), instigator of the Hippocratic Oath still sometimes taken by new doctors, stressed that diet, including herbs, formed the foundation of well-being. He separated health and medicine from superstition, and was one of the first Western physicians to use and recommend willow bark to ease childbirth and fever (it later gave us aspirin). His *Hippocratic Corpus*, a collection of seventy writings, is the oldest surviving complete medical text. Dioscorides (AD 40–90), a physician and botanist, wrote *De Materia Medica*, a five-volume encyclopaedia in Latin about herbal medicine, used by doctors for more than 1,500 years. Galen (AD 131–200) was a famous physician and herbalist who first listed common illnesses and their respective herbal remedies.

After the fall of the Roman Empire, the study of medicine moved east, and for the next 1,000 years the Arab world became the centre of scientific progress. Islamic scholars studied Greek and Roman texts. They refined Hippocrates' theories as Islamic physicians prescribed medicinal plants. So the knowledge was not lost during the Dark Ages, and it eventually filtered back to Europe. In the sixteenth and seventeenth centuries, the first physic gardens appeared, and herbal encyclopaedias were written by English herbalists such as John Gerard and Nicholas Culpepper.

Pedanius Dioscorides, the Greek physician whose herbal medicine writings are still referred to today.

Some early writings make fascinating reading. What party-giver could fail to be inspired by John Gerard's comment on borage (*Borago officinalis*): 'The leaves and floures of Borrage put into wine make men and women glad and merry, driving away all sadnesse, dulnesse, and melancholy, as Dioscorides and Pliny affirme.'

The very sight of borage's bright blue star-shaped flowers is enough to cheer you up.

Domestic use of plant medicines

Plant medicine was small-scale for centuries. Though medieval monasteries and convents prescribed, and sometimes grew, plant remedies, part of the housewife's job was to grow medicinal plants as well as food, and it was mainly village 'wise women' who helped local people. By the seventeenth century, professional physicians had largely taken over medicine, and the wise women were persecuted by the Church, which burned many of them at the stake for witchcraft. But families quietly passed down the know-how for growing and using herbal remedies by word of mouth and, later, in handwritten recipes. Some of us still remember our grandmother's potions and remedies – every family had their own 'witch'!

Sourcing herbs from hedgerows or cottage gardens gradually became more difficult as people migrated to the expanding cities. Later, as formal medicine switched to chemical and synthetic drugs, pharmacists stopped selling medicinal plants. But the physic garden remains a fount of knowledge for cultivating and using medical plants.

Old wives tales, magic & science

Why do plants heal? Magic, of course – or so it seemed in the old days. People often thought magic was the explanation. And strangely, sometimes science and 'magic' converge. The myths that have been passed down through the generations, myths that helped people to remember what herbs do, provide us with clues about their use today. For example, St John's wort (*Hypericum perforatum*), said to exorcise devils, is now known to relieve depression, once thought to result from demonic possession.

'Demon Dispeller', a sculpture of St John's wort in the Dilston Physic Garden.

From herbalism to scientific medicine

With the rapid development of biology and chemistry from the Enlightenment onwards, scientists began to look at *how* medicinal plants affected the human body. The history of how drugs from plants were discovered is as colourful as their flowers. It combines ancient wisdom, science, serendipity and human ingenuity. And it suggests potential life-savers in other undiscovered medicinal plants whose secrets are still to be tapped. Here are a few such stories.

The story of foxglove (*Digitalis purpurea*) starts at the end of the eighteenth century. A bright young Scot, Dr William Withering, came across a woman with dropsy (oedema, a sign of heart failure) who improved dramatically after a visit to the local herbalist. On examining the mix of twenty herbs she had been prescribed, Withering suspected that it was the foxglove that caused the improvement. He tested foxglove extracts on patients and, in

1785, published his results as *An Account of the Foxglove, and Some of its Medical Uses*. This book recorded case histories and the best and safest way of using the plant. With this, Withering was the first person to bridge the gap between mainstream and herbal medicine: he proved that an ancient remedy really did work. (However, it was another 100 years before digoxin was identified as the active chemical, and another 100 years after that before we understood exactly how it quiets a racing heartbeat.)

In 1804, Friedrich Sertürner, a twenty-one-year-old apothecary's assistant from Neuhaus, Germany, identified and isolated the active agent in opium poppy seedpods (*Papaver somniferum*) that relieves pain and promotes sleep. He called it morphine after Morpheus, the Greek god of dreams. This discovery started the chemical drugs revolution.

The foxglove plant (*Digitalis purpurea*) that changed the course of Western medicine.

Papaver somniferum, source of the potent painkiller morphine and of the soporific smoke of opium dens.

The opium poppy not only provides the most effective painkiller in medicine today, but it also led us to understand the biology and mechanisms of pain relief. Certain pain-sensitive molecules ('opiate receptors') on the exterior of brain cells detect and grab the morphine, preferring it to the endorphins (our natural brain chemical painkillers). This alters neural network activities, reducing awareness of the pain, and often comes with symptoms such as sedation and euphoria. The modified morphine molecule heroin is a quick-fix euphoric, far more addictive than morphine and potentially fatal.

Staying with euphoria-inducing plants, another story crosses cultures and centuries. When the Incas worked in the Andes creating citadels like Machu Picchu, they chewed coca leaves because they found these boosted their energy at high altitudes and dulled pain. Centuries later, in 1860, German chemist Albert Niemann isolated cocaine from coca leaves, having recognised that this was the active ingredient in the leaves. Sigmund Freud instantly extolled cocaine's virtues for treating depression and impotence. Throughout its subsequent history of use and abuse, chemists continually altered the cocaine molecule to increase its painkilling qualities. After a long series of modified molecules, we now have ropivacaine, the most effective, fast-acting local anaesthetic yet.

From whole plant to individual extracts

The scientific study of herbalism led to modern conventional pharmacology, but with that came another significant change: whereas herbalists usually prepared medicines from the whole plant, mainstream medicine extracts a single chemical (or synthesises it). This paved the way to linking the medical action of a plant to one chemical, and in the nineteenth century chemists started to make new synthetic molecules. Factories took over from herbalists as the producers of medicines, and eventually pharmacies switched to synthetic chemical drugs. Aspirin (acetylsalicylic acid), the most widely used of all medical drugs, was originally extracted from willow bark and, at the end of the nineteenth century, the first plant drug to be patented.

White willow, *Salix alba*, from whose bark is derived the most widely used drug, aspirin.

Today, half of new conventional drugs come directly or indirectly from an ingredient of common plants like snowdrops or foxgloves. So your physic garden can include these often beautiful plants, the unrecognised heroes that give us life-saving drugs.

Other mainstream drugs from plants were discovered as a result of scientific research rather than from traditional use. Galantamine, originally from the bulb of the snowdrop (*Galanthus nivalis*), raises the level of a brain chemical (acetylcholine) that strengthens memory. Alzheimer's disease destroys that chemical, an original finding of three British groups in the 1970s, one of which was ours at Newcastle University. Later, American entrepreneurs patented galantamine, which is now a standard prescription drug for Alzheimer's.

Snowdrop (*Galanthus nivalis*), source of a drug for dementia, portrayed by Dilston artist-in-residence, Pauline Aitken.

Another plant chemical, L-dopa, also emerged from neuroscience. It was isolated in 1913 from the faba broad bean (*Vicia faba*), an old Ayurvedic remedy for Parkinson's disease. Initial tests on mice indicated that the bean did not improve motor function (movement). Later it transpired that the original lab tests were not sensitive enough and that the bean did indeed improve movement. Fifty years on, the absence of the brain signal dopamine was found to be the root cause of Parkinson's disease. L-dopa, which converts to dopamine in the brain, is now the gold-standard treatment for the disease.

Dr Munroe Wall, a US cancer researcher interested in plants, tested hundreds of botanic extracts on tumour cells. His research team found that one from the Pacific yew (*Taxus brevifolia*), killed the cells. The extract contained the chemical paclitaxel (trade name Taxol), which is now a front-line drug treatment for breast, ovarian and prostate cancer. Mass production no longer depends on vast quantities of yew tree cuttings but on growing *Taxus* cells in labs.

For other drugs, plant cell cultures are modified genetically to increase production of the active chemical. Artemisinin, our fastest-acting antimalaria drug that led to a health revolution and a Nobel prize in 2015, was originally produced from sweet wormwood (*Artemisia annua*) but is now grown in genetically engineered yeast cells.

Sweet wormwood (*Artemisia annua*), source of the antimalarial drug artemisinin.

Recently there has been a dramatic increase in scientific papers on medicinal plants. In the 1960s and 70s there were about 500 papers annually; that doubled in the 1980s and 90s, and reached several thousands after the year 2000. Considering that herbal medicine had fallen from favour early last century, this demands explanation. Part of the reason is growing interest in new treatments for diseases like cancer or Alzheimer's. Another likely factor is that the pharmaceutical industry is prospecting for more plant-derived drugs like aspirin and artemisinin. The medical and commercial potential could be vast, with thousands of plants, fungi, algae and bacteria across the globe awaiting investigation. So far, Western medicine uses only a hundred or so drugs derived directly from plants.

Links between ancient folklore, plant magic and modern medicine

Before we embark on our voyage of discovery of plant chemicals and learn how plants are tested in the lab or on people, it's worth noting that we owe 'magicians' of old a great debt. Ancient beliefs in magic that were passed on helped to keep our knowledge of plant medicines alive long enough for today's scientists to follow up on those leads.

So far we have looked at the progression from 'traditional' or 'folk' medicine, which is largely plant-based, to modern conventional medicine, which relies largely on synthetic or single-chemical drugs. In fact, the transition has been neither sudden nor complete: scientific medicine has retrospectively validated many of the 'old wives tales' of folk medicine, and there are many more traditional-medicine plants still to be tested.

The remainder of this chapter describes plants that have been used traditionally, or ones that people believed had magic properties, but these are plants with a difference – their former uses not only match how they are used by herbalists today but they also have modern scientific backing. In gathering great 'tales' that translate into modern medicinal uses of plants, we identified some fascinating examples (see the table below). Some links are tenuous and depend on interpreting the meaning of old words in the context of modern medical terms. What, we might wonder, did the Druids mean when they said that hawthorn, one of today's best herbal medicines for heart disease, 'opened the heart'? They knew nothing about how heart muscles contract and how the plant contains a chemical to help the process. But today we know its flavonoids help the heart muscle to contract and regulate its beat.

Then there is the story about elecampane (*Inula helenium*), which always intrigues children who visit our physic garden and helps them take an interest in herb medicine. A common diagnosis long ago was 'elfshot', which may have been ME (myalgic encephalomyelitis or chronic fatigue syndrome). This is a disorder of the immune system, and elecampane, also called elfwort, is now established as an immune system booster that treats colds and flu just as well as echinacea. Plants like these could have been lost to medicine if such stories had not been told and passed down the generations.

Function suggested by form

In the sixteenth century, Paracelsus, building on the writings of Dioscorides and Galen, taught the 'doctrine of signatures' – that God shows us how to use plant cures by making the herbs resemble the shape of the parts of the body they can be used to treat. Oddly enough, this sometimes holds true! The spotted leaves of lungwort (*Pulmonaria officinalis*) supposedly resemble lung tissue; they are used by herbalists for pulmonary disorders. The tubers of lesser celandine (*Ficaria verna*), or 'pilewort', are pile-shaped; they relieve haemorrhoids. Walnuts (*Juglans*) look like human brains; they contain so much omega 3 they are indeed brain boosters. The sinister glint on belladonna berries reminds us that they enhanced a lady's beauty as eye drops which dilated her pupils; although *Atropa belladonna* (deadly nightshade) is poisonous, the active chemical atropine is still used in ophthalmology today.

Sinister-looking, deadly poisonous berries of *Atropa belladonna*.

From plant magic to medicine

PLANT	THE STORY Magic or folklore	THE FACTS Modern medical & scientific evidence
Angelica (European) (*Angelica archangelica*)	In a dream, an archangel held out a plant, at the time called wild celery, to a medieval monk who then used it to help cure the plague	Essential oil of angelica contains antibiotic chemicals and insecticides, which could have reduced the fleas on the rats and the bacteria carried by the fleas that caused the plague.
Apple (*Malus domestica*)	'An apple a day keeps the doctor away'	Regularly eating apples (containing flavonoids) is proven to reduce the risk of various cancers.
Belladonna (*Atropa belladonna*)	Italian women used to apply berries to their eyes to make them appear more beautiful	Contains atropine, which at low doses stops the pupil contracting, so enlarging the pupil and eye brightness.
Bramble / blackberry (*Rubus fruticosus*)	A child passed through the roots would be cured of cough	Antimicrobial, including antiviral activities in berries.
Cannabis (*Cannabis sativa*)	Believed to have been given by the gods for delight and courage	Releases dopamine (the brain's pleasure signal) and has neuroprotective and anticancer effects.
Coca (*Erythroxylum coca*)	Used by the Incas to increase energy and dull the pain of walking on bare feet (e.g. during the building of the citadel at Machu Picchu)	Cocaine in coca leaves increases noradrenaline (the fight or flight hormone) and works as a painkiller on brain molecules and opiate receptors.
Datura / thorn apple (*Datura stramonium*)	Used by native Americans in rite-of-passage rituals for the young so they can meet their spirit guides	Contains a powerful hallucinogen, which blocks a brain signal (acetylcholine), and induces visions of people and animals.
Elder (*Sambucus nigra*)	It was said that the witch living in the tree would hurt anyone who cut the tree down	Green parts of the plant are poisonous, containing toxic chemicals (cyanogenic glycosides), so only use the flowers and fruits.
Elecampane / elfwort (*Inula helenium*)	Protection against elfshot, a condition in Anglo-Saxon times believed to be due to arrows from invisible elves	The Anglo-Saxon disease may have been chronic fatigue syndrome; the herb boosts the immune system.
Garlic (*Allium sativum*)	Protected the house against all forms of evil, material or spiritual	The bulb is a potent antibiotic due to the action of its main chemical, allicin.

PLANT	THE STORY Magic or folklore	THE FACTS Modern medical & scientific evidence
Ginseng (*Panax*)	The Chinese believe this plant is the essence of the earth in the form of a man, curing sickness and rejuvenating the aged	Multiple proven health benefits of the root include: protecting heart and nerve cells; lowering blood sugar and cholesterol; anticancer; and antistress.
Hawthorn (*Crataegus*)	Used by the Druids to open the heart, hawthorn was given to the aged as a tonic against weakness	Leaves and flowers are used by herbalists today for heart conditions. Clinical trial evidence for treating heart arrhythmias and high blood pressure.
Henbane (*Hyoscyamus niger*)	The priestess at Delphi was believed to have inhaled fumes of the smoking plant to help prophesy	Contains the chemical atropine, which can induce hallucinations and expanded consciousness.
Juniper (*Juniperus communis*)	Protective bush under which Jesus was said to be hidden for safety during his flight to Egypt	Antimicrobial activities in juniper essential oil.
Lettuce (*Lactuca sativa*)	Venus threw herself on a bed of lettuce after Adonis' death to cool her desire	Wild lettuce latex promotes sleep due to chemicals that differ from morphine derived from the opium poppy.
Mandrake (*Mandragora officinarum*)	Used as an anaesthetic for surgery in the ancient Roman army	Contains alkaloids (like atropine and hyoscyamine), which are pain-relieving and sleep-inducing.
Mugwort (*Artemisia vulgaris*)	Also known as the witches herb, mugwort was used in ancient druid rituals to induce spiritual states of mind	Induces lucid dreaming, a state of being asleep but aware of, and able to control, dreams.
Rosemary (*Rosmarinus officinalis*)	Shakespeare (a neighbour of herbalist John Gerard) has the character of Ophelia (*Hamlet*) talking about rosemary for remembrance. Plant used for remembrance at weddings and funerals	In controlled clinical trials, the essential oil has been shown to enhance memory function.
Rowan, mountain ash (*Sorbus*)	In Christian belief, the red berries were a sign of life blood and protection	Berries have antioxidant and anti-inflammatory activities.
Skullcap (*Scutellaria*)	Seed heads resemble skulls, so, according to the doctrine of signatures, the plant will be good for the head	Herb extracts are effective in clinical trials as an antidepressant, and have anti-anxiety effects in lab models.

PLANT	THE STORY Magic or folklore	THE FACTS Modern medical & scientific evidence
Snowdrop (*Galanthus nivalis*)	Protected Odysseus and his men from Circe's poisons, which may have included belladonna. It being an hallucinogenic may account for the story that it turned the men into wild animals	Contains the alkaloid galantamine, which raises the level of the brain signal (acetylcholine), and so counters the effects of atropine in the belladonna. Now used to treat Alzheimer's disease.
St John's wort (*Hypericum perforatum*)	Dispelled demons and evil spirits, which were believed to possess and drive people mad	Extracts are antidepressant, as effective as drugs like Prozac, for people with mild to moderate depression.
Walnut (*Juglans*)	Shaped like the human brain, indicating application for mental conditions	Proven to enhance cognitive function; high in omega 3 and folate, which protect heart and brain.
Wolfsbane (*Aconitum*)	Also known as the devil's helmet; used as an ointment to turn people into werewolves	Leaves induce tingling sensations on the skin that can feel like growing hairs.
Wormwood (*Artemisia absinthium*)	Absinthe, the alcoholic spirit made from wormwood, was known in the nineteenth century as the green fairy. It induced a free state of mind, inspiring some poets and artists, and driving others mad	The chemical thujone, claimed to be hallucinogenic, has potent effects on the nervous system, including inducing convulsions.
Yarrow (*Achillea millefolium*)	Named after Achilles who used the plant for his wounds	Extracts are anti-inflammatory and wound- healing; effects clinically verified.
Yew (*Taxus*)	Celebrated as the tree of life by pagans	Yew leaves contain paclitaxel, a potent anticancer drug.

The next chapters of the book (which comprise Part I) deal with the science of medicinal plants in further detail. If you are primarily interested in the horticultural aspects of physic gardens, you could skip straight to Part II on first reading. We hope that the idea of growing 'evidence-based' medicinal plants will tempt you to discover more about the fascinating health-giving chemicals that plants make and learn about the gold-standard methods that medical scientists use to decide if the plants actually work just as those old herbalists and magicians said.

PART ONE
KNOW

The Science of
Medicinal Plants

1

Plant Chemistry

If medicinal plants are to move back into the mainstream and be used effectively and safely, traditional evidence has to be supported by modern science. That is the maxim we apply to our research and the physic garden we founded. So in this chapter we take you into human biology, plant ingredients and how they enhance our health.

Plants contain a host of ingredients of all shapes, sizes, colours, flavours and aromas that affect human and animal health. But why would plants evolve chemicals that can affect us beyond just being nourishing? When we've answered that, we can go on to consider how plant chemicals work their magic to keep us healthy (or poison us!).

The chemicals that plants produce are broadly divided into two classes, primary metabolites and secondary metabolites.

Primary metabolites are chemicals like carbohydrates and proteins that help the plant grow, photosynthesise and set seed, keeping it alive and functioning on a day-to-day basis.

Secondary metabolites, the ingredients of interest for health and medicine, are chemicals like flavonoids, polyphenols, terpenes and alkaloids that promote propagation or protect the plant against environmental threats. These phyto (meaning 'plant') chemicals deter predators, competitors, insects, fungi, bacteria and viruses, while others attract pollinators, serve as communicators between plants and act as preventative medicines for the plant, thereby preventing inflammation, free radical, cancer and UV damage. At the right dose, certain phytochemicals are health-giving, protective or medicinal for humans too.

Plant chemicals benefit human health

Plant and animal cells have much in common (nuclei, cytoplasm, mitochondria), which explains why what's good for the plant in the way of a phytochemical may well be good for the animal. As for the arsenal of plant chemicals that deter or poison us and other animals, it is a matter of dose (to get the dose of foxglove leaves right for the human heart and avoid digitalis poisoning, the pharmacist of old checked each batch on luckless pigeons). Beyond these obvious explanations of why we benefit from plant chemicals, there are fascinating Darwinian ideas about plant–animal co-evolution: plants adapting chemicals that people value in order to promote their own survival (cultivation), or fine-tuning chemicals to attract the best pollinating insects. Addictive or psychedelic plant chemicals come to mind!

Health-giving phytochemicals are central to the benefits of the five-a-day portions of fruit and vegetables promoted by our institutions. And phytochemicals explain why homegrown produce tastes better than supermarket vegetables. It's not our imagination. Streetwise homegrown carrots are full of fight and flavour because they have to produce chemicals to attract pollinators and defend themselves against attack from insects, fungi and bacteria, all of which requires many different flavoursome, health-giving plant chemicals. In contrast, polytunnel carrots usually have an easy life in an environment where their few threats are taken care of by externally applied fungicides, herbicides and pesticides. It doesn't have to produce as many chemicals for defence, or even for propagation if it's pollinated by hand.

With around half a million flowering plants on earth, there are hundreds of thousands of bioactive chemicals, with more yet to be discovered (and that's excluding those in the animal, fungi and marine worlds). These form a botanical pharmacopoeia, a 'library' of potential medicines for us to explore for individual drugs or for whole-plant extracts which contain the multiple chemicals ('multi-drugs') used by medical herbalists.

Take just one plant family as an example. The mints (Labiatae) has 240 subgroups, and just one subgroup alone, the sages (*Salvia*), can contain over 700 individual species. In turn, just one species of sage such as *Salvia officinalis* (common sage) can contain over 200 different plant chemicals. So you can see that the potential number of bioactive chemicals from plants is truly astounding.

A further subtlety in plant ingredients is that plants in the same subgroup don't necessarily contain the same chemicals. In fact many plants in the same genus can each contain very different chemicals. Moreover, the mix of chemicals within a single plant doesn't stay constant – proportions of a particular chemical can change from 1% to 40% depending on the environment, the needs of the plant, the season and even the time of day.

So there remains much to be discovered: more plant chemicals, how they work, and learning their science and medicinal powers. More and more scientists worldwide are investigating plant chemicals as a way to maintain human health and treat disease. You too can be part of this crucial resurgence, growing and using your own physic garden plants.

Plant ingredients that affect mind and body

Some of this amazing array of plant chemicals have a powerful and protective effect on our body and brain. They are active compounds – 'active' as they cause biological changes in our body, and 'compounds' as they're made by the plant from atoms of carbon and hydrogen, with oxygen, nitrogen or occasional sulphur atoms added on. The aroma, taste and colour of plants is determined by how these atoms are put together to form each chemical. For example, the distinct taste and smell of cabbage and other brassicas is produced by nitrogen and sulphur atoms in a bowl-shaped molecule with a side chain (called glucosinolates). They protect cruciferous vegetables, such as young broccoli plants, from predators, but they have also been studied over the last three decades for their key cancer preventative effects in humans.

It's the exact structure of plant ingredients – how each atom is aligned, whether in a long chain, or in a ring, or in linked rings – that determines how it will affect you. Whether a plant molecule stops an enzyme working, switches on a brain signal, gets broken down in the gut or transformed by the liver into a more active molecule, or even whether it passes through you unchanged, is all determined by the molecule's shape and size. Each different molecule can cause different reactions in the body, and some work together to produce their effect. For example, plant ingredients can dilate veins to increase blood flow, dull nerves to pain, boost the brain's calming signal, increase or slow the heart rate and even stop the production of tumour cells. Many of these plant chemicals work to prevent something, like cancer, inflammation, free radical damage or bacteria. Using the prefix 'anti-' (meaning 'against' or 'opposite'), there are plant ingredients that are anticancer, anti-inflammatory, antioxidant, antibacterial, antiviral, antifungal, anti-anxiety.

Let's meet some of the plant chemicals that are of vital importance for our health and as medicines.

Medicinally useful plant ingredients

Asked to name some plant ingredients, you might choose capsaicin in chillies (*Capsicum*), which lowers inflammation and pain, curcumin in turmeric, which is anti-inflammatory, or catechins in tea (*Camellia sinensis*), which are antioxidant. Or you might choose caffeine in coffee, tea and chocolate, or nicotine in the tobacco plant (*Nicotiana tabacum*) which are both stimulants. All are useful and affect us in different ways.

To help understand how these chemicals work they are classed according to their shape, because similarly structured compounds usually have similar, but not identical, biological effects on the body. For example, *steroids* are four-ringed molecules with particular atoms added on to the rings that lead to families of steroids with specific physiological functions. Here are a half dozen of the most interesting families of phytochemicals.

Main classes of bioactive plant chemicals

Class	Main subclass	Example chemical and plant containing it	Action of example chemical
alkaloids	pyridine, quinoline, isoquinoline, tropane, quinolizidine, pyrrolizidine, indole, steroidal, alkaoidal amines, purine, amino acids, lectins	caffeine coffee (*Coffea arabica*)	stimulant
		morphine opium poppy (*Papaver somniferum*)	narcotic, analgesic, hypnotic
		vinblastine Madagascar periwinkle (*Catharanthus roseus*)	antileukaemic
		reserpine Indian snakeroot (*Rauwolfia serpentina*)	hypotensive, sedative, tranquillising
		mescaline peyote cactus (*Lophophora williamsii*)	hallucinogenic
		strychnine strychnine tree (*Strychnos species*)	poison
glycosides (can be phenol, quinine, terpene and steroid)	anthraquinones, cardiac, cyanogenic, glucosinolates, iridoid, phenylpropanoid	oleandrin dogbane (*Nerium oleander*)	cardioprotective, cytotoxic effect
		amygdalin almond (*Prunus dulcis*)	toxic (bitter principle in almonds)
phenols	coumarin, quinone, phenolic, phenylpropanoid, salicin, salicylate, stilbene	curcumin turmeric (*Curcuma longa*)	anti-inflammatory, cognitive-enhancing
		salicin willow (*Salix species*)	analgesic, anti-inflammatory
polyphenols	anthocyanin, flavonoid subgroups, lignan, tannin, catechins	apigenin German chamomile (*Chamomilla recutita*)	anti-anxiety, antioxidant, anti-inflammatory, anticancer, neuroprotective
terpenes	monoterpene, di-, sesqui-, tetra-	1,8-cineole common sage (*Salvia officinalis*)	Boosts brain's memory signal (acetylcholine) (action similar to anti-Alzheimer's drug galantamine)
		menthol peppermint (*Mentha x piperita*)	antispasmodic, used for irritable bowel syndrome
		Taxol yew tree (*Taxus brevifolia*)	cervical and breast cancer
triterpenes and saponins	phytosterols, saponins, cardiac glycosides	digoxin foxglove (*Digitalis purpurea*)	heart conditions
fixed oils and alkamides	omega-3, essential fatty acids, alkamides	linoleic acid sunflower (*Helianthus*)	cholesterol metabolism, inflammatory processes
polysaccharides	gum, mucilage, pectin	inulin elecampane (*Inula helenium*)	blood sugar stabilising

Alkaloids: affecting the nervous system

The large alkaloid family contains many of the well-known drugs in the medical world, some recreational drugs, some common stimulants in everyday foods, along with many more drugs that are very toxic. Caffeine, nicotine, codeine and cocaine are all alkaloids. Alkaloid molecules contain a nitrogen atom, their names all end in 'ine' (caffeine for example), and broadly speaking they make up one of three main groups of plant ingredients (secondary metabolites), phenols and terpenes being the other two. Alkaloids are generally colourless solids derived mostly from amino acids, the building blocks of proteins.

Only around one in five flowering plants contain alkaloids, including the poppy family (*Papaveraceae*) and the tomato family (*Solanaceae*). Alkaloids have been much studied, used and abused. Over 10,000 alkaloids have been identified from over 300 plant families. Many are very toxic, causing hallucinations, loss of coordination, vomiting, convulsions and death. Coniine

Piperine in the pepper plant is being investigated for anti-asthmatic and anti-ulcer activities.

Alkaloids at home

The more domestic alkaloids include the spicy, tongue-tingling piperine in pepper (*Piper nigrum* and *Piper longum*), and quinine, the antimalarial from Peruvian *Cinchona* bark, which is the bitter ingredient in tonic water. Tonic water was originally produced in colonial India to prevent malaria – the quinine kills the parasite that carries the disease. Tonic water today has less quinine than before, but its bitterness is still an essential part of a good gin and tonic.

Caffeine, the world's most widely used psychoactive chemical, found in everyday drinks.

in spotted hemlock (*Conium maculatum*), for example, causes death by paralysis and was the chosen method of execution in Ancient Greece. Socrates was its most famous victim. Curare, from the tropical curare vine (*Chondrodendron tomentosum*), is used in the Amazon as an arrow poison causing similar effects to coniine. Still others are cutting-edge medicines such as vinblastine from the Madagascar periwinkle (*Catharanthus roseus*), used as an antileukaemic.

Alkaloids can have powerful – even drastic – effects, predominantly on the nervous system.

They interfere with it in two ways: either by blocking molecules (receptors) on nerve cells that normally respond to (transmitter) signals, or by blocking enzymes that control the level of these signals. These effects deter predators from ever eating the plant again after a first nibble, and it's no coincidence that many plants which contain alkaloids also have attractive seed pods or tubers – their chemicals keep predators at bay in spite of attractive appearances aimed at propagators.

The opium poppy is the source of morphine, which is our best pain reliever in medicine. However, the poppy latex contains over forty other alkaloids, only 10% of which is morphine. The closely related Iranian poppy (*Papaver bracteatum*) is the source of another popular painkiller, codeine.

One of the largest groups of alkaloids, known as indole alkaloids, are two-ring molecules that plants make from amino acids. They are found in psilocybin, 'magic' mushrooms, and the mood-boosting tryptophan that you get from bananas is also based on an indole alkaloid. Tryptophan works by increasing the production of serotonin, which is calming and mood-boosting.

These indole alkaloids form the basis of several pharmaceutical drugs, including reserpine from the Indian and East Asian *Rauwolfia serpentina* used to treat hypertension and psychosis, and physostigmine from the Nigerian calabar bean (*Physostigma venenosum*), used to treat glaucoma. Both are limited in use because of their adverse effects. But also included in the indole alkaloid group are some poisons such as strychnine, which causes convulsions, disproving the myth that anything 'natural' is, by definition, good and health-giving.

Nicotine usually has less drastic effects than strychnine, but it's still a fatal poison in quantity. Surprisingly to many, it occurs in a variety of plants of the Solanaceae family other than tobacco, like tomatoes and potatoes, and even in mosses. Nicotine is made from nicotinic acid, otherwise known as vitamin B3, which is widespread in the plant kingdom.

Codeine from a chemical in the Iranian poppy (the alkaloid thebaine) provides relief from mild to moderate pain.

Alkamides: hot and spicy

Capsicums, the bell pepper family, contain alkamides. Alkamides also contain nitrogen atoms and are present in a large number of medicinal plants. They have a pungent taste; for example, the alkamide capsaicin produces the hot numbing effect of eating chillies, and because of this numbing action, chillies can be used to manage toothache. Capsaicin also decreases inflammation, oxidation, microbes and viruses, as well as protects DNA from carcinogens.

Polyphenols: the aroma, taste and colour of our food

One of the largest and most important groups of plant secondary metabolites is the phenols (from the Greek *phaino*, to shine). A phenol molecule has a simple ring of hydrocarbon linked to hydrogen and oxygen atoms. In chemistry, this ring structure is called aromatic because the molecules first found to contain it had distinctive odours. Phenols are alcohols found in nearly all families of plants. Plants create them to defend against environmental stress and to protect from UV radiation, infection, bacteria and parasites. But we humans use them in the food industry as flavourings, colouring agents, aromatics and antioxidants.

There are around eight groups of phenols that are of pharmaceutical interest, ranging from the simple to more complex polyphenols like lignans, tannins and flavonoids. The simpler phenols include caffeic acid, the phenolic acid in tea, coffee and chocolate. Caffeic acid is anti-inflammatory and tranquillising and promotes efficient intestinal action. Salicylates (the source of aspirin) are also simple phenols, and plants containing salicylic acid, like willow, have a long history of use for relief of pain and inflammation.

Curcumin is another simple but famous phenol since it's one of four colourful curcuminoids in turmeric. It is the yellow pigment responsible for the turmeric root's anti-inflammatory, antioxidant, anticancer and new-blood-vessel-forming properties. You might think it had only recently been discovered as a remedy, but China has been producing medicinal curcumin commercially for the past twenty years.

Camellia japonica, closely related to the *Camellia sinensis* tea plant, also makes good tea.

Another in the phenol group, not to be confused with curcumin, are the coumarins. First isolated from the coumarou or tonquin bean, they have the familiar odour of cut grass, used in perfumes. Coumarins have anti-inflammatory, fungicidal, antimicrobial and anticancer effects. They used to be described as blood-thinning, since cattle fed sweet clover (which contains 0.4% coumarins) develop a bleeding disease. But this was due to bacterial action on the damaged hay they were fed, which turned coumarins into dicoumarol, a slow onset anticoagulant. From dicoumarol the powerful and more complex phenol warfarin was developed. This is used as a blood-thinning drug to treat blood clots and prevent stroke. It's also used as a rat poison, while a warfarin-like chemical occurs in dying ragweed which is dangerous to horses and cows that eat it.

Crystallised angelica is a sweet green confection used to decorate cakes. In fact, the angelicas (*Angelica archangelica* in Europe; *Angelica atropurpurea* in North America and a number of species in China) contain furanocoumarins, such as archangelicin, that are reported to have powerful coronary vasodilator (blood-vessel-dilating) effects, and to lower blood pressure. (They relax blood vessel walls by blocking calcium from entering the cells). In plant medicine, angelica root is traditionally used for bronchitis associated with vascular deficiency.

Rosemary (*Rosmarinus officinalis*) contains rosmarinic acid, a phenolic ester (a phenol with a bit on the side). It's widespread in the plant kingdom, especially in plants of the Labiatae family, of which rosemary and sage are members, and widely investigated as cell-protecting, antidepressant, antioxidant, anti-inflammatory and skin anti-ageing.

Lignans are more complex phenols, familiar as a major source of the phytoestrogens present in pulses and grains. Lignans have oestrogenic, antitumour and antioxidant properties.

Tannins and flavonoids: tea, berries and autumn leaves

Other larger phenols, the polyphenols ('poly' because they have more than one ring in their molecular structure), are also known for their antioxidant and anti-inflammatory effects. Widely studied for their health benefits, they include the tannins and flavonoids.

The astringent sensation you get from wine and chocolate comes from tannins. Another tannin in all those black and green teas is epigallocatechin, a powerful antioxidant. Beware though: tannins can reduce absorption of other nutrients such as proteins and iron. However, they have their uses in cases of heart disease, preventing bleeding, reducing inflammation and relieving diarrhoea.

The Japanese regard fried autumn maple leaves (*Acer*) as a delicacy, rich in flavonoid-related anthocyanin and carotenoid chemicals.

The polyphenol group you'll certainly have heard of for their health properties, the flavonoids, are also responsible for autumnal leaf colour alongside the carotenoid terpenes. Like tannins, many plants contain them as they make red and yellow coloured flowers and leaves, and are in many fruits and vegetables. Apparently, we each consume on average 1g of flavonoids per day in our fruit and vegetables. The flavonoid-related anthocyanins are responsible for the red, blue and black colours of raspberries, grapes and blueberries.

Flavonoids protect the plant from UV radiation, are antioxidant, and have other roles in energy transfer, hormones and growth. They're the white blood cells of the plant world, and they increase when a plant is injured. There is evidence to prove their antioxidant, antiviral, liver-protecting, anti-inflammatory and blood pressure-lowering actions in humans. Apigenin, one of the most famous flavonoids, is in chamomile tea, which has anti-anxiety and sedative effects. The subgroup isoflavones, which include genistein, are also oestrogenic and well known for their presence in soya milk products.

Glycosides: sweet ingredients

The glycosides are another major plant secondary metabolite chemical group. They contain a sugar add-on, attached to the active part of the molecule. This is significant because they are inactive until they are broken down in the bowel, so they can have a planned, delayed reaction. Plants store some chemicals as inactive glycosides. They're a fairly widespread group, and are found not only in seeds of pulses and in flowers, but also in shoots and tubers (like potatoes). A number are toxic, although cooking removes the toxicity.

The cardiac group of glycosides are important medicinally and used in the treatment of congestive heart failure and arrhythmia. Foxglove leaves contain glycosides like digoxin. This slows and strengthens the heartbeat and is still widely used in Western medicine. In Chinese traditional medicine, *Nerium oleander* is proven to be cardioprotective and cytotoxic (cell-destroying), which again is good in some circumstances. It contains oleandrin, a toxic cardiac glycoside also investigated for its use in cancer treatment. Cyanogenic glycosides like prussic acid, the cyanide so beloved of crime and spy fiction, are also significantly toxic. The glycoside group also includes members such as echinacoside, found in *Echinacea angustifolia*. Widely used for its antibiotic and antiviral properties, echinacea is one of the accepted plant medicines found on supermarket shelves.

Terpenes: the aromas of plants

Finally, meet one of our physic garden favourites, and one of the most important biologically active phytochemical groups, the terpenes. Many terpenes are responsible for the scents of plants and, like other plant chemical classes, they're split into groups according to size. Mostly just molecules containing carbon and hydrogen atoms, they have oxygen atoms added on in various ways that determines their individual biological effects. Some are ring-shaped and others are open chains, and with an estimated 20,000+ known structures, they are an imposing and diverse group – from carotenoids to cucumeroids – and are just as diverse in their bioactivities.

The smallest and most common terpenes are the monoterpenes (terpenes are named after the number of their chemical building blocks, 'mono' for one, and so on). Monoterpenes are responsible for the familiar scent of common culinary and medicinal herbs such as sage and lavender. The familiar Christmas tree smell of pine is due to a pinene, a volatile chemical that is disinfectant, antiviral, antibiotic, anti-inflammatory, insect repellent and works in the human brain to boost memory. Being volatile, some monoterpenes help plants attract pollinators, and the plants increase production of these in the midday sun; plants also communicate with each other. Monoterpenes are important commercially and are used in flavouring and perfumes, but they are also of growing interest in science because, being small and oil-loving, they easily cross the blood–brain barrier to work on our brains. They're the major ingredient of essential oils.

Another group present in essential oils, the sesquiterpenes ('sequi' meaning 'one and a half'), are responsible for the base-note scents of plant aromas. Sesquiterpenes also possess antitumour, antileukaemic, cell-destroying and antibacterial powers. They include the antimalarial artemisinin from sweet wormwood (*Artemisia annua*) mentioned earlier.

The next size up in the terpene group are the diterpenes (only a few are found in essential oils), which include tree resin acids (such as in turpentine). They often taste bitter and many are antibacterial and anti-inflammatory. Taxol, the anticancer medicine from yew, is a diterpene.

Scots pine (*Pinus sylvestris*), the longest-lived tree in the Caledonian forest, contains chemicals that are antiseptic and also boost memory.

Another diverse terpene group, the triterpenes, include the saponins, which produce the soap-like effects in many plants such as soapwort. Saponins have detergent, wound-healing and anti-inflammatory effects. They are widely used in the cosmetic and pharmaceutical industry.

One last terpene group worth a mention is the largest group, the tetraterpenes. These include the colourful carotenoids, occurring widely in plants (and animals) and familiar to us as the red, orange and yellow pigments in vegetables and fruits. They participate in photosynthesis, the process in which plants make sugar using sunlight. Citraurin gives the orange in tomatoes, while the red in tomatoes is from lycopene, a chemical that, along with other carotenoids, is studied for antioxidant and anticancer effects. The most famous carotenoid is beta-carotene from carrots, which converts to vitamin A in our digestive system. Vitamin A deficiency causes night-blindness, and carrots have traditionally been said to help night vision.

Squeeze a few soapwort leaves (*Saponaria officinalis*) to feel one of nature's gentlest detergents.

These various plant ingredients we've described are only a few examples from the half a million or so that exist. There are at least fifty other major chemical classes and subclasses, (summarised in the chart), which gives an idea of the numbers of pharmaceutically relevant chemicals in plants. While the same chemicals can occur in many different plants, we've highlighted only those that contain a large amount of the chemical (where they play a key role in the plant's survival), and that have biological effects relevant to health. Bear in mind that the actions listed under the heading 'Action' are just a few examples from hundreds.

This chapter about the chemical ingredients of plants helps to explain how plant medicines work. When plants are used as traditional medicines it's the whole plant that is used, and many of its chemicals – often acting synergistically – produce an effect. In order to confirm the traditional medical herbalist's use of a plant, the whole plant extract has to be tested and subjected to scientific analysis in lab tests and in human studies. The science is more complex than for single drugs, but the testing procedures for plant extracts are the same as for drugs.

Testing in clinical trials is an exciting new area for medicinal plants (the last half century of their long history). As this book is grounded in science, testing is explained in the next chapter in a way that will allow you to assess the evidence yourself.

2

Testing and Approving
Herbal Medicines

What the herbalist knows about a plant as a medicine, based on hundreds or thousands of years' use, is the cue for the scientist. The first step in investigating a traditionally used plant medicine is usually biological research to see what the plant does. Scientists test potential drugs on cell-lines in animal or human tissue slices isolated in test-tubes ('in vitro'), or on live mice or other animals ('in vivo'). On humans, they use blood samples and cutting-edge imaging scanners to detect changes in our body functions, as well as assessement scales that detect changes in physical or mental states.

While the results from test-tube or animal studies in the lab can be impressive, the gold standard is clinical evidence from trials (drugs or plants) on humans. The 1980s and 1990s brought a flurry of reports on controlled clinical trials on plant medicines: St John's wort (*Hypericum perforatum*) *did* help mild depression, and ginkgo (*Ginkgo biloba*) *did* improve memory. More and more, researchers in labs are studying other traditional medicinal plants to determine whether and how they work. Plant medicine is moving from village kitchen to laboratory, funded by medical research councils or charities combating diseases like cancer.

Although the ethics of animal research in general are controversial, there are some reassuring factors. First, it helps to know that animal-based research has undeniably improved the quality and length of many of our lives (Americans For Medical Progress (www.amprogress.org/) lists benefits that have flowed from such research). Second, the laboratory testing of, specifically, traditional plant medicines that have already been taken by humans for centuries is a fairly benign process. The animals used to test plants are usually laboratory mice or rats. Any reservations we had about enlisting them for our university research were relieved by the animal house technician who always had time to play with his white mice, which all lived longer than those in nearby research centres or even in the wild. Other animals exposed to plant extracts include zebrafish, which are,

A plant sign at Dilston Physic Garden that bamboozles visitors with 'in vitro' and 'in vivo', the scientific terms for lab ('test tube') and 'animal model' tests.

surprisingly, genetically similar to humans and less sensitive to stress. Nematode worms or fruit flies are widely used to study protective anti-ageing plant substances. It turns out that curcumin and a chemical found in many essential oils called beta-caryophyllene can actually prolong their lives, even in the face of stress or toxins.

Three stages of testing

There are three stages for testing whether a plant medicine (or medical drug) works and is safe.

1. Open-label trial. A small number of volunteers are tested to confirm that the plant medicine has no major side effects and to see whether the volunteers respond in the desired way. Both volunteers and researchers know that the real treatment is being used.

If the open-label trial is successful, the next step is …

2. Randomised, double-blind controlled trial. Some volunteers are given the real treatment, others a harmless, ineffective lookalike – a placebo. Neither patients nor researchers know who gets what, which ensures that if someone feels better, it's not simply because they are taking a pill (the placebo effect).

If the results of a controlled trial are promising, other researchers repeat the trials on other volunteers. As more of these trials are completed, scientists then scrutinise the findings to combine the best-run trials to form a …

3. Meta-analysis. Results of these independent trials are analysed together (pooled) to give an overall picture of effects on different people at different times and places. 'Meta' means 'beyond' or 'after', and a meta-analysis provides sound statistics on all preceding studies. The end result indicates whether positive outcomes are due to the remedy alone, or whether there is some confounding variable interfering with the result.

Sometimes, the results of just one or two trials are leaked to the media before proper meta-analyses have been undertaken, perhaps to encourage further research funding. This often leads to false hopes for patients suffering from the condition being studied because the effect of a plant or drug isn't considered to be truly backed by robust scientific evidence until the combined results of tests on hundreds or, more often, thousands of subjects confirm it.

A complication can arise with meta-analyses. The results of early analyses, which are based on a smaller number of trials, can be contradicted by later analyses which are based on more trials. Outcomes in different populations can vary too. For example, a Cochrane review (2008) indicated that St John's wort works better as an antidepressant in people in Germany compared to other countries. (No reason for this national difference was apparent.) In initial trials, *Ginkgo biloba* was considered to be the plant 'saviour' for dementia, but later meta-analyses varied in outcome, some being negative. A 2014 meta-analysis then identified positive results only for people on higher doses.

The value of controlling trials

The word 'placebo' comes from the Latin 'I shall please'. In medical trials, the 'placebo effect' means that if you *think* something is going to do you good, it probably will. This mind-over-matter effect has now been detected in the human brain using imaging in people being tested. And expectations extend beyond the person being tested to people round about – hopeful doctors, nurses or carers. So a double-blind control means that neither the person being tested nor the expert assessing the outcome is aware of who's on the test agent or on the placebo. A single-blind study is valuable too, but only the person being tested is 'blind' to the test or placebo option. This means experimenters' expectations that the pill will work (or not) could affect the outcome. For double-blind, the gold standard is the randomised controlled trial or RCT – people are allocated to the test or placebo group by chance alone, which means that there are no concerns about any bias in group selection. So if you delve into the scientific literature on medicinal plants, pay particular attention to trials that are RCT as these are the most reliable.

Obtaining reliable information about plant medicines

The media is so full of conflicting, often sensational, headlines on the effects of drugs or plant medicines that you could be excused for ignoring the whole lot. One day it's claimed that red wine does protect the heart, the next day that it doesn't. One glass of wine can threaten a pregnancy, yet drinking champagne can prevent Alzheimer's – or so anyone might think from reading social media. Currently, according to medical authorities in the UK, everyone over the age of forty should take statins. Yet other authorities say none of us should risk the sometimes lasting and severe side effects of taking statins. When you want to decide which medicinal plants are safe and effective, how do you find out the truth behind the headlines? The following two sections explain. First, we discuss the causes of the confusing information and second, how to assess the evidence on controlled clinical trials.

Epidemiological studies and contradictory advice

One cause of confusion and contradictory advice is epidemiology. This involves observational studies on populations without any intervention. They are 'cross-sectional', which means that data has been collected from different populations at one specific point in time. Epidemiology is thus not about controlled trials or based on any intervention. Instead, it looks at the prevalence of disease in different populations to see if any obvious factor can be linked to the disease. There are shortcomings in these kind of studies, but no one would dispute that Richard Doll's studies, linking smoking to lung cancer, saved millions of lives. Epidemiology points the finger at the possible cause of a disease or a factor in prevention.

However, difficulties do arise. The fact that two things are correlated doesn't mean one causes the other – 'correlation isn't causation'. If one thing increases, and another also increases in the same group of people, it may just be coincidence and the two things are completely unconnected, or they may both be caused by a third factor. A classic example is the baby boom and the rise in the number the storks' nests in Copenhagen after WW2.

Dilston Physic Garden volunteers enjoying a glass. But how much red wine is good for you? Latest research suggests you would have to drink far more than could possibly be good for you to match health-protecting effects.

The explanation was not, as some fancied, the old folk myth that more storks brought more babies in their beaks. The real reason was that both birds and men were returning to their homes after wartime exile. Other humorous but equally spurious correlations include the almost perfect association, in the early twentieth century, between the numbers of radios being used and people in insane asylums, and, more recently, of margarine consumption and the divorce rate in Maine, US! So make sure the headline linking coffee or champagne and health is based on sound gold-standard clinical trials, and not just epidemiology.

How to obtain reliable evidence

This book provides you with up-to-date information about controlled clinical trials, but only relating to our own selection of plants and within the constraints of the space available. Two important online databases or libraries inform our assessment of medicinal plant research today. The first is specifically concerned with clinical trials, assessments and diagnostics:

The Cochrane Library

Its website describes it as follows:

> Cochrane exists so that healthcare decisions get better. During the past 20 years, Cochrane has helped to transform the way health decisions are made.
>
> Cochrane is for anyone who is interested in using high-quality information to make health decisions. Whether you are a doctor or nurse, patient or carer, researcher or funder, Cochrane evidence provides a powerful tool to enhance your healthcare knowledge and decision making … Our global independent network gathers and summarizes the best evidence from research to help you make informed choices about treatment and we have been doing this for 25 years.

It is a comprehensive database of evidence-based health care that is constantly updated by experts, and it can be searched by topic. There are three main ways to access the library:

(1) follow their instructions for obtaining information from the website.

(2) search for 'Cochrane review' and your subject of choice through a search engine like Google or Bing (or on PubMed – see below). For example, search for 'Cochrane review' and 'ginkgo for dementia' and you can view all the published Cochrane reviews of clinical studies on that subject over the years, focus on the latest picture, and see how conclusions change over time.

(3) you might like to become a 'citizen scientist'. You can be one of the first to see new examples of scientific proof as they appear online and, at the same time, make a contribution to the spread of knowledge about herbal medicine and other medical advances. Go to the Cochrane website, sign up and/or log in, then click 'Join Cochrane'. Look under 'What you can do' and choose from the resulting list. If you pick 'Screen records with Crowd', they will explain how you can help to screen newly arriving articles and studies for whether they are randomised controlled trials (RCTs) on human subjects. Once you learn how to do this it's quite fascinating as you can prioritise areas of special interest and they'll push those your way. RCTs are the most trustworthy for whether medication works, though some of the 'reject' articles also have value if they are observation studies of techniques or treatments on specific groups of people. You can 'give it a try' before beginning your screening.

PubMed

PubMed is a comprehensive online hub for accredited scientific papers where you can obtain more detail on individual trials, and information about other plants and their chemical ingredients, or about lab tests of plants and their chemicals. Most of the papers are reports of individual studies carried out by the authors. For clinical trials, this contrasts with the Cochrane Library where reviewers are enlisted to analyse results of studies conducted by others.

In each abstract, PubMed papers tell you: the aim of the study, the methods used and the results, followed by implications and a conclusion.

The reason we rely so much on PubMed is that each paper will have been sent out for review by experts (peer-reviewed) and only accepted for publication by the editor of the journal if the reviewers are satisfied that the study is satisfactory, something we well know can take some doing. Reading and responding to critical comments on our own papers can be a challenge, but one we learned to accept as essential, adding to the value of the report. Needless to say outright rejection is not uncommon! One word of warning – while a published report on a lab study may show a biological effect of a plant, it does not mean that this effect will translate into humans. Don't try it at home! – toxicity studies may not have been done yet.

To use PubMed choose search terms that are as precise as possible. The number and relevance of 'hits' can vary enormously depending on the words used. You will learn by experience how to access papers that are directly relevant and how to avoid those that are inappropriate. One of our first searches on sage, a favourite medicinal plant, generated a host of citations on Sage software!

Talking of citations, another key to evaluating a PubMed paper is to check the 'citation index'. This is a measure of how frequently a paper or papers in any one journal have been referred to. We don't want to suggest just going for journals with the highest citation numbers like *Nature* because plant medicine is mostly not that high profile (not yet – it's still a relatively new area of research). We need to take on board all reports in reputable journals that publish peer-reviewed science.

While PubMed itself is free, not all the articles listed are freely available online. Options for obtaining a copy include: contacting the author; accessing the journal through an institution (university library, for example); buy the article or journal yourself; or (in the UK) contact the British Library.

Complications from statistics, and from the placebo effect

Statistics lie at the heart of all clinical trial analyses. Usually two data sets – one, the results from the test group, and the other, from the placebo group – are compared. There are set methods for determining if differences between the two can be considered real or just the result of chance. Specific tests are applied to the data that take into account the number of observations and variability in the data (you may have heard of 't-test' and 'p-value').

The strength of the meta-analysis lies in the power of its larger numbers, but as numbers rise so too does the prospect of statistical significance – the probability that the result is more than just chance (rejecting the 'null hypothesis' that is by chance). Small or borderline measurable effects are more likely to show up as statistically significant as the number of observations increase. And these effects may not be 'significant' in real life, not having any impact on or altering clinical practice, for example. It calls to mind the aphorism, 'There are three kinds of lies: lies, damned lies, and statistics.'

Then there is the placebo effect, described earlier, which can muddy the waters. Large placebo effects are often seen in trials relating to disorders of the mind (brain). Even in other trials, the extent of the placebo effect can be amazing: the power of belief is so strong it can lead to placebo (simulated) heart or knee surgery patients improving. And even though controlled trials are designed so that neither patient nor doctor know whether the real treatment is being administered or not, often one or both can be aware. Side effects are said to alert patients that they are on an antidepressant drug, for example. And in one clinical trial that we heard of testing a fairly large dose of turmeric for cognition, the people taking the real turmeric knew very well, as their faeces turned bright yellow! To get round these kind of giveaway signs, people in RCTs are often asked to guess if they were on test or placebo and their response is then taken into account to ensure that any significant outcome was not affected by an 'accidental' placebo effect.

Agrimony (*Agrimonia*) has many traditional uses (sore throats and upset stomach, for example) not yet backed by clinical trial evidence.

Clinical trial protocols are the best objective evidence we have about the formal assessments of medicinal plants for outcomes, including their safety. We label the plants in our physic garden with signs giving the relevant evidence, although the pace of research means we are forever having to update these signs. Subjective impressions may be good enough if you just want to test-drive a plant medicine yourself, but there is much greater comfort in successful formal trials. So we still advise you to consult a competent authority before taking any plant medicinally.

Though this testing chapter may have 'blinded' you with science, it has hopefully given you some ideas about growing and using evidence-based medicinal plants in your physic garden. In practice, any physic garden would be lacking if traditionally used medicinal plants still awaiting science backing were excluded. It's the tradition that inspires the science, and for medical herbalists today their idea of 'evidence-based' is long-standing traditional use.

We welcome any medicinal plant that will live in our physic garden, and mark ones without scientific evidence as 'traditional'.

The next chapter looks at traditional herbal medicine and how it compares with mainstream medicine. It explains how medicinal plants, irrespective of scientific track record, are used effectively to treat disorders today. In the West (as opposed to China and India, for example) plant medicine still sits outside the realm of mainstream medicine and we need to see the science from this perspective.

3

Herbalism as Complementary Medicine

If medicinal plants are to cross back over into mainstream use, uncovering the science behind how they work is essential. In the previous chapters, we've highlighted active chemicals, biology and RCTs. For any new chemical drug, RCTs lead to a consensus that it is safe and effective, and often result in a regulated medical product. But these scientific guidelines have yet to impact on medical herbalism as a whole. We still live in parallel universes in many Western societies, with a dividing line between clinical trial evidence-based medicine on one side and 'alternatives', like herbalism, based on long-standing traditional evidence on the other.

In this chapter we explore how this partition impacts on medical practice, regulatory procedures and commercial aspects. We encourage you to join us in growing and using evidence-based medicinal plants in your physic garden. It's a small step on the road towards medicinal plants moving back into mainstream medicine. Meantime, it's important for the physic garden venturer to know about the implications of the divide. So we now cast a scientific eye on principles and practices of herbal medicine.

The holistic herbalist

Some herbalists argue that the methodology of clinical mass trials – where everyone gets the same medicine for the same condition – doesn't apply in medical herbalism, and they make a valid point: herbalists prescribe a combination of plant extracts that are prepared to the exact needs and overall health condition of the individual patient with the aim of treating the root cause of the disorder, as well as the symptoms. So, for example, a migraine may be treated not just with pain relief but also with a mild sedative to aid sleep and reduce anxiety. Interestingly, these 'multi-drug' and individual 'tailoring' approaches are now evident in mainstream medicine too. Patients are often given more than one drug to combat a medical condition. And choosing the right drug(s) can be influenced by what is referred to as a 'patient-centred framework', which takes into account individual traits, including genetics, for example.

Plant combinations

Combinations of herbs are just emerging in Western medicinal plant research. Whatever herbalists prescribe in the way of mixtures, scientific research is still focused on 'one plant–one symptom (or condition)' (see Chapter 8). But the scene is changing, thanks to research in the Far East. When we first shifted the focus of our university brain research to medicinal plants, most studies were based in Western institutions. Not so now. Countries in the East and in Asia are the source of more and more research studies. And we only see the tip of the iceberg in the articles that are translated and published in English language journals.

Traditional Chinese herbal medicines consist of formulations of different plants (over 100,000 have been recorded over time), and there can be as many as a dozen in any one mixture. While these Chinese herbal medicines have been used for thousands of years, it is only recently that scientists have begun to run controlled clinical trials to check their efficacy.

Traditional Chinese medicine jars from which individual prescriptions are made up for each person.

Many peer-reviewed reports are appearing about trials of Chinese herbal formulations (some individualised, i.e. adapted to suit each person in the trial). Most of this research is supported by universities in the Far East. This expansion of Chinese herbal medicine research is raising the profile of medicinal plant science as a whole, even though it might leave some of us in the West lamenting the lack of local funding for research in the area.

Just one example of a study in an area of research we are involved in illustrates the quality (not to mention complexity) of the new studies emerging from China. A group at the University of Traditional Chinese Medicine in Tianjin, China, reported (2015) in an open access peer-reviewed journal (*PLOS One*, one of the more highly regarded journals for medicinal plant research reports) that a formulation called 'Yishen Huazhuo decoction' (YHD) was more effective than the treatment drug Donepezil. The trial involved 144 patients with mild Alzheimer's disease. We might struggle on the botanical side as they list the ingredients of YHD (Yin Yang Huo (*Epimedium*), Nu Zhen Zi (*Fructus ligustri lucidi*), Bu Gu Zhi (*Psoralea* fruit), and seven more), but still appreciate this study as an important development in Alzheimer's research.

Single-chemical drug versus whole-plant medicine

The divide between supporters of single-chemical plant-derived drugs (or their synthetic equivalents) and those who use whole-plant extracts containing many active ingredients can lead to ferocious debates. We have seen this in our Dilston herbology classes, attended by both medicinal plant diploma students and practising conventional doctors. Doctors are trained in the pharmacology of single-chemical drugs, whereas herbalists are trained in the use of whole plants containing a 'polypharmacy' ('multi-drug'). However, it's not all fighting, as few on the holistic plant side would object to a shot of morphine when in agony, and few on the drug side would argue against the long-term benefits of healthy food and drinks prepared from plant products.

The pros and cons of both sides of the argument are detailed in the table below, but here are some of the major issues:

- A single-chemical drug can be measured precisely to ensure that the dose is the same each time, year in and out. The plant on the other hand has an array of active chemicals, none of which alone is solely responsible for a specific health benefit.
- Even if the amounts of the individual components could all be measured, their proportions change, according to environmental factors – growth conditions, time of year (and sometimes time of day) and even insect attack. (For scientists like us, this issue can be as near as it gets to giving up on identifying exact molecular mechanisms for all the ingredients in a plant medicine.)

However, plant medicines can be standardised to their main bioactives. In other words, the medicine can be made up so that the quantity of one specific active ingredient is always the same in the prepared pill, tincture or other formulation (though the idea of what the principle active ingredient is can change, as it does with St John's wort).

Plants have held on to their reputation as medicines over centuries – millennia, in some cases. Their complex mixture of chemicals, even as it varies, has been demonstrated to have a consistent overall health benefit.

Pros and cons of whole-plant extracts versus single drugs from plants

	Medicinal whole-plant extracts	Single drug derived from plants
PROS	Long-standing traditional use supports safety and efficacy	For a single-chemical constituent, the action and dose are more easily controlled
	Contain multiple chemicals that have different health benefits	Chemicals can be patented with commercial advantages
	The costs are generally low, especially if you 'grow your own'	Chemicals can be easily matched with an inert chemical in placebo-controlled trials
	Wide choice of options for effective formulation like teas, tinctures and topical oils	Some have more confidence in man-made (when the plant chemical can be synthesised)
	Some consider 'natural' to be best	Pharmacology of a single chemical is more easily understood
	Animals have evolved their own pharmacology partly in parallel with plant ingredients so there are less likely to be untoward side effects	Patenting makes it easier for manufacturers to fund R&D and clinical trials
CONS	Growing, harvesting and preparing plant extracts needs to be controlled in order to standardise the dose (due to natural variability in proportions of plant ingredients and in different formulations)	The necessary lab and animal testing of an isolated chemical (not backed by traditional use) requires extensive funding and resources
	Often difficult to provide acceptable placebo in controlled trials because some plant preparations can be recognised (by patient and/or doctor) or by distinctive taste or smell	Some view conventional medicines as 'synthetic' or 'unnatural' and, therefore, undesirable
	Some view plant medicines as 'new-age', based more on wishful thinking than effectiveness	Purity means advantage of combined ingredients in whole plant is lost
	Most commercially available preparations are not subject to strict regulation and can therefore be adulterated	

Explaining how arrays of chemicals in a single plant work together is still a challenge. The tendency for testing a plant medicine is to focus on a single chemical because this makes testing easier, but this has led to unexpected outcomes. In some trials of St John's wort (*Hypericum perforatum*), for example, the extracts used to treat depression had been standardised to the amount of the single ingredient hypericin (i.e. each prepared extract always contained a specific amount of hypericin). However, it was then found that a different constituent, hyperforin, was more active in lab tests – it caused the release of more serotonin, the brain signal that maintains mood. But neither of these, or other chemicals in the plant, looks like becoming nature's new 'prozac' type of drug; it's the whole St John's wort plant extract that is as effective as conventional drugs.

It's not often that the chemists hit the jackpot, as they did with the likes of the foxglove or poppy, when one chemical stands out as the principal active. For many medicinal plants we are going to be dealing with, it is combinations of active chemicals working together that make the plant effective.

In our view, the strongest 'pro' for whole-plant medicines is their legacy.

Commercial tablets of St John's wort are standardised to a single chemical (like hyperforin), even though benefits are not due to any one chemical.

If a plant has been used for hundreds or thousands of years, it must have retained its reputation for safety as well as efficacy. Put bluntly, if the plant was harmful, or if it was easy to mistake it for a dangerous lookalike, its users would have sickened or died and wouldn't (or couldn't!) have kept using it. In effect, the toxicity and safety testing, essential for new drugs, has been done already, and largely on human guinea pigs. We have generations of ancestors to thank for passing on this ancient knowledge gained by trial and sometimes tragic error, and we should think of it as a kind of family heirloom.

Regulating herbs for health

It's herbalists, not doctors, who prescribe plant medicines in most of the Western world, although it varies. Pharmacies in France and Poland provide herbal medicines as well as chemical drugs. A Polish pharmacist joined our physic garden herbal dispensary with the bold vision of 'converting' UK pharmacies to dispense herbal medicines just as they do in Poland. But where health is nationalised, as in the UK, medicines are almost all synthetic chemicals.

Regulations designed for conventional medicines can't always be easily applied to plant products. If commercial plant preparations are sold as 'oral medicine', they *are* regulated (in the UK they require Traditional Herbal Registration), but there are other cases (some good, some bad) where they are *not* regulated (as for medicines). Some foods and teas are deliberately labelled as 'food supplements' to bypass regulation, even though it's clear that most people will buy the products for medicinal use. In the US, herbal supplements are regulated by the FDA, not as drugs or foods but as dietary supplements.

There are other cases where, surprisingly, the regulations just don't apply. When planning formal trials of herbal teas, our university group met with the UK medicines regulatory body and was astonished to learn that teas from medicinal plants are not classed as 'medicines' since they are common foodstuffs and therefore didn't need approval. That simplified our work, but the downside is that a producer could label plant medicine as tea, and there would be no regulation or checks that the product was authentic, properly prepared, and not adulterated with anything harmful.

But on the plus side, there are regulatory procedures for processed food, drink and cosmetic products sold commercially (requiring monitoring for toxins like insecticides, bacteria or fungi, and ensuring stability within 'sell by' dates). Of course, regulation clearly isn't needed when we are eating food plants and herbs that have health benefits. Curry cuts the risk of Alzheimer's, many fruits and vegetables reduce the risk of cancer, and spices like cinnamon reduce blood sugar and inflammation. This all makes sense, as health-enhancing substances exist in many foods and spices, not just in plants used solely as medicines. We'll come back to 'nutraceuticals' and their cosmetic equivalents, 'cosmeceuticals', in later chapters.

Commercial development of plant medicines

What are the commercial prospects for herbal medicines? In much of the West, herbalism remains a minority therapy whereas in many Asian and African countries, primary healthcare for most people is still plant-based – herbal medicines are grown or gathered for sale (and often used in parallel with medical drugs). It's big business: new plant formulations are constantly being developed and sold for use in China, where the uninterrupted use and current demand for Traditional Chinese Medicine ensures ongoing research and development, and protection of China's herbal medicines. Cynics claim that science

A local farmer harvests coriander in Rajasthan, India.

Flowers in the Mayfield lavender farm in Surrey (UK).

research in the Far East is carried out mainly so they can promote sales of Chinese herbal medicines in the West. But as long as production, formulation and packaging are subject to stringent testing and regulation, it's a welcome development.

But the marketing of plant medicines as such will happen in the West only when enough people start to value plant medicines and demand new policies on sales. Meanwhile, the size of the Western market for medicinal plants in health foods, essential oils and cosmetics is enormous. Dietary supplements were reportedly worth $50 billion worldwide in 2016, and herbal products are expected grow annually by 1 per cent in the UK to reach £466 million in 2021.

Spectacular lavender beds in Europe may not officially be making medicines, but they provide countless products – from bath oils and balms to biscuits and perfumes – from a herb with many evidence-based benefits for mind and body. Health food shops, like the one in our local town, not permitted to mention medicinal use on their labels, display 'wellness' products for things like 'nervous tension', 'sleep', 'skincare'.

A new initiative in the marketing of oils and lotions made from such herbs is labelling that lists references to published studies that support the health benefit of the plant. As we in the West wait for the revolution that might bring medicinal plants into line with synthetic drugs, herbs for health continue to make their presence known.

The next chapter takes us back into the research scene to explore ways in which the 'gap' between traditional plant medical practice and mainstream medicine can be bridged in areas like drug resistance, and chronic conditions such as dementia.

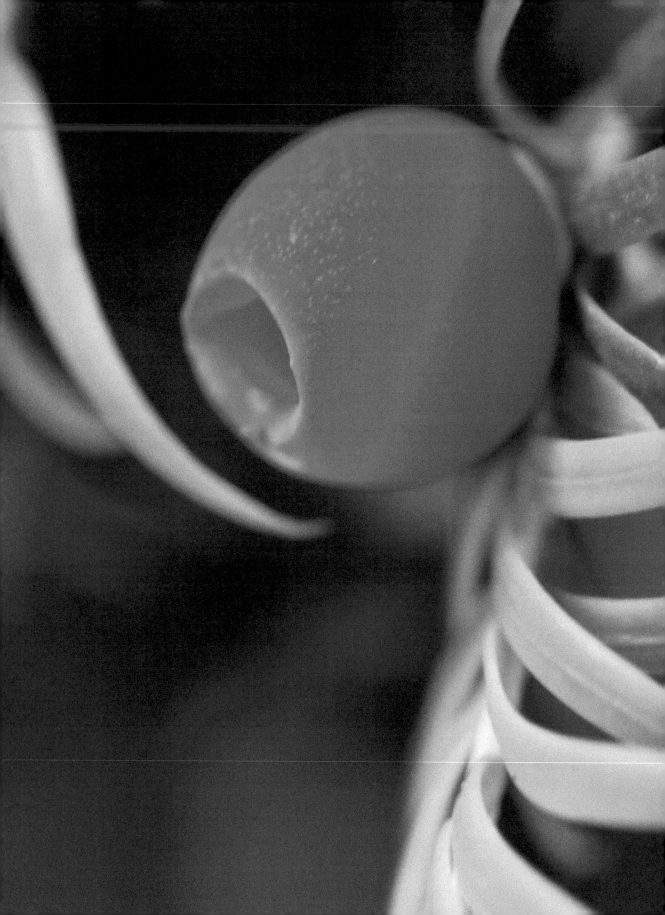

4

Plant Medicines for the Future

Despite the dramatic rise in medicinal plant research this century and new evidence that traditional, time-tested medicinal plants really work, mainstream medicine is not paying much attention. Only one herbal medicine has made it mainstream in the UK.

But plant medicines *could* attract the attention of Western health professionals in situations where conventional medical approaches are failing. 'Have you a plant for my arthritis?' or 'Can anything help with my mother's dementia?' are typical of questions often asked at our physic garden (see Chapter 8). Here we look at how plant medicine may help in the search for new antibiotics, how herbal extracts are used in conjunction with other treatments for chronic conditions such as dementia and in palliative care. And for cancer, once viewed as a chronic or untreatable condition, we see how medicinal plants are leading to new treatments.

New antibiotics to overcome drug resistance

More and more germs are becoming resistant to antibiotics. However, few if any new antibiotics are being found that can counter the resistant bugs, so we risk returning to the 'bad old days' before antibiotics – when babies and children often didn't survive common illnesses and adults commonly died from minor infections. Florence Nightingale reported from the Crimean War that more soldiers died from infections than from enemy action. As

One herbal medicine (whole-plant extract, not an isolated chemical) is part of mainstream medicine in the UK. Doctors prescribe peppermint oil (taken orally) to ease gastrointestinal pain in irritable bowel syndrome (IBS) or after abdominal surgery. Why this one has 'made it' and not others, like ginger for nausea or lavender for sleep and anxiety, is not clear. Drug company monopolies could be involved, or there may be restrictions in adding further healthcare prescription costs for products that are freely available to buy, though at costs five times that of over-the-counter medicines; paracetamol is also available on prescription in the UK. It may also be because medical students in most Western universities don't learn anything about plant medicine.

one researcher put it pessimistically, 'If we don't get new antibiotics soon, elective surgery could become a death sentence' (hospital patients could risk catching a potentially fatal infection with no effective antibiotic).

The prospects for plants helping in the antibiotic resistance crisis are good. After all, penicillin, the original antibiotic that stopped so many deaths after the 1940s, was from a natural source (fungus). Mainstream medicine does not yet use plant chemicals to fight infection, but some plant extracts are strongly antibiotic. Essential oils from tea tree and eucalyptus and their chemicals are used as over-the-counter herbal medicines and backed up by laboratory studies.

The number of scientific reports on medicinal plants as antibiotics is substantial (about five per cent of all papers dealing with plant medicines). The focus is mainly on bacteria. For example, a range of randomly selected articles published in 2015 report: newly identified active chemicals (like carvacrol) in essential oils of thyme and clary sage; the skin infection bug *Staphylococcus aureus* wiped out by Cameroonian medicinal plants; antibacterial activity in lemon juice; cranberry juice capsules reducing half of urinary tract infections (UTIs) after surgery; and local plants in India and Pakistan screened for antibiotic activities.

Eucalyptus leaves contain one of the most effective antibiotic essential oils (due to ingredients like cineole).

A plant has one great advantage over any man-made chemical – it has been doing battle against invading microbes for generations, and has developed an armoury of multiple and changing chemical weapons against viruses, bacteria and fungi. Essential oils have been billed as the new antibiotics. Early concerns that they could promote resistance to other antibiotics in bacteria are not apparently founded. A 2012 review of published studies concluded that essential oils are effective antiseptics against many types of bacteria, including multiple drug-resistant bacteria such as methicillin-resistant *Staphylococcus aureus* (MRSA) and vancomycin-resistant *Enterococci*. Cinnamon bark is one of the most potent.

Treatment for chronic conditions

There is a crying need for new treatments in chronic conditions where there are few or no effective mainstream medicines. Examples are palliative care and dementia – especially important since people are living longer than ever and therefore an increasing percentage of the population is being affected. Plants (and alternative) medicines are often sought by people with these conditions, and they have a new and progressively well-founded place in these areas of medicine.

Even when patients are already receiving conventional treatment, plant medicines can be useful. The treatments often focus not on curing the disease but enhancing quality of life, boosting immunity and managing the stress response. They also give some sense of control back to the patient. Common treatments of this type are herbal medicines and aromatherapy, as well as nutraceuticals.

A classic success story about a plant long used to fight infections, that has provided a life-saving mainstream medicine, is sweet wormwood (*Artemisia annua*). Used in China for thousands of years to treat fevers, the chemical artemisinin (a sesquiterpene, or its derivatives) prevents malaria (from the *Plasmodium* parasite). But this remarkable plant has many more antibiotic properties. Its chemicals destroy other parasites, bacteria and even viruses. Wild wormwood chemicals kill bacteria as effectively as streptomycin, and one of its antimalarial drugs even reduces cancer cell proliferation in patients with cancer (colorectal).

However, so far there hasn't been very much high-quality scientific work in this area. Scientific studies can be hard to assess or even find, and reports often appear in low-profile journals. Editors of high-profile scientific journals often don't risk ratings by including reports on 'complementary' medicine. Scientific papers are ranked by 'impact factor' – an indication of how important they are based on how often they are referred to in other papers. Journals on natural products and alternative or complementary medicine typically have an impact factor of 1 or 2, compared to 30 or 40 for heavyweight journals like *Nature* or *Science*. Moreover, the use of terms like 'herbal medicine' and 'aromatherapy' without naming the actual plants involved is frustrating for anyone looking for scientific support for plant medicines in chronic conditions. Even so, plant-based therapies, especially essential oils, are increasingly used in care homes and hospices by nurses.

Salvia Officinalis: (mixed media) by Jill Tattersall
(collection of Clare & Graham Herring).
Latin text: 'Why should man die who has Sage in his garden?'

A medieval manuscript extols the virtues of sage (*Salvia officinalis*) for longevity. Plaque illustration in Dilston sage garden provided by artist Jill Tattersall

Dementia: plant hopes for the ageing brain

Whereas plant medicines target single cells, like bacteria, or relentlessly dividing cancer cells, they also help treat complex bodily systems – the ageing brains in people with Alzheimer's for example. With periodic, misleadingly triumphant headlines (which soon prove to be false dawns), some drug companies that backed such studies have pulled out of the field. But 'hope springs eternal.'

In the US, the proposed 2016 federal budget allocated an additional $350 million for Alzheimer's research, more than doubling the total funding. Around the same time, the UK launched a Dementia Discovery Fund (a partnership between the government and international drug companies) and a Dementia Research Institute (involving the Medical Research Council and universities), both involving hundreds of million pounds. As far as we know, none of this new research includes the potential of plants for treatments, even though one of the few prescription drugs, Reminyl, originated in snowdrops (as galantamine). That said, a new dementia research institute at the University of Wessex, UK, will explore the role of nutrition. But it is mostly left to smaller groups (ours is one of just a few in the West) to run low-budget 'pilot' research projects, which may prompt more studies.

Plants have much to offer dementia treatment and many research papers explain the reasons why. In one of our reviews on medicinal plants for dementia (2011), promising plants included sage, *Ginkgo biloba*, and complex mixtures of other traditional remedies (for cognitive symptoms), and lemon balm and lavender (for behavioural and psychological symptoms). In a 2017 review of effects of medicinal plants on Alzheimer's and memory deficits from universities in Pakistan and Japan, over 70 plants are listed as worth following up based on their traditional uses, lab studies or clinical trials. They included familiar plants like coriander, curcumin, gingko, melissa and sage, and many others not familiar to Westerners, such as *Centella asiatica*, *Bambusa vulgaris* and *Cordia millenii*.

Our own original research into the chemical pathology of Alzheimer's helped lead to the use of the very few drugs, like Reminyl and Aricept, that are effective against the disease, even though they only work for a limited time. It was research on Alzheimer's that led to the creation of Dilston Physic Garden where we grew traditional plant medicines for the brain and studied the science of whether and how they work.

Apart from a few drugs like galantamine from snowdrops, which appeared in the clinic over twenty years ago, there has only been one new drug for memory loss or confusion. Yet herbs like sage, rosemary and lemon balm have a long history of aiding learning and memory. Europeans drank sage tea for hundreds of years. The Chinese, long famed for their knowledge of plant medicine, so valued sage that they would trade six chests of their tea for one of European sage. Sage was renowned for 'strengthening' the brain; in 1597 English herbalist John Gerard said it was 'singular good for the head and brain and quickeneth the nerves and memory'.

Students in our lab found that sage affects the same brain molecule as dementia drugs like Donepezil, an enzyme that increases the level of the brain's memory signal, acetylcholine. This was so surprising that the students had to repeat the experiment several times. Since

Black or blue fruits contain brain protective polyphenols.

then, others have shown that sage improves memory in people with and without dementia. In our latest trial, a community team (medical herbalist, physic garden and local therapy centre staff) found that a combination of plants (sage, rosemary and lemon balm) doubled the rate of word recall of middle-aged volunteers.

As memory fades in the ageing brain, the stress of confusion leads to further problems like anxiety and agitation. Lemon balm (*Melissa officinalis*) is one of many herbs that helps boost memory and keep you calm. John Evelyn, medical historian of the seventeenth century, wrote 'Balm is sovereign for the brain, strengthening the memory, and powerfully chasing melancholy.' Our lab work showed that lemon balm affects a brain molecule (nicotinic receptor) that is involved in both calming and alerting effects. This is the same brain target for nicotine, the alkaloid in tobacco, which was itself once extolled for many medicinal virtues like curing convulsions and the 'shaking palsy' (Parkinson's), before its other, less desirable, effects became obvious. Our trials in young people and in people with dementia showed that melissa essential oil reduced anxiety.

It's not really surprising that a plant can have effects on the human brain even though it is the most complex system in the known universe. Consider alcohol or marijuana: one drink or 'joint' can ease stress, while taking either in quantity can eliminate short-term memory. Plants like lemon balm and lavender have the advantage over these in helping with anxiety, though they don't have the 'street appeal' of more common recreational drugs.

Research into other types of medicinal plant extracts containing polyphenols like flavonoids (see Chapter 1) is now focused more on discovering new therapies for the core symptoms of dementia, and less on treatments to improve quality of life. In contrast, studies of plant-derived food and drink are more concerned with disease prevention than cure, giving us good evidence-based reasons to increase our risk-reducing dose of fruit juice, chocolate, red wine and curry (all full of flavonoids and other polyphenols)!

Palliative care

Plant medicines also impact on symptomatic relief for patients in palliative care. This is an area where complementary medicine, herbal medicine and aromatherapy are often used in addition to conventional treatments, but where scientific research to provide the evidence has been largely lacking.

There have been isolated trials of aromatherapy (one indicating the effects of sandalwood essential oil in reducing anxiety), and more trials of Chinese plant medicines. One impressive controlled trial conducted in 2008 on 2,466 patients showed that, compared to a normal hospital diet, a Taiwanese traditional diet, including analgesic plants (peony and liquorice root), was effective for pain management in terminal cancer patients.

More systematic investigations are emerging, providing more reliable guidance for future studies. In reviews (2016) of randomised controlled trials (RCTs) of therapies for symptom management in palliative cancer care, Chinese herbal medicine added to conventional treatment significantly reduced pain (three trials) and constipation (six trials). Around the same time, Chinese herbal medicine alone or with acupuncture improved quality of life in patients with various types of cancer in two analyses of RCTs. These studies by Chinese authors, which include analyses of original Chinese language reports, are potentially groundbreaking, given the previous lack of controlled trials of herbal medicines added to palliative care.

Medical cannabis is often mentioned in relation to palliative care. Evidence based on a 2016 systematic review of trials (RCTs) of cannabinoids (with meta-analysis) indicated significant benefits, including relieving pain, and improving sleep and appetite. An interesting opinion was expressed that same year by medical experts in the middle Eastern countries where plant medicines (including cannabis) are widely used (Israel, Egypt and Turkey):

> The presence of integrative physicians with training in complementary and traditional medicine can help patients and their healthcare professionals reach an informed decision regarding the safety and effective use of these products.

With the legalisation of cannabis products for medical use in many countries, the scene is changing. In a 2018 review, use of cannabinoids for refractory symptoms (those not responding to treatment) in palliative care patients is supported, despite the lack of strictly controlled trials.

The role of psychedelic drugs or plants to help relieve fear and anxiety of imminent death could be described as a 'back to the future' area of investigation. Isolated reports on benefits of LSD, for example, in the 1960s and 70s were not followed up at that time. But international trials are now underway to revisit the role of agents like mescaline (from the peyote cactus) and psilocybin (from magic mushrooms) in assisting patients with terminal cancer, and to investigate anxiety-inducing 'existential' issues surrounding their illness. Psychedelic plants are also being researched in people with depression or addiction (with significant benefits of psilocybin for depression and ibogaine, from an African plant, for addiction).

From physical pain to subtle states of mind, 'plants in palliative' is a 'watch this space' area for plant medicine moving mainstream in the future. There is clearly scope for applying plant medicines to comfort and calm those approaching the end of life, but until there are more formal trials, incorporating them into mainstream medicine remains only a hope. And for those already on prescribed medication, the question of mixing medicines (contraindications) arises. How plant medicines and prescription drugs do (or do not) go together is formally known for only a few plants and drugs.

But where prognosis is poor and no other options are available, introducing traditional plant medicines – even if short on scientific evidence – may be justified, under the direction of a registered medical herbalist or aromatherapist. After all, in mainstream medicine too, new drugs not fully tested in clinical trials are given, with consent, to patients diagnosed with terminal conditions. Further application of science to plant medicines may lead to remedies that address situations of great and currently unmet human needs.

Cancer

A beacon for plant medicines impacting mainstream medicine is cancer research and therapy. Cancers that spread belonged to the untreatable or terminal disease category not so long ago. It was in the 1940s that soldiers exposed to chemical weapons were found to have suppressed tumours, and this led to the first use of chemicals closely related to the mustard gas for therapy. Plants used traditionally for cancer entered mainstream medicine in the 1960s, with the use of the plant alkaloid vincristine from the Madagascar periwinkle (*Catharanthus roseus*), in combination with synthetic drugs.

Cancer is currently the most active area for medicinal plant research: of all scientific publications on plant-based therapy, ten per cent relate to treating cancer. It's an area of increasing need. The average lifetime risk of cancer for people born in the UK after 1960 is one in two. Genetic factors, lifestyle, pollutants in the environment and unhealthy diet all contribute to the risk. So does living longer, because in one sense cancer is a disease of the aged – before we had antibiotics and improved surgical interventions, people didn't live long enough for cancer to become the cause of death for a large proportion of the population.

With chemotherapy, an increasing proportion of patients now live for months or years with malignant cancers. Even so, chemotherapy can be hard to fine-tune to individuals and often has side effects like nausea and fatigue. There is an opportunity for plant medicines here, especially as they have a good track record. Taxol (paclitaxel) from the yew tree is not only used to treat a range of cancers, but it has fewer side effects than other (synthetic) chemotherapy drugs.

Scopolia japonica, Japanese or Korean belladonna, closely related to *S. carniolica*, which is being investigated for anticancer effects.

Success stories in oncology

Meta-analyses of multiple studies of plant medicines (2013–15) indicate improved quality of life and reduced side effects (such as hot flushes from chemotherapy) in breast, lung and oesophageal cancers. However, in many studies the herbs are traditional Chinese medicines, often with no mention of individual plant species – common or Latin names – making it difficult to find evidence for a specific plant.

Many plants and their active chemicals are being tested on cancer cells in the lab or in animals. Selecting at random from reports in one year (2015): curcumin stops gastric cancer cells growing and spreading; mistletoe (*Viscum album*) attacks breast and other types of cancer cells (it also works in patients); a ginkgo extract kills prostate cancer cells; and a chemical from the henbane bell (*Scopolia carniolica*) is effective on liver cancer cells. Soya, peppercorns, curcumin and even cannabis were all being researched as anticancer agents that same year.

Many essential oils are also active against cancer cells. In recent lab research these include cinnamon, rosemary, eucalyptus and frankincense, as well as common essential oil chemical ingredients like beta-caryophyllene and several monoterpenes. Geraniol, a chemical present in rose, lemon, geranium and other oils, stops cancer cells acquiring immunity to anti-cancer drugs. Where specific essential oils have been part of clinical trials, it has been shown that frankincense reduces oedema-induced pain (pain from swelling due to fluid retention), and ginger reduces nausea and vomiting.

Frankincense resin, the 'tears' from the Boswellia tree, alters mind and mood, while the oil has promising anticancer effects.

A mysterious-looking medicinal plant in our physic garden, *podophyllum*, is the source of an important anticancer drug.

Success stories in cancer treatment for plant chemicals (other than paclitaxel) are the vinca alkaloids from the Madagascar periwinkle and two drugs (etoposide and teniposide) derived from podophyllotoxin found in the mayapple (*Podophyllum peltatum*). This plant is slow-growing and said to thrive only in the Himalayas. Because of the scarcity of the species, another plant, tobacco (!) is being genetically modified to produce the chemical. A related species, *Podophyllum hexandrum*, also used to produce these drugs, does survive in our physic garden, although in ten years it has barely doubled in size.

Regarding food plants as medicine – at its simplest, eating fruit and vegetables – the epidemiology (see Chapter 2) indicates that this reduces the risk of some types of cancer as well as improves general health. There have been only a few studies to see if any specific diet helps patients with particular types of cancer to survive. It's early days for drawing conclusions, but in a 2016 study of early-stage breast cancer survivors, those on a low-fat diet had a decreased recurrence of their cancer. In a review (2016 again) of the role of different dietary polyphenolics, the Mediterranean diet showed the most promise for keeping the cancers from recurring. Polyphenols (Chapter 1), rich in olive oil and other ingredients of this diet (like rosmarinic acid in sage and rosemary), have antioxidant, anti-inflammatory and anticancer effects.

Complementary therapies in cancer treatment

One third of cancer patients use a complementary therapy, including plant medicine, at some point. Cannabis and its constituent cannabinoids are said to help with pain and chemotherapy-induced nausea. But controlled trials are lacking, and the conclusion so far is that they 'may' be useful. Nonetheless, the National Cancer Institute recognises medicinal cannabis as providing relief for pain, loss of appetite, nausea, vomiting and anxiety in cancer. Cannabis is increasingly being legalised for medical use, so it is likely that more definitive evidence, whether pro or con, will emerge.

Controversial cannabis is finding its way back as a plant medicine for pain in many conditions, including cancer.

Why plant chemicals affect cancers

Why would plant chemicals be able to cure human cancers? Plants, as explained earlier (Chapter 1), evolved chemicals for self-defence. Humans, and self-medicating animals who know which plant to chew for which ailment, discovered these plants and used them for our benefit. A possible mechanism is that some of these plant chemicals act as signals to kickstart helpful anticancer natural processes like apoptosis. (Apoptosis is programmed, deliberate cell death, used to get rid of redundant cells as in malignant tumours.) Plants produce anticancer chemicals to defend themselves against cancers. Growths or 'galls' on oak trunks are formed from uncontrolled cell division (usually induced by wasp larvae), but in plants the cancer cells locked inside rigid cell walls don't spread. Ancient Druids associated these oak apples with magic, and the high tannin content is medicinal.

Some plants actually *cause* cancer. For example, the betel nut (*Areca catechu* seed), used as a mild stimulant and aphrodisiac, causes mouth cancer. This is presumably because, in chewing betel nuts for long periods, the mucous membranes of the mouth are over-exposed to toxic betel chemicals, which switch on a portion of DNA that promotes cell division and cancer. But the vast majority of the many thousand studies on plants and cancer are reports (on PubMed) relating to treating cancer.

From knowing to growing

This ends the science section of the book: explaining what we think is important about medicinal plant chemical ingredients, testing effects, why plant medicines sit outside mainstream medicine, and how this may be changing.

We move on from knowing about medicinal plants to growing such plants in your physic garden. We suggest how to choose your plants, and we introduce a few of our favourites. The reading will be easier for plant-lovers new to plant science, but the science is still in there and adds a compelling dimension to creating a twenty-first century physic garden.

PART TWO
GROW

Ideas for Creating
Your Physic Garden

CARDOON

5

Physic Gardens, Then and Now

Before you think about what to grow, or even what your physic garden might look like, we visit other physic gardens, from the past (mainly European) to the present (across the globe), looking at their purpose and design. Then we give you reasons to be inspired to grow your own physic garden, tailored to your interests, and ideas to help you plan your garden. After that, you have our unique charts of plants, each for different health systems, from heart to mind, followed by detailed profiles of our favourite plants. And finally, and not before time, come practical details on cultivation – sourcing, growing and maintaining medicinal plants in your physic garden.

Plants have been used for medicine all over the world, and gardens for healing, research and experimentation have a distinguished history. For example, Aristotle is said to have had a physic garden in Athens for botanical studies. However, the prototype Western physic garden came later, planted by medieval monks and nuns, with areas set aside for medicinal plants for themselves and for nearby communities and hospitals.

We get an idea of what the gardens might have been like from a ninth-century plan for a physic garden at St Gall in Switzerland, laid out near the kitchen garden in sixteen beds. Two centuries later, there was a physic garden at the famous medical centre of Salerno, Italy, and at other monasteries in Italy and Spain.

Further south, Muslim authorities founded a medical school at Montpellier in 1221, recognising the need to educate lay physicians working in Moorish France, Spain and Sicily.

Subsequently, the Republic of Venice authorised a physic garden in 1333, and the Holy Roman Emperor, Charles IV, established one at Prague a few decades later. Then in the next century, Pope Nicholas V dedicated land within the Vatican gardens for the study of medicinal plants by university students.

History of physic gardens in the Mediterranean

It seems unlikely that Europeans knew of the royal physic gardens that had already been established in China, India and Persia. However, the Spanish were astonished by the medical plant gardens they encountered in Mexico and South America in the early sixteenth century, especially those made by the Aztec chief Montezuma II. They saw plants such as *Nicotiana tabacum*, tobacco, lauded as a wonder drug (treating everything from pain to infections) and thereafter popular in Europe from the 1580s onwards; *Guaiacum officinale*, the 'holy wood' hoped to be a cure for syphilis, which was epidemic in Europe; *Cinchona officinalis*, quinine, the Peruvian bark used in the seveneenth century for malaria (and, later, in tonic water with gin); and *Cannabis sativa* used as a medicine in sixteenth-century Europe and also as a sop to prolong working hours of slaves in the Spanish-run silver mines in the Andes.

The heyday of the physic garden ran from the sixteenth to the eighteenth centuries. While the Spanish explorers brought back plants and knowledge, they did not immediately set up physic gardens. Rather, these were created by the North Italian universities, which were undergoing a renaissance in their teaching of 'physic' – the old word for medicine. Classical studies in Italy from the mid-fifteenth century had included Greek and Latin masterworks on medical plants. Formerly, academic physicians had relied on apothecaries and chemists to supply medicines for their prescriptions, sourced from traditional texts, whereas the new physic gardens made it possible for them to identify the species described by Dioscorides, Pliny and Galen.

Padua, the University of Venice, and Pisa had set up their own gardens in the mid-1540s. The Paduan Orto dei semplici ('garden of simples' – 'simples' are individual plants combined in prescriptions) still exists on its original site. Its circular design is unusual, but its purpose was common to others that came later in that its layout represented the four 'corners' of the known world. It included specimens from the Americas and the East, and valuable species from the Mediterranean region.

Also in Italy, Bologna set up its physic garden in 1568 under the influence of the great medical teacher Luca Ghini, and medical students were encouraged to read the original descriptions for themselves and go on expeditions to seek the plants. On their return, plants were dried in a herbarium (an innovation of Ghini's to ensure correct plant identification), but increasingly they were transplanted into physic gardens attached to the university where lecturers instructed the students in the identification and use of simples.

History of physic gardens in Northern Europe

Following the Italian example, universities in Northern Europe created their own physic gardens at Zurich, Leyden, Paris and Heidelberg, among others, attracting distinguished physicians and botanists. At Leyden, a rectangular garden with rows of beds in each quarter representing different species and different usages was run by Carolus Clusius. He had already set up a medical garden for Emperor Maximilian II in Vienna, and was responsible for introducing into Europe the horse chestnut tree and tulips from Turkey.

Foundation dates of European physic gardens, 16th–18th centuries

c. 1545	Padua	1620	Strasbourg
c. 1545	Pisa	1621	Oxford
1550	Florence	1655–7	Uppsala
1560	Zurich	1670	Edinburgh
1568	Bologna	1673	Chelsea, London
1571	Leipzig	1679	Berlin
1577	Leyden	1682	Amsterdam
1597	Paris (from 1635, Le jardin royal des plantes médicinales)	1704	Glasgow
1598	Montpellier	1759	Kew, London
before 1600	Heidelberg	1760–3	Cambridge

Some physic gardens were re-founded (e.g. Uppsala, Cambridge) and/or changed sites repeatedly (e.g. Edinburgh).

In England, aristocrats like William Cecil, Lord Burghley, collected medical and food plants, although Cecil's gardener, John Gerard, writer of the famous *Gerard's Herbal* in 1597, urged him in vain to establish a new garden for Cambridge University. However, in 1621 Oxford University set up a physic garden on the site of the old Jewish cemetery on a bend of the Cherwell near Magdalen Bridge. This, the oldest physic garden in England, still retains its ceremonial entrance, its surrounding wall and the layout of 'order beds', which deal with a single species or a group of plants; eight of these are still devoted to medicinal plants. By 1648 the first curator, Jacob Bobart, had acquired over a thousand different specimens. Bobart's son set up a seed exchange and extended the garden, which continues to supply medical specimens for lectures and research to Oxford University.

Meanwhile, the London apothecaries set up their own physic garden on a riverside plot in Chelsea, donated to them by Sir Hans Sloane in 1673. Chelsea produced a series of distinguished directors, especially Philip Miller who was in charge of the garden for fifty years. Chelsea received many specimens brought back by explorers, including Sir Joseph Banks, who established the first rockery there. Chelsea still maintains its brief: to provide authenticated specimens for medical students and to educate the public. It includes an area dedicated to world medicine, demonstrating different plants and different medical traditions.

While European gardens included plants imported from the colonies, some colonists also set up gardens in the Americas. In the mid-seveneenth century, the Dutch created

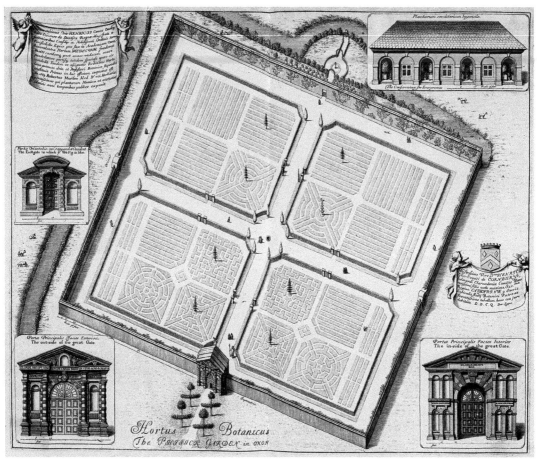

The ordered beds of the Oxford Physic Garden.

zoological and botanical gardens in what is now Recife in Brazil. In 1765, General Robert Melville, aided by the military surgeon Dr George Young, set up a garden on the Caribbean island of St Vincent, gathering information about local remedies and their uses from slaves and the remaining elderly Carib residents. In 1808, by which time the Portuguese had reclaimed Brazil as a colony, John VI of Portugal ordered a botanical garden to be created in Rio de Janeiro for the purpose of acclimatising valuable spices such as cinnamon and nutmeg.

The Chelsea Physic Garden in its early days.

It was becoming obvious that the continuing discovery of new medicinal and food plants required an understanding of their botany. Linnaeus (Carl von Linné) had created a classification system for every known genus and species. A physic garden was established in Linnaeus' home town, Uppsala, in 1655–7, and it became a centre for botanical identification and seed exchange when it was re-established in 1787.

Around 1728, the first English garden in North America was set up near Pennsylvania by John Bartram, for the proper scientific study of useful plants and how they grew. Meanwhile, back in England, Kew Gardens was created in 1759 by Augusta, mother of King George III, and her superintendent, William Aiton, to focus on botany. Kew was partially landscaped by 'Capability' Brown, with exotic buildings and follies by Sir William Chambers while collectors such as Banks supplied seeds and cuttings. Today, Kew acts as a world seed bank and database, but the Queen's House still includes a medicinal garden of some plants listed in *Gerard's Herbal*, and it continues to investigate plants for commercial and medical use. Likewise, as part of its brief, Edinburgh Botanic Garden preserves cuttings from its yew hedges for research on the tree's anticancer actions. In this way, the functions of the physic gardens of the sixteenth century are still carried on in some of the current botanic gardens.

In the nineteenth century, as new, beautiful or strange plants were brought back as trophies from distant European colonies, some physic gardens evolved into simple botanic gardens with collections of plants for display while medicinal plants, often modest in appearance, gave way to showier species. Today, Oxford is referred to as a 'botanic garden', as are Glasgow, Cambridge and Edinburgh.

Present-day botanic gardens of medicinal plants

It seemed that the history of physic gardens in the West might have ended there, as medicine moved from plant-derived drugs to synthetic chemicals. Then in the late twentieth century came renewed interest in plant medicine and with it the urge to collect, grow and learn about the healing power of plants. This interest was, and still is, worldwide. New physic or medicinal plant gardens sprang up across the globe, and long-standing botanic gardens, many attached to universities, revived their physic garden plants. Globally, there are now hundreds of medicinal plant gardens to visit: botanic, physic, university, herb or community gardens, and we feature a selection below.

From this modest medicinal yarrow (*Achillea millefolium*) spectacular bright red and yellow cultivars have been developed for their looks rather than for medicines.

British Isles

Here we've chosen gardens with special features to inspire you with themes, layout, activities and choices of plants or trees. We start with the Chelsea Physic Garden in London, the only one to retain its identity in the same location for centuries. Its 1.2 hectares (3 acres) hide behind a high, old, red-brick wall along a quiet road on the north bank of the Thames. It has been open to the public since 1983, and you can feel the history straight away. The Worshipful Society of Apothecaries established the garden in 1673, although they no longer run it, but it still cultivates healing plants, shares seeds and has a thriving visitors' centre.

As befits its historic London location, this physic garden is laid out in formal beds, divided by immaculate grass-edged gravel paths. In the Pharmaceutical Garden area, plants are grouped according to the ailments they treat, while in the Garden of World Medicine, they are laid out according to the countries or cultures using them.

The Chelsea Physic Garden today.

Appropriately enough, the Royal Colleges of Physicians (RCP) in London and Edinburgh have their own physic gardens. The London garden is just a few miles north of the Chelsea Physic Garden. The new RCP building was designed by Denys Lasdun (who also designed the National Theatre in London) to reflect the five hundred-year history of the college. There are over a thousand species of medicinal plants in the tranquil garden: herbs with folk histories; those providing pharmaceutical drugs; fibre plants used to make bandages; and plants with Latin names commemorating eminent physicians. Yam (*Dioscorea*), for example, is named after the famous ancient Greek physician Dioscorides, while lobelia is named after the lesser-known Flemish botanist and physician Matthias de l'Obel.

The physic garden in the Edinburgh RCP sits behind the Georgian college building in the New Town. It is still a secluded spot for guests and the public, and it houses an invaluable library of beautifully illustrated old books on medicinal plants. Nearby were other physic gardens that supplied doctors, one in Hollyrood Palace and another near Edinburgh Castle. The Edinburgh

'The Respiratory Ward' where the relevant plants are grown in the Urban Physic Garden, London.

Long view of the Dilston Physic Garden.

Royal Botanic Garden (ERBG) was a small physic garden, and as it evolved into a botanic garden, a cottage was built for teaching students. This was left behind when the gardens moved again, but it has recently been relocated, stone by stone, into the ERBG. The garden runs a certificated course in herbology and, at the time of writing, a new garden is being established at Hollyrood Palace inspired by the original physic garden in the palace grounds.

Recently, new English physic gardens have been created. One is our own, Dilston, in the north-east of England. This was set up to carry out university research, taking neuropathology in the then unlikely direction of botanicals for the brain: testing plants that were said to relieve memory disorders. Another is the Urban Physic Garden in Southwark, South London, which began in the summer of 2011 as a pop-up temporary land-use project on a disused building site, but which is now partnered with King's College London, Tate Modern and other institutions. Unique features include plant beds set out in 'hospital wards' specialising in orthopaedics, obstetrics, cardiology, and so on.

Continental Europe

The world's oldest botanic garden, still at its original site, is the Orto Botanico di Padova in Padua, Italy. It began as a physic garden, and still grows medicinal plants as well as poisonous plants. It also has a collection of plants from the surrounding Euganean Hills, and a section for the preservation and study of plants in danger of extinction.

Elsewhere in Europe are a number of medicinal plant gardens with special features. The Research Institute for Medicinal Plants at Budakalász in Hungary produces pharmaceutical raw materials, develops and manufactures medicinal and cosmetic products, breeds plants, and carries out molecular biological and genetic research. The Wala Garden in Germany combines expertise in medicinal plants with herbal horticulture and cosmetic formulation. The founder, Rudolf Hauschka, is well known for organic skin products. Less well known, he was inspired by the philosopher and social reformer Rudolf Steiner to introduce the idea of rhythm into plant growing and preparations. He converted a boggy meadow near the Swabian Mountains into a thriving garden for medicinal herbs. This continues to produce cosmetic products from plants that grow there biodynamically.

In France a number of gardens started as physic gardens and expanded later to become botanic gardens. These include the Jardin des Plantes in Montpellier created in 1594, the Muséum National d'Histoire Naturelle created in 1635 and others linked to pharmacy faculties in Lyon, Paris and Lille.

In Chemillé in the Loire valley, Le Jardin Camifolia, also known as Le jardin des plantes médicinales et aromatiques, was established in the 1970. It grows around five hundred medicinal and aromatic plants trad-itionally used for tinctures, beauty products and perfumes. Typically French in style are the abundant water features and mature trees.

The Wala Garden in Germany established by Dr Rudolf Hauschka.

Botanic Garden, Grasse, by the perfume museum Fragonard.

In Provence, the medieval village of Grasse, centre of the perfume industry, has an international perfume museum with a nearby perfume garden, devoted to the preservation of species like *Rosa centifolia*, jasmine, tuberose, geranium and orange blossom. Although once essential in the perfume industry, these sweet-scented plants, each with its own health benefits, are now largely superseded by synthetic chemicals in most of today's perfumes.

A. Vogel Tuinen (A. Vogel Gardens) are based in t'Harde, Netherlands, and are open to the public. Despite being grown for mass production of herbal remedies, they are designed to be educational and beautiful. Alfred Vogel was a Swiss proponent of herbs for healing and health, with a philosophy of living and working in harmony with nature. Bioforce, the company he set up in 1963, together with its sister company Biohorma, globally market their health products developed from organically and sustainably cultivated plants like echinacea.

The Americas

New World countries had no physic gardens as such at the same time as the European apothecaries. However, indigenous populations in the Americas and Australia gathered their own healing plants, while colonists imported their favourite plant foods and medicines, some setting up public gardens for botanical education. Today, colleges and botanic gardens in the USA, Canada, New Zealand and Australia boast first-class medicinal plant gardens, which developed with

Echinacea bed at A. Vogel Tuinen in the Netherlands.

the growing public interest in medicinal plants, prompted by the introduction of herbal products in health food shops.

A major medicinal garden in the USA, the University of Mississippi National Center for Natural Products Research, is where investigators explore medicinal plants as alternative crops, 'to identify botanical products with the potential to improve human health and to enable the safe, effective and proper use of high-quality botanical products by healthcare professionals and consumers.' The garden is designed to blend harmoniously with the labs and lecture facilities.

Another medicinal garden in the USA with many indigenous plants was added in 2003 to the Indiana Medical History Museum, Indianapolis, dedicated to archiving the region's healing arts. It occupies most of the old pathology building of the former Central State Hospital. The museum is said to be haunted: the violent criminally insane used to be kept in underground tunnels, which are now demolished.

In Mexico, medicinal plants are used by many, and there are a growing number of medicinal gardens such as the Botanical Garden of the Institute of Biology, Mexico City, developed in 1959. In South America, the Maya Traditions Foundation was created in 1996 by Jane Mintz to help Maya women in Guatemala to learn skills and trades, and to preserve their ancient culture, including the use of medicinal plants. Even now, modern medicines and medical help are either too expensive or non-existent in more remote areas, and community health programmes work with local herbal healers to run health clinics using and teaching ancestral knowledge of medicinal plants. Part of this is teaching Maya women to grow the medicinal plants currently in San Juan la Laguna.

Medicinal Plant Garden, Indiana Medical History Museum, Indianapolis, USA.

Africa

Lowveld National Botanical Garden (Lowveld NBG) is one of nine, soon to be ten, botanical gardens managed by the South African National Biodiversity Institute (SANBI). SANBI is devoted to the conservation of native wildlife and plants, restoring ecosystems and educating the public about their plant heritage. 'Useful plants' are very much part of their focus. Located in a dramatic setting between two rivers with spectacular waterfalls, Lowveld NBG has a medicinal garden area, as do Free State and Pretoria NBGs.

Maya Traditions Medicinal Garden, San Juan la Laguna, Guatemala.

Asia

There are over three hundred medicinal plant gardens in India according to the list on their National Medicinal Plants board website. One visionary enterprise in the Rishi Valley Education Centre teaches local children to care for their own health. The surrounding hills are abundant in Ayurvedic medicinal plants, but urbanisation and the move to modern synthetic drugs have endangered their continued use. The Arya Vaidya Pharmacy is another unique Indian medicinal garden. Situated in the Centre for Indian Medical Heritage, next

Medicinal Garden, Lowveld National Botanical Garden, South Africa.

71

to an Ayurvedic medicine factory, it cultivates and conserves medicinal plants, and trains college and school students. Through medical camps and awareness programmes it promotes the use of herbs for primary health care.

The Great Himalayan National Park Conservation Area in India is a natural site of around 300 sq. miles (750 sq. km). In 2014 it was added to the UNESCO list of World Heritage Sites. A key objective is to develop alternatives to provide local people with income, preserving the natural and delicate ecosystem that nurtures the medicinal plants.

In the Far East is Singapore Botanic Gardens, the first and only tropical botanic garden with UNESCO World Heritage status. It incorporates a brilliant healing garden, founded in 2011. Containing over four hundred varieties, it features medicinal plants traditionally used in Southeast Asia. It is laid out in the shape of a body, planted with appropriate remedies for head, neck and throat; respiratory and circulatory systems; the digestive system; muscular, skeletal, skin and nervous systems; and reproductive organs. The website enticingly invites you to 'immerse yourself in the beauty and serenity of the healing garden and discover the power of plants to heal and enhance the quality of our life.'

A common theme for public physic gardens in developing parts of the world is conservation, often to preserve the diversity of species threatened by loss of interest in traditional folk medicines. At the opposite extreme is the danger of conservation areas raided by outside traders in lucrative herbal medicines, removing wild plants previously harvested sustainably for local use only.

Healing Garden, Singapore Botanic Gardens.

Across the world, physic gardens have long been supplying people with indigenous plants for their health. Physic and medicinal gardens are now seeing a resurgence because of the increasing need for sources of new drugs and to conserve biodiversity. By creating your own garden of natural plant medicines, you will take your place in this great, global tradition. Wherever you live, there will be indigenous species that may need to be nurtured, and perhaps protected, in your physic garden.

Knowing about these wonderful physic or medicinal plant gardens, with their visions and diversity, and perhaps also visiting some of today's gardens, may well inspire you to grow your own. But anyway, you can discover more reasons to grow your own in the next chapter.

6

Reasons to Grow Your Own

Creating a physic garden is a great adventure. It's exciting to discover the hidden powers of plants and follow ways of growing and using healing herbs from other times and climes. Reading old herbal folklore on winter days, and then tracking down seeds and seedlings, and growing and using them is a source of endless satisfaction. With a rich array of herbs on hand, you can experiment with tastes in teas and salads and scents for lotions and oils, and figure out what suits the needs of your body and mind. From medicine to magic, your physic garden will take you places you never dreamed of.

There are probably as many different reasons for creating a physic garden as there are gardeners, but here we summarise a few, from the pure pleasure of gardening, through growing plants for your own medicinal use, to the social, artistic and educational opportunities your garden can provide.

A garden with a difference

A physic garden is a place of peace and tranquillity. The atmosphere of calm and joy as the healing plants spread out in their new home is not all in the imagination. The blend of colours and scents brings you benefits and a sense of well-being just from spending time savouring your garden. For those with health issues, it might be a cup of fresh herbal tea or a barefoot walk on the chamomile patch that inspires you, or sets your mind at rest.

Growing remedies you can rely on

Taking your well-being into your own hands is empowering. Public medicinal plant gardens typically provide guidance only on plant uses but not on fresh products derived from those plants. In your own garden you can grow and use the plants *you* want. As you cultivate each species, you take responsibility for their quality, use and safety, engaging actively in your own healthcare.

Moreover, some disreputable commercial medicinal plant products can be adulterated, contaminated or deliberately spiked to mimic the intended use. Sometimes they even may not contain the advertised ingredient at all (see Chapter 11). By growing your own, you can be sure your source of seeds or plants is reliable, that your soil is not contaminated and that the plant was not compromised by artificial fertilisers or chemical pesticides. You can cultivate organically, and grow enough of your favourite herbs to see you through the year using reliable drying or tincture-making techniques.

Roots of elecampane (*Inula helenium*), as effective as echinacea as an immunostimulant, can be dried in spring or autumn to use all year.

Visitors to Dilston often remark that our fresh herb teas taste so much better than their teabags at home. Freshly picked leaves lose none of their powers nor suffer the chemical depletion that occurs when they are dried, crushed and stored at varying temperatures. (Whether the fresh infusion is more medicinal has not been investigated, but it feels like it!) Dried herbs are more concentrated, weight for weight – more active chemicals per gram of plant material – but this is at the cost of potential loss of active volatile agents and flavour (see Chapter 15).

Outreach and teaching

The original purpose of physic gardens was teaching and growing sufficient identified plant material, but medical students don't study botany any longer, and few doctors are taught the benefits of medicinal plants (although herbal medicine is formally taught as a degree course). So who needs a physic garden to learn about medicinal plants? The answer is simple: anyone who is interested in looking after their own health or in understanding the medicinal power of plants, and, crucially, anyone who wants to inspire the next generation to forge new paths for plant medicine in the future.

Physic gardens are a magnet for groups, from gardening clubs to institutes on a mission to learn. Healthcare professionals in your area or people with conditions such as cancer or disabilities, together with their carers, may come to see how plants might help or just to relax in a beautiful natural space devoted to healing.

Depending on what you want, and on the size of your physic garden, more organised activities such as workshops can be appropriate. Popular topics at Dilston are tree medicine, hedgerow medicine, first-aid herbs, wild plant food for health, spring tonics and botanic brain boosters. Making a lotion or syrup to take home is a great bonus for younger students, while perfume-making takes aromatic herbs into the realms of the exquisite.

We found ourselves collaborating with many others in diverse areas, from aromatherapy to veterinary medicine. An aromatherapist and medical herbalist introduced courses in root and bud medicines. Professional cooks demonstrated the use of health-boosting herbs in delicious dishes. Teachers of mindfulness meditation added a psychological dimension to our Botanic Brain Booster workshops. Courses by various experts are now part of our yearly programme of engaging the public and sharing our physic garden.

The Dilston Physic Garden phoenix signifies the rebirth of a twenty-first century physic garden from medieval models.

The physic garden as art studio

Any garden is enhanced by art, but in the physic garden art pieces draw attention to key concepts, prompt questions and fix health benefits in visitors' memories.

We found ourselves drawn into creating artworks inspired by aspects of our physic garden, and you may find the same in your garden. Sculptors and ceramicists created outdoor artworks that add to the experience of our plants. Sculptures of a medieval plague doctor, an angelica archangel, and a demon-dispelling figure of the antidepressant St John's wort, made in weatherproof metal and set in concrete, tell their own stories about how modern medicine depended on ancient physicians and plant folklore. Our phoenix sculpture expresses how a modern physic garden is reborn after the demise of the old models. A witch called Belladonna stands for a plant that can make a woman look beautiful but it is also highly dangerous (it's commonly known as deadly nightshade).

Medieval doctors filled their face masks with medicinal herbs to keep out the plague and held a long rod to keep the patient at a safe distance!

Art classes can range from meticulous botanical watercolours to impressionistic paintings inspired by anthropomorphism, Rudolf Steiner's philosophy that attributes feelings to plants. Creative arts classes include writing poetry or stories prompted by the appearance, scent, folklore and intriguing names of our herbs. Poisonous medicinal plants (grown for interest, not use of course!) not unexpectedly fascinate children, and are a source of inspiration for murder mysteries in adult creative writing classes. But it doesn't have to be a formal workshop – just enjoy drawing or writing a poem to a medicinal plant in your physic garden.

While most herbs and shrubs with medicinal powers are modest beauties rather than showy plants, medicinal trees or shrubs, like yew and box, lend themselves to topiary. Willows can be grown into sculptures, adding another artistic touch to the physic garden at relatively low cost, although they do require a lot of maintenance.

On the artistic side, musicians, writers, poets, painters and sculptors add something different to the hundreds of fact-packed plant signs throughout our garden. And these, with their information about wonderful old plant names and strange afflictions, can inspire on their own. A young singer and violinist standing among the wood betony playing her composition as a tribute to her favourite herb is a treasured memory. Others are a poem inspired by the deadly nightshade's angelic beauty and diabolical powers, a tribute to our triangular 'Mind, Body and Spirit' tranquillity pool, and a quantum haiku in the form of floating wooden words. Quite how these unexpected blessings arose is a mystery, one you may well share in your own physic garden.

Artwork by Dawn Hopps inspired by spirals and colours of herbal seed heads and flowers during a course on Vedic Art at Dilston Physic Garden.

The physic garden as research laboratory

Botanic gardens worldwide conduct research. In Cambridge University Botanic Garden, originally a physic garden, William Bateson initiated genetic research in 1901. Building on Mendel's famous experiments on pea plants, he brought the principles of heredity to the English-speaking world. There is still a genetics garden there for new crop species. At the Royal Botanic Gardens, Kew, renowned today for plant classification, conservation and chemistry, an exciting new initiative researching plant chemicals for dementia is linked in part to our own research at Dilston, testing medicinal plants on memory.

You can use your physic garden as a laboratory without buildings or benches. Research is defined as making observations with the aim of establishing facts and reaching new conclusions. So in your physic garden this could include observations like: growing conditions for the most strongly scented lavender flowers; the most effective drying methods for plants that die back in winter; which species protect or nourish other medicinal plants; or the most palatable herbal tea recipes. You might, as we do, get feedback from visitors on medicinal plants they use, why, and whether they work, or ask them to report on the effects of inhaling after crushing aromatics like our chamomile lawn.

None of these suggestions is too academic for an amateur physic gardener. After all, it was observations by individuals that inspired new herbalist practices in the first place and eventually triggered the first clinical trials. Alert, interested observers in villages and farms often discover new medicinal plants and new uses. You might notice which plants sick or injured animals eat to self-medicate, or which species people with particular disorders are drawn to. You might discover a whole new use for a known medicinal plant! Obviously, discovering new medicinal plants would involve a special area of your garden, with precautions in case of toxicity.

This potential for new discoveries is one more reason to embark on the adventure of growing medicinal plants. Scientific research may be run at great expense by experts in institutes, but you as a physic gardener could make your own contribution to the cause of medicinal plants.

Traditionally used to help 'ground' people, wood betony (*Stachys officinalis*) inspired our musician in residence to write a song about the plant.

A garden of cultural diversity

Your physic garden vision can focus on species from one culture or country: African, Asian or Australian Aboriginal medicinal herbs, for example, or plants used in traditional Chinese or Ayurvedic medicines, or those used by the ancient Greeks or medieval monks. Each culture

The hallucinogenic mescal cactus (*Lophophora williamsii*) used in shamanic rituals.

has its own *materia medica*, or catalogue of medicines. For instance, Dilston has a 'Time-Space' area for those medicinal plants used in different places (countries) and in different times (history) that thrive in our region. It's a reminder that plant medicine is global and still essential for more than half the world's population. Designing signboards for our plants brought home to us the different cultural theories of health, causes of disease and how plants heal, from moving chi energy (as in Traditional Chinese Medicine) to Western ideas on material mechanisms (like molecules). Interweaving many cultures in a physic garden creates new ideas on integrating world medical herbalism.

Particularly popular with visitors are plant spirit medicine and 'plants of the gods' workshops. A past PhD student in pharmacology regularly returns with his psychedelic cacti to recount his adventures with shamans in South America, explaining how the exotic plant chemicals they use act on the brain to induce visions. Visiting shamans and herbalists specialise in spirit medicine. Gowned members of the Order of Bards, Ovates and Druids celebrate the Celtic seasonal festivals in our own henge of oak pillars carved with local spiritual icons (from Celtic and pagan to Buddhist and Christian), a striking reminder that a physic garden can also provide a spiritual space.

Plant wines and spirits

A popular country craft was the making of wines and spirits from local plants, and there is no shortage of medicinal plants you can grow that make heavenly drinks.

Recipe
Spirit of sweet cicely

Cicely (*Myrrhis odorata*) makes a delicious, aniseed-flavoured spirit, sweet without the hazards of sugar, and with the added benefits of being a digestive. Pick fresh leaves in the spring and cover in vodka in a closed jar, leaving it to extract for 2-6 weeks depending on how strong a flavour you want. Strain through muslin and store in dark glass bottles. Add a measure to a glass of ice cubes, with water as required, and it will turn cloudy like the anise drink.

Sweet cicely (*Myrrhis odorata*), a naturally sweet medicinal plant.

Monks are renowned for making wines and liqueurs, often with healing herbs as ingredients. Benedictine and Chartreuse are still produced in monasteries in Normandy and Grenoble, France. The recipes are secret, but some of the 150 herbs in Green Chartreuse are known, and are medicinal: cinnamon, lemon balm, hyssop, peppermint, thyme, costmary, arnica and angelica. Italian Galliano liqueur is made from vanilla and star anise.

Herb wine is a veritable home industry. Elderflower champagne and wines made from elderberry and rose petals are some of our favourite homemade tipples. The Mother Earth Living website has exciting recipes to try. The ingredients have established antibiotic, tonic or soothing properties. There is hardly a herb that has not been made into wine (by fermentation or infusion) or spirit (by distillation or infusion). Combining healing herbs with conviviality and pleasure is a double benefit your physic garden can supply.

The rising sap of silver birch (*Betula pendula*) makes a fine tasting wine. Birch is traditionally used as an antirheumatic, and lab tests indicate anticancer effects.

If wines and spirits don't appeal, or if you avoid alcohol, you can make herb vinegars or grow health-promoting spices instead. Turmeric, ginger, cinnamon and cloves have potent health benefits. Spices don't just grow in tropical or desert climates. Caraway, fenugreek and juniper thrive in Northern Europe. A fascinating compilation of spices from countries around the world is the Geographic Spice Index, in which almost every plant listed is medicinal as well as flavoursome.

Fenugreek (*Trigonella foenum-graecum*) is a metabolic and menopausal aid supported by science. It grows in temperate zones to produce spicy green leaves.

Nature in the physic garden

Animal visitors may not be in your physic garden design but they will remind you of one of the reasons why plants have medicinal effects: chemicals that attract pollinators or propagators or that repel too-greedy predators are beneficial to human health. Wild creatures enhance your garden for human visitors. Leave undergrowth for birds to nest in and they will stay to enjoy blossom buds, nuts and fruit. In Australia, dramatic and much-loved birds like rainbow lorikeets, king parrots and kookaburras match the drama of tropical medicinal plants, as do enormous fruit-eating flying fox bats.

Rainbow lorikeet, a welcome garden visitor in Australia.

Some animal visitors may threaten your plants, such as rabbits raiding tender leaves. Sun-basking physic garden cats and kittens keep them at bay and also delight visitors young and old. Squirrels, while cute, can be the worst vandals, destroying nests and digging up bulbs. Fruit bats can break thin branches as they gorge on fruit, though others catch insects. You decide how to deter them. Our cats even catch the grey squirrels that are so invasive in the UK they are killed legally and sold to eat! Or you welcome nature in, in the hope that a natural balance will result. Medicinal plants evolved to cope with natural 'enemies'. Damage stimulates the defence mechanisms of the plant, making more of those medicinal ingredients, those plant secondary metabolites that, at the right dose, benefit human health (see Chapter 1).

Butterflies, moths and other pollinating insects find sanctuary in the garden and add their beauty. Beehives on site provide delicious honey flavoured with aromatic flowers from all those healing plants. The drowsy hum of honey bees visiting the lavender and oregano beds on a sunny day is a delight, as is their 'physic' honey from the hive. We have large beds of lemon balm (*Melissa officinalis*) for teas and dried herbs for the winter. A visiting beekeeper told us that if you rub yourself all over with melissa, the bees will not sting you. It must calm them, just as it did for the human subjects of our early university research, when we treated them with melissa essential oil. This solved a great puzzle for us as 'melissa' means honeybee in Greek (from 'meli', the Greek for honey), allegedly because bees love it. We have never seen a single bee on its tiny white flowers, so people may have confused melissa (or lemon balm) with bee balm (*Monarda*) that attracts them in droves. Your physic garden will bring you fascinating facts that you won't find in textbooks!

Sharing your physic garden with other people

There is great joy in sharing your healing garden. Friends, family or friendly passers-by will love to take a freshly picked herbal tea and hear the latest on healing herbs. Visitors will bring you ideas, seeds and new opportunities. Formally or informally, your growing, changing physic garden will stimulate conversations.

Friends and unexpected guests helped to set up our physic garden and still lend a hand today. A computer-literate colleague set up our system of signs. One beautiful summer's day we opened the garden in aid of a local charity, and to our delighted surprise it attracted hundreds of visitors. This prompted regular public openings, and in 2005 led us to make the physic garden an educational registered charity.

Children are often interested in the special features of gardens, physic or not. Historic Alnwick Castle in Northumberland, UK, is a location used in the Harry Potter films, and has a 'poison garden' that is very popular with young visitors. Stories about herbal magic and medicine sow seeds of interest in young minds. Potion clubs liven up our physic garden scene for youngsters, and treasure hunts and quiz trails provide them with life-changing medicinal plant knowledge. They also learn that it was ancient Roman soldiers who brought healing herbs to Northumberland two millennia ago.

Visitors who come to learn or just out of curiosity, and volunteers looking after the medicinal plants often forge new friendships. For the physic gardener, the efforts of growing your own medicinal plants are endlessly rewarded.

In Northumberland imported herbs were used by the Roman army doctors, stationed along this Roman wall.

Commercial opportunities

If you are considering operating commercially, growing medicinal plants or products for sale could profitably fill a gap in the market, since there are currently only a few sources of remedies made from rare and authenticated species. Plants that thrive in your physic garden are the ones to consider for this, because you want to be sure you will have an adequate supply of the plant materials you need. You might create a niche market for specifically targeted foods, teas and toiletries (but be aware of strict restrictions and regulations for marketing a herbal product for medicinal use).

Before we opened to the public, we held a charity event and assumed that visitors would want to find out about healing herbs. Most, however, just wanted to know where the tea and cakes were! So now we provide herbal teas, cakes and biscuits as 'tasters' of medicinal plants. This adds to visitors' enjoyment and perhaps also a little to their education. A physic garden on its own or attached to another enterprise could usefully have an on-site restaurant using herbs grown in the physic garden, attracting those who like 'food as medicine'. The dishes at the The Physic Garden Café at Chelsea Physic Garden are flavoured with herbs and help draw people to the garden.

If the notion of creating a physic garden of whatever size has caught your fancy, then the next chapter will provide ideas about how to design it.

SAGE GARDEN

This area of the garden (sheltered against the prevailing westerly wind) contains over 20 species of medicinal, culinary or ornamental sages.

The Chinese used to exchange six cases of their green tea for one of our common sage (Salvia officinalis).

7

Planning Your Physic Garden

Originally, physic gardens were for educating and supplying physicians, but today your physic garden is for you, your needs, and you can be as flexible as you want. Whatever the site, its size and purpose, your physic garden begins in your mind, and much of the fun is in designing it. As well as providing the plants you want, your physic garden should work in harmony with your available climate, space and resources, and here we cover all these aspects.

Where?

Is the physic garden only for you or friends and family under your supervision, or will the public, students, specialist groups be visiting? If your physic garden is for your own pleasure and interest, your home plot or allotment is fine. You can grow a physic garden almost anywhere, including in pots in the back yard, but of course some of the larger-scale features, such as a chamomile lawn, or a woodland area, are suitable only for larger gardens.

For individual use, the physic garden could be as near the kitchen door as possible to facilitate fresh-picked herbal teas or salads. Drying your herbs near an open window (out of direct sunlight) or making tinctures in the kitchen is fine on a small scale, but a herb-drying cabinet and tea-making area are necessary for herbal products on a larger scale.

For public access and interest, get creative! Local authorities may allow you to convert a public park or waste area, or a community garden on reclaimed land or attached to a local school, church or museum. Our Dilston Physic Garden emerged in wild Northumbrian countryside when we purchased an acre of pasture to grow medicinal plants for our university research into the science of memory plants.

A variety of ecosystems provides a richer range of medicinal plants. Natural or created meadow, hedgerow, waterside and woodland plants added to traditional beds reproduce the experience of foraging for medicinal plants in the wild. Wherever you are, certain species will outstrip others in unpredictable ways. We have carpets of woodruff rather than wild garlic spreading through the wooded area, horseradish and Jerusalem artichokes taking over in the culinary garden, mugwort and wild lettuce invading every corner.

How climate affects your choice of plant

Whether your local climate is arctic or amiable, aquatic or arid, there will be medicinal plants that will flourish, and of course there will be others that just aren't suitable. For example, in Northern Europe holy basil, which is valued for medicinal and culinary qualities, will only thrive inside on kitchen windowsills.

Holy basil (*Ocimum sanctum*) is revered in India as the sacred plant tulsi. Widespread evidence-based benefits include stress relief and cognitive enhancement.

Our approach for a diverse physic garden is to grow all and any medicinal plants that will thrive in your local climate and soil. A few seasons will tell you what survives or thrives. Long ago, we stopped replacing plants like liquorice that were killed by our cold winters, whereas friends in north-western Australia gave up on lavender and rose bushes as they wilted away in the heat and humidity. The sky-brushing silvery eucalyptus is a powerful antiseptic; it's native to Australia but somehow survives deep frozen winters in Northern Europe. A magnificent *Eucalyptus gunnii* of ours, apparently dead after one such winter, suddenly resprouted two years later and, with its long shallow roots, went back to stealing water from the nearby local plants which risked dying in the drought. Therefore, you must be cautious about introducing aliens, and think about how the physic garden is set in the local landscape.

In temperate zones the best site for most medicinal plants is well-drained, and in full or partial sun where aromatic plants produce more essential oils ('sunshine oils'), as shown by both scent and chemical analysis. Lavender, sage or thyme in shaded temperate zones are sorry sights. Failure to thrive is also a symptom of wet roots for many woody perennials. But then others such as woodruff, wild garlic and mints love shade or damp.

In subtropical regions, full sun and humidity are the enemies of perennials like lavender, which only survives in the winter, unable to cope even with shade. Variations in rainfall, mean temperature, frost-free periods, sunshine duration, soil pH, soil organic matter and available minerals influence not only growth and survival but also the active agents in medicinal plants. This varies for each plant and its therapeutic chemicals. A study in north-west China measured active chemicals in one medicinal plant related to the mayapple (*Sinopodophyllum hexandrum*),

Woodland ground cover of sweet woodruff (*Galium odoratum*) which has traditional uses for digestive and uterine conditions, yet to be subjected to scientific scrutiny.

in different growing conditions: the type of active chemical is unaffected, in this instance podophyllotoxins (antiviral and derived anticancer agents), but the levels increased with less rain and more organic matter. Other scientific papers and websites provide information on growing conditions for crops for maximum medicinal or nutritional chemical content (for example, for the intensely sweet glycosides in stevia).

To find out which species from other countries will grow in your area – for example Traditional Chinese Medicine (TCM) species in Northern Europe, or northern European species in Southern Australia – study gardens that have succeeded. Chelsea Physic Garden has its world medicine area with beds of TCM, Ayurvedic, Maori, Australian aboriginal and South African tribal medicinal plants, which all grow in the temperate London climate. Up to twenty species for each culture are listed on their website.

Chinese medicinal plants that survive further north include the *Ginkgo biloba* 'memory' tree, numerous rampaging bamboos considered to be cooling and phlegm-eliminating, and giant rhubarbs including the Himalayan rhubarb (*Rheum australe*).

As you 'test' plant, you can choose or control conditions for optimum results. For those plants that you want but which won't thrive anywhere, there are 'behave-alikes'. For example, liquorice doesn't grow well in Northern Europe, but anise hyssop (*Agastache foeniculum*) and sweet cicely (*Myrrhis odorata*) both flourish, taste of aniseed, have some similar chemicals such as anethole and, where investigated, similar

Himalayan rhubarb (*Rheum australe*), closely related to the Chinese medical species (*Rheum officinale*) used in India and Nepal for over fifty different ailments (circulatory, digestive, respiratory).

Anise hyssop (*Agastache foeniculum*), one of several hardy liquorice-tasting plants, contains the same chemical (anethole) as liquorice.

digestive properties (see our sweet cicely spirit recipe in Chapter 6). A hardy ginger lily (*Hedychium spicatum*) has a ginger-smelling rhizome used for coughs and fevers (with traditional uses backed up by lab tests).

For growing exotics like ginger and turmeric in temperate zones you can create an artificial climate using a hotbed, glasshouse or biodome. However, these pampering and protected conditions may not encourage the plant to make those bioactive self-defence chemicals. It is only by fighting to survive in a natural environment, subject to adverse weather and full of life-threatening microbes and ravenous animals, that many of those plant molecules that benefit our health are produced (see Chapter 1).

What to plant?

You may have a specific purpose in creating your physic garden or perhaps you just want to grow as wide a variety as possible. While we have happily followed both routes, judging by most physic gardens, comprehensive collections are most popular. But pursuing your special interests makes your physic garden unique and can be more rewarding for you and your visitors. You could consider starting as we did, with a kind of 'collectomania', scooping up as many medicinal plants as you can find and grow. You can then narrow your focus as you see which plants thrive and which you use most for flavour, health or medicine.

Deciding which species to grow in order to prevent or treat a condition can be complicated. There are often dozens of medicinal plants used traditionally for one symptom or disorder. And, conversely, one plant can treat many different disorders. Which ones to use depends not only on your personal choice, but also on how the plant works in your body and with any other medical conditions. You might find a herbalist in your area who could tell you which herbs grow well locally and relate to your needs. Chapter 8 provides detailed charts for selecting your plants by medical condition, and Chapter 9 has more information (including growing details, habit, size, aspect and zone) for popular plants that are safe and widely used.

Designing and laying out

Your physic garden plan is intimately linked to the design, taking into account your purpose in creating it, herbal remedies, the habits of the plants and any other people involved.

Medicinal plants, being wild, are beautiful though modest in colour and size of blooms. Ordering them in beds for specific uses with informative signs is traditional for a physic garden. For most of us growing healing herbs for health, a simple design works well, though novel ideas like using the human body and its parts as a template for planting the different medicinal plants, as they do at Singapore Botanic Gardens, can be tempting.

Walled and knot gardens, courtyards and structured foregrounds of buildings are extremely elegant but don't necessarily suit the character of wild medicinal plants, and immovable beds and permanent paved or gravel paths don't accommodate the roving habits of many wild species. The St John's wort bed at Dilston is forever shifting because after a year or two and having exhausted their favourite nutrients in the patch of ground, the plants won't regrow but instead seed vigorously in all *except* their own bed. Movable dividers and signs solve this problem. We use felled tree trunks and lopped or pruned branches laid on the ground to divide beds. As a bonus all sorts of wood fungi decorate them, and they are wildlife habitats too. As the wood rots, some of these saprophytic fungi look marvellous, though beware – some can be poisonous. The appropriately named Funeral bell (*Galerina marginata*) can grow on decaying wood in the UK. But other physic gardens, *do* use bounded beds to contain the nomads. As well as clear boundaries, you will also want to provide easy access with paths or central space.

Your design will certainly be shaped by the unexpected habits of your healing herbs. They may drive you to create a new feature. Our Dilston chamomile lawn grew of its own accord out of a small patch of Roman chamomile (*Chamaemelum nobile* 'Treneague'). It never flowers but constantly spreads, especially if people walk on it, which they love to do, inhaling the relaxing aroma. Shakespeare knew that chamomile thrives underfoot and had Falstaff advise: 'For though the camomile, the more it is trodden on, the faster it grows'

(*Henry IV, Part 1*). The Dilston chamomile lawn may be unique in being solely chamomile. Keeping it that way, small as it is (100 square feet), takes our volunteer team half a day's weeding each week. The famous and much larger chamomile lawn in the grounds of Buckingham Palace dates back to the reign of George V, though it is mostly common grass with only occasional chamomile plants visible. In its full (dare we say) pure glory, a chamomile lawn is soft to sit on, sweet to smell and calming to be near. Our visitors relax and sometimes fall asleep, crying kids fall silent, even the weary weeders smile, just as the properties of the plant determine. The title of Mary Wesley's first bestselling novel, *The Chamomile Lawn*, which later became a hit TV series, refers to a fragrant lawn stretching down to the cliffs in the garden of the aunt's house.

The chamomile lawn at Dilston. Small in size is major on maintenance!

How much space does each plant need?

If you're growing a herb for the occasional cup of tea it's up to you, but if you're wanting a medicinal dose, quantities for planting and dosage are easy to work out. Here's an example. Let's say you want to take sage for menopause or memory at five grams a dose, three times a day. Over a year that comes to 5g X 3 X 365 = 5,475g (5½ kg) so you need enough plants to provide 5½ kg of leaves each year. While these would ideally all be harvested in early summer, fresh leaves can be picked all year round. The flavour mellows in winter and ingredients change (camphor is higher in winter and borneol higher in summer), but what happens to the health benefits is currently unknown.

Formal and geometric layouts

For a formal design you can get ideas and inspiration from some of the classic physic gardens of the world (see Chapter 5).

The circular design of the Orto Botanico – Padua Physic Garden – of old.

Cowbridge Physic Garden in Wales with its fountain, herb borders and Roman-style gazebo.

The Cowbridge Physic Garden, in an old market town in Wales, is formally and delightfully laid out with inviting paths and ornamental structures, all set among old stone buildings.

The classic knot garden beloved of Tudor gardeners is perennially popular for herb gardens of all kinds, with divisions for aromatic, culinary and medicinal plants. You might like to base yours on a pattern that has meaning for you – perhaps a Celtic symbol, or spiritual one like a mandala (symbolic of the cosmos) from Indian religions, or something significant to your culture or area of interest. Keeping the tiny neat boundary hedges in order is high maintenance but worth it.

The Lewes Priory garden in Sussex, UK, is modelled on the original monastic garden there, with dozens of herbs set out in the site of the old hospital where, long ago, monks and nuns kept herbal medicine alive in local communities.

Or you could consider planting in beds that replicate the shape of the human body, with subsections of plants for different body parts, or allocating plants to beds named after hospital wards, as in London's innovative Urban Physic Garden.

Informal or wild layouts

The natural look is increasingly popular. For medicinal plants, wilderness, wild meadow and woodland are particularly appropriate as the plants originated in the wild. This also accommodates plants migrating naturally as they deplete their original soil nutrients, similar to crop rotation. With so many medicinal plants being wild, visitors sometimes wonder why our physic garden is so full of 'weeds'!

Working with nature, if the laws in your area allow, you could go so far as to ditch the design and fence off a section of wilderness or woodland. Nowadays, land around towns and cities is allocated to farmers, while woods are used for timber or turned into manicured parkland. Such monocultures lead to the extinction of many medicinal plants, so today's conservation work of botanic gardens and physic gardens is taking on a new importance.

Your local landscape lies behind your plants, trees, paths and artefacts, and you may need to do some blending, structuring or screening to accommodate it. Unless yours is an enclosed walled garden, background settings like hillsides, buildings, trees or lakes will influence your layout – a wild meadow area in a town, or formal knot gardens in remote countryside may not be ideal. Long-line beds and paths in Chelsea Physic Garden suit its location in the heart of a capital city, while our random Dilston garden

The wild look of Dilston Physic Garden fits its Tyne Valley rural environ.

layout blends with its rural river valley setting. Nurturing self-seeded plants fits with a time-honoured principle. According to Ayurvedic medicine, plants that spread naturally are more potent than cultivated specimens. They certainly look more lush when they themselves choose where to grow.

The Piedmont Physic Garden in South Carolina.

The Piedmont Physic Garden in South Carolina 'celebrates the natural landscape' by concentrating on plants native to the south Appalachian corridor. Matching physic garden plants to the surrounding flora is one of our natural landscaping strategies at Dilston. It depends on identifying local medicinal plants and trees growing in the wild, and acquiring those species without breaking the law relating to wild flora. In fact, local plants constantly take up residence of their own accord: seeds blow in with the winds or arrive in bird droppings.

A new physic garden in the form of a medicine wheel being constructed in Kenya. The idea and development of the Nairobi Physic Garden is due to Deborah Coulson, a Dilston Foundation in Plant Medicine student.

To our delight a student on the Dilston plant medicine course decided to create a physic garden near Nairobi, Kenya. And to our surprise it's a large formal medicine wheel construction with walls and dividers.

Labelling: the vital feature of any physic garden

Identifying individual species, especially in mixed beds such as those dedicated to particular bodily systems, needs vigilance as plants spread, seed and encroach. Therefore, signage is an integral part of physic garden design, and is especially important in wild or informal gardens with less structured beds and in gardens visited by people seeking information. Even in a private garden, clear labelling is essential, so there is no possibility of misidentifying plants. For signage, stones carved with plant names or, as we spotted in one Scottish garden, indelibly marked razor sea shells are attractive. For adding information that is going to be updated, our sign designs (A4-sized laminates on stainless steel plates) have evolved over the years to weather well and allow easy updating and relocating. We position the labels knee-high and slanted upwards to save the backs and eyesight of visitors and gardeners alike.

For physic gardens with visitors, signs do more than label the plant; they add important information and interest. Our signs have room for the common name, plant family, Latin name, and brief notes on traditional herbal medicine use, clinical and scientific evidence, and folklore. Details on parts of the plant used, growing and harvesting seasons, formulations and dosage would answer many visitors' questions, but at that point the signs would overshadow the plants!

HIBISCUS
Hibiscus

Digestive, tonic, diuretic, hypotensive. Clinically proven to reduce blood lipids in diabetics. Used in Ayurvedic medicine to strengthen hair roots. In vitro evidence for antioxidant, in vitro & in vivo evidence for anti-atherosclerotic activities. Significant antitumour activity of H. sabdariffa L.

Dilston medicinal plant signs are regularly updated as new scientific studies emerge.

Variations on a theme

If you are a gardener who prefers a more planned approach, you can arrange your plants as parts of an overall garden theme while still producing all the medicinal plants you want for health purposes. Here are some suggestions about themed planting layouts that may appeal.

Themed planting

Aromatic herbs/sensory garden	Conservation of rare or indigenous species
Cosmetics & beauty aids; perfume species	Creative arts, e.g. botanical painting, creative writing
Culinary: vegetables & spices; fruit & nuts	Plants for mainstream drugs, e.g. willow, yew (many toxic)
Ecosystems, e.g. arid, rock, water, tropical plants	Flower essences & flower medicines
Folklore & history: plants with good stories	Ritualistic or recreational – safe psychedelic plants
Herbal teas & infusions	Wines & spirits
Spices	Monastic herbs used by monks
Woodland/tree medicines	Spirituality - incense, smudging, sacred ceremonies

Other attractive features common to physic or healing plant gardens over the ages that you might like to include are: reclining seats in aromatic areas; a meadow of wild medicinal plants; a wilderness for seed collections and self-seeding of medicinal plants; world plant medicine collections; or that labour of love – the chamomile lawn.

While our Dilston garden is firmly founded on medical science, our visitors also love the magic and folklore of herbs. You can grow trees still used in Wicca (pagan witchcraft) to make wands and divining rods, or if you dare, grow witchy species like belladonna and mandrake in marked-as-toxic corners. Or you could feature plants symbolic for life's rituals, like rosemary for remembrance. The wedding bouquet traditionally held herbs symbolising good fortune, aphrodisiacs, fertility and even stress relief for nervous brides – Queen Victoria had myrtle in her bouquet. For funerals, herbs such as garlic, clove and sage were used to help the spirit move on and avert hauntings. Such uses are short on scientific evidence but have long traditions behind them. However, clinical evidence for the anti-acne actions of myrtle do provide one possible reason for wedding-day benefits!

This wooden henge and mosaic in the Dilston garden celebrate different spiritual ways and plants used in rituals.

The Angelica Archangelica figure in the Dilston garden highlights how angelica was discovered as a cure for the plague through a monk's dream (the plant has antibiotic properties).

Non-botanical features

For extra visual impact and allure, we add an occasional iconic artwork linked to the healing properties and folklore of the plants, or allow more spectacular species to rampage in areas between the signed beds. Iconic art forms are both useful and ornamental, as are sculptures, birdbaths, sundials, seats, gazebos or shelters. A beautiful as well as practical physic garden is a stronger advocate for medicinal plants.

Before you start planting: balance and aesthetics

Before digging in the plants and placing signs, it pays to stand back and survey the design. Without form and colour to delight the eye, your physic garden will not attract attention. Plant medicinal trees to punctuate beds of unassuming species. Low-growing trees like rowans, elders, hazels, chinchona or cocoa may work better than water-hogging willows or towering eucalyptus. Clusters of trees and shrubs add an irresistible urge to see what's behind them.

To add architectural interest for visitors, painters or photographers, plant spectacular trees like palm – the benefits of coconut oil are endless; red maple for sore eyes; camphor tree (*Cinnamomum camphora*) to clear catarrh; eucalyptus for respiratory ailments; white birch for water retention; and eye-catching plants like yucca, which are anticancer and anti-inflammatory; cardoon (*Cynara cardunculus*), proven to aid digestion, mullein (*Verbascum*), also antitumour, or aloes and agave to soothe soreness.

The wild artichoke (*Cynara cardunculus*) is one of the most dramatic medicinal plants, treating dyspepsia and hepatitis C in clinical trials.

If lavender thrives in your region and if space allows, a glorious sight and scent is a spacious bed of the medicinal variety *Lavandula angustifolia*. Just as the flowers open, a shimmering sea of blue draws in the honey bees. Adding the gentle buzzing of bees to enticing scents of aromatic herbs also works with oregano and thyme. Non-aromatic medicinal plants like viper's bugloss (*Echium vulgare*), echinacea, bacopa or (toxic) foxglove also attract bees as well as butterflies. Or you might want a lawn as an area for relaxation, or just an open grass space to create perspective or for children to play.

Inspired by a reason and driven by a plan, the next move is choosing plants to fill the space that's going be your unique physic garden. That reason and that plan are bound to change as you go over the options of medicinal plants and see how they grow with you. It's a two-way plant-propagator process that is part of the enjoyment of being a physic gardener. In the next two chapters we offer a choice of plants for different aspects of health, and provide essential details on knowing, growing and using our favourites.

SIMON Y. MILLS — The Essential Book of

BARTRAM'S ENCYCLOPEDIA of HERBAL MEDICINE — Thomas Bartra

THE · MACDONALD · ENCYCLOPEDIA · OF Medicinal Plants

TISH HERBAL PHARMACOPOEIA 1996 — BH

Herbal Medicine · Second edition — elmann

Encyclopedia of Herbal Medicine FIRST EDITION

8

Deciding Which Plants to Grow

To help you decide which plants to grow, this chapter provides charts, arranged by bodily systems (e.g. 'Cardiovascular system', 'Skin') and related medical conditions, listing the healing plants for these conditions. Then, when you have decided which plants are appropriate for your condition(s), you can find out more about them and how to grow them.

First, though, please take note:

- Conventional and herbal medicine differ in their philosophy, definitions and diagnosis of symptoms, systems and disease. Conventional medicine is reductionist (diagnosis, followed by standardised treatment), whereas herbal medicine is governed by integrated holistic approaches often tailored specifically to the individual.

- Different medical herbalists may use many different plants for any one condition. Conversely, a single plant can be used to treat several different conditions.

- We include many plants that have controlled clinical trial evidence (**in bold**) to support the traditional use.

- Some studies support the mainstream Western approach – i.e. one plant or drug is used for each condition – and others support the herbalist style of using plant combinations for treatment (although combinations are increasingly used in mainstream pharmacotherapy).

- There is a vast body of information on medicinal plants used in Traditional Chinese Medicine , Ayurveda and other non-Western cultures. We haven't included those sources here because we are concentrating on medicinal plants that are both easy to grow in the West and can be obtained readily. Nevertheless, most research in plant medicine today is carried out in the East, not West.

Therefore this chapter is deliberately not exhaustive. Instead, we recommend about twenty plants each for the dozen or so symptoms or conditions associated with different bodily systems. These are plants used widely by herbalists in the West today, are safe to take and, in most instances, are easy to grow.

The health conditions and complaints that we consider suitable for treating with plant medicine are:

1. Common medical conditions identified at accredited clinical organisations such as the Mayo Clinic (US) or NHS (UK). Generally *not* included are serious conditions requiring immediate medical attention where there are extremely effective mainstream medical treatments.
2. Conditions commonly treated by practising herbalists identified in classic modern medical herbal texts and on reliable websites (full references in the resources at the end of the book).
3. Conditions generally recognised as suitable for self-medication and not requiring medical supervision – the type of problems for which people seek advice from pharmacists and that can be treated with non-prescription remedies.
4. Minor ailments that people in our survey said they would use herbal medicine for.
5. More serious conditions where there are no effective, safe, well-tolerated mainstream treatments, but where safe, long-term protection and prevention are still needed.

This chapter divides the health conditions into eight bodily systems:

- Cardiovascular system
- Central nervous system
- Digestive system
- Infections and infestations
- Musculoskeletal disorders
- Reproductive system
- Respiratory function
- Skin

For each category we recommend (based on standard herbal texts) suitable medicinal plants to help you choose the plants to grow in your physic garden. A unique feature of our charts is scientific evidence. Increasing numbers of plants in the charts are backed with clinical verification (one or more controlled clinical trial supporting traditional medical uses).

The chart information has also been checked for accuracy by practising medical herbalists and a UK General Practitioner. Bear in mind what we have said throughout – that when it comes to using any of these plants for your health, any conditions, medications and contraindications have to be taken into account.

We have not provided 'preclinical' evidence (based on in vitro and in vivo lab tests), which is accumulating for many more plants than listed here; we may soon see clinical trials for these. So while our charts will help you choose plants for your physic garden now, you can update them yourself as new tests are run (see Chapter 2).

Frequently Asked Questions

Dilston's practising herbalists regularly answer questions from visitors. Ross Menzies's answers to questions about plants for specific conditions give you a glimpse of the astonishing diversity of plant medicines for common conditions – the depth of nature's medicine chest.

Recommended plants for:

Anxiety: chamomile, lemon balm, mistletoe, motherwort, pasque flower, passion flower, skullcap, valerian, vervain, wild lettuce, wild oats, wood betony

Arthritis: devil's claw, goldenrod, meadowsweet, nettle, silver birch, turmeric, willow

Eczema: barberry, blue flag, burdock, cleavers, dandelion root, echinacea, mountain grape, nettle, red clover, sarsaparilla

Insomnia: chamomile, hops, Jamaican dogwood, lime flowers, passion flower, skullcap, valerian, wild lettuce, wood betony

Irritable bowel: angelica, chamomile, dogwood bark, fennel, gentian, meadowsweet, peppermint, slippery elm, vervain

Memory: capsicum, ginkgo, hawthorn, lavender, lemon balm, rosemary, sage, turmeric

Menopause: agnus-castus, black cohosh, evening primrose, hops, lady's mantle, motherwort, pasque flower, red clover, sage, sarsaparilla, St John's wort

Psoriasis: barberry, blue flag, burdock, burdock nettle, cleavers, figwort, mountain grape, poke root, sarsaparilla, yellow dock

Rheumatism: devil's claw, echinacea, meadowsweet, Siberian ginseng, silver birch, turmeric, wild indigo, willow

Run down/energy depleted: ashwagandha, echinacea, Korean ginseng, liquorice, nettle, rhodiola, sarsaparilla, Siberian ginseng, slippery elm, wild oats

Pasque flower (*Pulsatilla*) prescribed by medical herbalist Ross Menzies for insomnia.

Ross added to his responses above, by way of explanation:

> These are chronic states of imbalance. Prescribing herbs requires a personal understanding of why and how, the cause and managing symptoms, all best supported by a herbalist. However, those herbs listed are commonly used by myself and other herbalists to help manage the conditions. A herbalist will always ask the question, What changes are the symptoms asking the person to make? These changes can be dietary, lifestyle, emotional or deeper personal change. The herbalist will support the patient in a process of reflection and change and the medicines prescribed will be used as part of this process. Healing is often gradual and, as change can be difficult for people, it can also be a demanding process. However, it can be transformative and is well worth the effort.

The conditions listed in the box on the previous page are not well managed in mainstream medicine, and many were identified in our web-based survey as the complaints most commonly treated with herbal medicines.

We conducted the survey in 2016 in conjunction with Newcastle University. The 170 respondents cited arthritis/joint pain, coughs, fever, headache/migraine, hypertension, injuries, mental problems, menstruation, sleep and stomach pain. Fewer than 5% mentioned cancer, heart disease or prostate problems, presumably because these are covered by mainstream medicine or are perceived as too serious for herbalism.

Responses to the survey also reflected those conditions often referred to pharmacists for advice: skin conditions (mild acne and eczema), coughs and colds, minor cuts and bruises, constipation, haemorrhoids (piles), hay fever and allergies, pain (headaches, earache or back pain), indigestion, diarrhoea and intestinal threadworms, period pain and thrush, warts and verrucas, mouth ulcers, cold sores, athlete's foot, nappy rash and teething.

In our charts we don't show anti-inflammatories, antioxidants and immunostimulants as separate categories because so many different plant species have these qualities. And we have excluded herbs like ephedra, lily of the valley or lobelia which are too strong for self-medication.

As this section of the book is so fact-filled, we lighten it with extra information about the stars of the plant world. We also include some traditional/anecdotal uses because there is a powerful argument that long-standing use of a plant as safe and effective is as good an evidence-base as any (and indeed, the science often backs this up).

We use plants' common Western names in the charts unless the plant is unfamiliar or there are closely related species, in which case we will also give the Latin name to specify exactly the species we mean (on first mention only). For many conditions there are also numerous reports on the efficacy of Chinese herbal combinations.

Parts of the plant used are not specified for almost all; for many plants it can be more than one part. You will find the most commonly used part in the resources.

Plants in **bold** have one or more controlled clinical trials verifying their traditional medical uses, some in combination with others.

Cardiovascular system

Condition	Medicinal plants (those in bold are based on controlled clinical trials)
Anaemia	ashwagandha (*Withania somnifera*), blueberry, coriander, **dandelion**, nettle, pine (nut), plum, soy, yellow dock (*Rumex crispus*)
Angina	arjuna (*Terminalia arjuna*), astragalus, *Angelica archangelica*, forskolin (*Coleus forskohlii*), **garlic**, **hawthorn**, motherwort, **Panax ginseng**, **roseroot**, *Salvia miltiorrhiza*, Siberian ginseng
Anticoagulant	**dong quai (*Angelica sinensis*)**, feverfew, garlic, ginger, ginkgo, ginseng, hawthorn, horse chestnut (*Aesculus hippocastanum*), motherwort, St John's wort, turmeric, willow
Antihaemorrhagic/stops bleeding (styptic)	agrimony (*Agrimonia*), arnica, capsicum, lotus, oak (bark), plantain, **rhubarb (*R. officinale* and *nobile*)**, salad burnet (*Sanguisorba minor*), selfheal (*Prunella vulgaris*), witch hazel (*Hamamelis*), woodruff (*Galium odoratum*), yarrow (*Achillea millefolium*)
Arrhythmias/palpitations	*Angelica archangelica*, barberry, hawthorn, **lemon balm**, motherwort, passion flower, skullcap, valerian
Arteriosclerosis	bilberry, blueberry, **garlic**, ginkgo, hawthorn, lime, mistletoe, pine (**Pinus eldarica**), turmeric, yarrow
Cholesterol control	***Achillea wilhelmsii***, alfalfa, **aloe**, apple, **arjuna**, artichoke (globe), **ashwagandha**, avocado, **black cumin (*Nigella sativa*)**, blueberry, coconut, evening primrose, **fenugreek**, **frankincense**, **garlic**, ginger, grape seed, green tea, **hawthorn**, holy basil, Mojave yucca (***Yucca schidigera***), **oats**, onion, Persian hogweed (*Heracleum persicum*), **plantain**, **rhubarb**, **rosehip**, **sage (*S. officinalis*)**, sesame, **soy**, **turmeric**, **walnut**, **whortleberry (*Vaccinium arctostaphylos*)**, yarrow
Circulation (improving), general	blueberry, capsicum, cinnamon, **cocoa**, coriander, **garlic**, ginkgo, ginger, **ginseng**, gotu kola, hawthorn, **horse chestnut**, horseradish, mustard, peppermint, **red vine (leaf)**, rosemary
Congestive heart failure	**arjuna (*Terminalia arjuna*)**, **cocoa**, garlic, **ginseng**, green tea, **hawthorn**, motherwort, pomegranate
Haemorrhoids	bistort (*Bistorta officinalis*), calendula, capsicum, ginger mustard, **ginkgo**, horse chestnut, lady's mantle, **leek (*Allium ampeloprasum*)**, lesser celandine (*Ficaria verna*), passion flower, prickly ash (*Zanthoxylum americanum*), silverweed (*Argentina anserina*), tormentil (*Potentilla erecta*), yarrow
Hypertension	**blueberry**, **cocoa**, cramp bark, **cranberry**, dandelion (leaf), **elder**, **garlic**, ginkgo, gotu kola, **hawthorn**, **kudzu (*Pueraria tuberosa*)**, lemon balm, lime flower, mistletoe, **motherwort**, **nigella**, **rhubarb**, **rosehip**, *Hibiscus sabdariffa*, **rosemary**, **sesame**, Siberian ginseng, valerian, yarrow
Ischaemic heart disease	**arjuna**, astragalus, capsicum, garlic, ginkgo, hibiscus, onion, **sea buckthorn (*Hippophae rhamnoides*)**, turmeric
Phlebitis, venous microangiopathy, leading to ulceration	ginkgo, **gotu kola**, hawthorn, **horse chestnut**, lime, mistletoe

Stroke prevention	astragalus, bilberry, capsicum, **carrot**, evening primrose, garlic, **ginkgo**, ginger, green tea, pineapple, turmeric
Varicose veins (most for external use only)	apple, arnica, bilberry, blueberry, **butcher's broom (*Ruscus aculeatus*)**, cabbage, calendula, comfrey (*Symphytum*), dog rose, garlic, ginkgo, gotu kola, grape (seed), hawthorn, horse chestnut, pine (bark), witch hazel, yarrow

Star plant for circulatory conditions

In the physic garden, a couple of safe herbs have a great reputation for heart health. One is hawthorn (see Chapter 10). Of the other, motherwort, John Gerard said: 'Divers [folk] commend it against infirmities of the heart', and Culpepper wrote: 'There is no better herb to drive melancholy vapours from the heart, to strengthen it and make the mind cheerful, blithe and merry.' The second part of motherwort's Latin name, *Leonorus cardiaca*, reflects its use for heart conditions. (The first part of the Latin name relates to its appearance: the ancients thought its leaves resembled a lion's tail.) The plant originated in Asia and Southern Europe but is now grown worldwide as a plant medicine.

Motherwort
(*Leonurus cardiaca*).

It's a powerful-looking plant with tough leaves and barbed seed heads that get caught in clothes or hair and are troublesome to remove. It is used traditionally as an aid for women, easing menstrual tension and cramps, for example, but its bitter taste precludes its use in herbal tea and it is neither sweet-scented nor pretty. However, our charts show that traditionally (only one clinical trial so far) it has justified its reputation for a whole range of conditions other than circulatory.

Phytostatins control cholesterol

At the top of the list for circulation-enhancing herbs are those that lower blood levels of LDL ('bad') cholesterol and, uniquely, the majority have been verified effective in controlled clinical trials. Again, there are far more of these than space allows in our chart. The promising results from some of these plants, and their side effects (variously hyped as alarming or tolerable), are driving a lot of scientific investigation in this area. Yet despite this level of scientific support for plant remedies, synthetic chemical statins are still widely prescribed for treatment and prevention. But the good news is that a variety of medicinal plants can be eaten for treatment or prevention.

Cautionary note on anticoagulants

For heart disease, hypertension, stroke and other serious or life-threatening symptoms, the first line of treatment is still the doctor. It is not known how most traditionally used anticoagulant herbs work. Some conventional anticoagulant drugs such as warfarin rely on reducing vitamin K effects on blood-clotting proteins while others act independently of vitamin K. (Warfarin is now being superseded by drugs that are not affected by diet.)

Central nervous system

Condition	Medicinal plants (those in bold are based on controlled clinical trials)
Addiction	kudzu (*Pueraria lobata*), liquorice root, lemon balm (*Melissa officinalis*), milk thistle, oats, **passion flower (*Passiflora incarnata*)**, **rosemary**, skullcap, **valerian (*Valeriana officinalis*)**, vervain (*Verbena officinalis*)
Anxiety/stress/tension	***Angelica archangelica***, ashwagandha, **bacopa**, **bitter orange (*Citrus x aurantium*)**, **black cohosh (*Actaea racemosa*)**, California poppy, **catnip**, **chamomile (German and Roman)**, cramp bark (*Viburnum opulus*), **echinacea**, **hemp (CBD rich)**, holy basil, **hop**, hyssop, Jamaican dogwood, **kava**, lady's slipper (*Cypripedioideae*), **lavender (*Lavandula angustifolia*)**, **lemon balm**, lime blossom, **motherwort (*Leonurus cardiaca*)**, oats, pasque flower, **passion flower**, **rose (essential oil)**, **rosemary**, **roseroot**, Siberian ginseng, skullcap (*Scutellaria*), **St John's wort (*Hypericum perforatum*)**, **valerian**, vervain, wild lettuce (*Lactuca virosa*)
Cognitive function, memory and attention deficits and dementia	**ashwagandha**, **bacopa**, **blueberry**, cowslip (*Primula veris*), **cocoa**, coconut, ***Angelica archangelica***, **ginkgo**, ginseng, goji berry (*Lycium barbarum*) gotu kola, **holy basil**, lavender, **lemon balm**, **nigella**, **peppermint**, periwinkle, **pine**, **rosemary**, **roseroot (*Rhodiola rosea*)**, **saffron**, **sage (*S. officinalis*)**, **turmeric**, **walnut**, wood betony, wormwood
Depression/mood uplift	**bacopa**, betony (*Stachys officinalis*), **catnip**, **chamomile (German)**, **cocoa**, damiana (*Turnera diffusa*), gotu kola, **hop**, lady's slipper, **lavender**, **lemon balm**, lime blossom, oats, **rose (essential oil)**, rosemary, **roseroot**, **saffron**, Siberian ginseng, **skullcap (*Scutellaria*)**, **Spanish sage (*S. lavandulaefolia*)**, **stachys (*Nepeta menthoides*)**, **St John's wort**, **turmeric**, valerian, vervain, **viper's bugloss (*Echium vulgare*)**, wild oat (*Avena fatua*)
Epilepsy (drug-resistant) (Caution: some other herbs are contraindicated)	bacopa, betony, blue cohosh, **cannabis**, **chamomile (Roman)**, groundsel (*Senecio vulgaris*), kava, mugwort (*Artemisia vulgaris*), peony, skullcap, valerian, vervain
Headache, including migraine	ashwagandha, betony, **butterbur**, **capsicum**, chamomile, **chaste tree (*Vitex agnus-castus*)**, **citron (*Citrus medica*)**, elderflower, **feverfew**, ginkgo, gotu kola, Jamaican dogwood, lady's slipper, **lavender**, **lemon balm**, *Lippia alba*, marjoram, meadowsweet (*Filipendula ulmaria*), pasque flower, **peppermint**, **rose (Damask)**, rosemary, rue (*Ruta graveolens*), skullcap, **sweet violet (*Viola odorata*)**, thyme, valerian, vervain, wild lettuce, wild oat, wormwood
Insomnia	**ashwagandha**, bacopa, banana, **black cohosh**, California poppy (*Eschscholzia californica*), **catnip**, **chamomile (German and Roman)**, cherry, **hop**, Jamaican dogwood, **kava**, **lavender**, **lemon balm**, lime blossom, **passion flower**, rose, **valerian**, **viola**, **wild lettuce**
ME (myalgic encephalomyelitis)	ashwagandha, **astragalus**, bacopa, evening primrose, liquorice, rosemary, roseroot, **sage**
Stimulant, tonic	**astragalus**, **coffee**, cola nut, damiana, **ginseng**, **roseroot**, **tea**
Vitality / antifatigue	astragalus, **ginseng**, **rosemary**, **roseroot**

Senses	Medicinal plants (those in bold are based on controlled clinical trials)
Balance/equilibrium disorders	**ginkgo**
Earache	almond, chamomile, echinacea, elder, garlic, ground ivy (*Glechoma hederacea*) , goldenrod (*Solidago*), goldenseal (*Hydrastis canadensis*), hyssop, lavender, mullein (*Verbascum*), olive (oil), plantain (*Plantago*), St John's wort, tea tree
Neuralgia	bacopa, black cohosh, betony, California poppy, **cannabis**, capsicum, ginseng, hop, Jamaican dogwood, lavender, meadowsweet, passion flower, pasque flower, rosemary, St John's wort, wild oat
Pain/analgesia (uses vary according to causes; overlap with headache)	**aloe**, **arnica**, **bitter orange**, California poppy, **cannabis**, capsaicin, **chamomile**, **comfrey**, **dill**, **feverfew**, ginger, ginseng, holy basil, kava, **lavender**, meadowsweet, **nigella**, passion flower, peppermint, **Russian olive (*Elaegnus angustifolia*)**, St John's wort, **sweet wormwood (*Artemisia annua*)**, **thyme**, turmeric, valerian, **willow**, wintergreen (*Gaultheria procumbens*)
Tinnitus	Bay (*Laurus nobilis*), black cohosh, fenugreek, ginkgo, goldenseal, horsetail (*Equisetum*), onion, plantain
Vision – tired, dry or infected eyes	**bilberry**, chamomile (Roman), clary sage (*Salvia sclarea*), **cocoa**, elder (flower), eyebright (*Euphrasia*), ginkgo, grapeseed, green tea, marigold, rose

NOTE: for butterbur, here and in other charts, long-term use is not recommended.

Star plant for brain/mind conditions

One of the best plants for the central nervous system is skullcap, even though it doesn't have much significant clinical approval yet. It is a modest little blue-flowered plant that covers several brain/mind conditions. One of its other names is 'mad dog' skullcap, as it was used to treat rabid dog bites. (It didn't save rabies victims, but it helped them to die more peacefully.) Skullcap (American skullcap (*Scutellaria lateriflora*) is most often used) has blue flowers that turn into tiny white seed heads shaped like skulls, which fit with its common name and tie in to the 'doctrine of signatures' that claimed the appearance of plants tells us what to use it for. Medical herbalists today use it for anxiety, nervous tension and convulsions.

Skullcap (*Scutellaria*) flowers resemble medieval skullcaps.

Common causes and connectivity

Notice that some plants appear in several places in the chart. This is because they perform several different functions. For example, valerian appears seven times in the above chart; skullcap, five; lavender and ginkgo, four. This says something about the diversity of plant chemicals within each plant giving it different functions. It also tells us about the way the brain connects: mood or mental fatigue affect cognition; anxiety or pain interfere with sleep (see also Chapter 16 and our book *Botanical Brain Balms*).

Plant painkillers

A great many herbs are used to relieve pain. Our list includes just some of the analgesic plants used by herbalists. In many instances, how they work is not fully known, though meadowsweet and wintergreen contain salicin, which is the chemical in willow that gave us aspirin. Willow bark, incidentally, has the great advantage over aspirin of not causing gastrointestinal irritation or bleeding.

The American Pain Foundation listed specific herbs for pain management: ginseng for fibromyalgia; kava for tension headaches and neuropathic pain; St John's Wort for sciatica, arthritis and neuropathic pain; and valerian root for spasms and muscle cramps. Since then, cannabis (containing THC) and hemp (containing CBD) have hit the headlines for pain control. Herbal analgesics (numbering many more than space allows us to list here) are widely used because conventional drug analgesics are sometimes ineffective, or cause side effects or addiction.

Adaptogens

While 'tonics' and antifatigue remedies affect multiple bodily systems, we have included them in our brain chart because 'mind over matter' plays a part in people's individual experience of pain, illness or well-being. 'Adaptogenic' herbs stabilise physiological processes, decreasing our sensitivity to stress and boosting immunity. Ginseng, roseroot and ashwagandha are adaptogenic herbs verified as countering fatigue. One view is that they do this by stimulating the adrenal glands.

Digestive system

Condition	Medicinal plants (those in bold are based on controlled clinical trials)
Appetite stimulants	agrimony, calamus (*Acorus calamus*), **cannabis**, cardamom, **chamomile (Roman)**, coriander, dandelion, fenugreek, gentian, ginger, mugwort, wormwood, yarrow
Appetite suppressants, slimming aids	**capsicum**, **caraway**, chickweed (*Stellaria media*), **cocoa (chocolate)**, fennel, goji berry (*Lycium barbarum*), green tea, pineapple, **plantain**, tamarind (*Garcinia cambogia*), **walnut**
Colic	calamus, **chamomile (German)**, cramp bark, *Angelica archangelica*, **fennel**, gentian, **lemon balm**, **peppermint**, valerian, wild yam
Constipation (laxative properties)	aloe, **buckthorn (*Cascara sagrada*)**, *Cassia alata*, dandelion, **elder (*Sambucus*)**, **fennel**, fenugreek, **fig**, linseed, liquorice, **plantain (*Plantago psyllium*)**, rhubarb, **senna**, yellow dock
Diarrhoea	agrimony, **apple**, astragalus, bayberry, bistort, **carob bean**, cinnamon, cranesbill, goldenseal, lady's mantle (*Alchemilla*), marshmallow, meadowsweet, oak (bark), plantain, raspberry (leaf), silverweed, **tea (black)**, tormentil
Digestive aids	**chamomile (Roman and German)**, cinnamon, dandelion root, elecampane (*Inula helenium*), ginger, hyssop, lemon balm, **liquorice**, **peppermint**
Diverticulitis	aloe, apple, chamomile, liquorice, marshmallow, peppermint, slippery elm, valerian, wild yam
Flatulence	asafoetida (*Ferula assa-foetida*), calamus, cardamom, capsicum, cinnamon, clove, coriander, dill, *Angelica archangelica*, fennel, gentian, ginger, peppermint, **plantain**, **turmeric**
Gastritis	aloe, anise (*Pimpinella anisum*), calamus, **capsicum**, chamomile, **cinnamon**, cranesbill, elm, goldenseal, Irish moss (*Chondrus crispus*), liquorice, marshmallow, meadowsweet, oak, plantain, quince, *Schisandra*, slippery elm, strawberry
Indigestion/dyspepsia	artichoke (globe), black pepper, calamus, capsicum, **caraway**, cardamom, **celery**, centaury, **chamomile (German)**, **cinnamon**, fennel, ginger, lemon balm, **nigella**, **peppermint**, thyme, **turmeric**, valerian, wormwood, yam, yarrow
Heartburn/acid reflux	chamomile, ginger, goji, **Indian gooseberry (*Phyllanthus emblica*)**, **liquorice**, marshmallow, meadowsweet, peppermint, **quince**
Irritable bowel syndrome	agrimony, aloe, chamomile, cramp bark, fennel, **frankincense**, **ginger**, hops, lemon balm, meadowsweet, myrrh, **peppermint**, **plantain**, **turmeric**, vervain, wild yam, **yarrow**
Nausea and vomiting	black horehound (*Ballota nigra*), **cannabis**, **celery**, chamomile, cinnamon, clove, dill, fennel, **ginger**, **globe artichoke**, **lemon**, **liquorice**, marshmallow, meadowsweet, nutmeg, **peppermint**, slippery elm
Obesity/weight control (as well as herbs to stimulate digestion)	**asparagus**, black pepper, **caraway**, capsicum, cardamom, cinnamon, coriander, cumin, dandelion, **elder**, fennel, *Garcinia atroviridis*, **ginger**, ginseng, gotu kola, **goji berry (*Lycium barbarum*)**, hawthorn, **magnolia**, mustard, **nigella**, *Salacia chinensis*, thunder god vine (*Tripterygium wilfordii*), turmeric, **veldt grape (*Cissus quadrangularis*)**
Ulcerative colitis	agrimony, aloe, **berberis**, *Boswellia serrata*, chamomile, liquorice, marshmallow, **plantain**, tormentil, turmeric

Related functions: fat and sugar digestion, metabolism, detoxification and excretion

Condition	Medicinal plants (those in bold are based on controlled clinical trials)
Gall bladder, including stones	artichoke (globe), **berberis**, betony, **curcumin**, curry plant (*Helichrysum italicum*), dandelion root, fenugreek, marshmallow, milk thistle (*Silybum marianum*), sorrel
Kidney, including diuretic and cleansing	berberis, **Chinese rhubarb (*Rheum palmatum*)**, cleavers (*Galium aparine*), **cranberry**, **dandelion (leaf)**, goji, goldenrod, gravel root or Joe Pye weed (*Eutrochium purpureum*), horsetail, hydrangea, marshmallow, **nettle**, parsley, pumpkin, wild carrot, wild celery, **yarrow**
Liver, including tonics	artichoke (globe), **astragalus**, berberis, blue flag (*Iris versicolor*), bog bean (*Menyanthes trifoliata*), **cassia**, **Chinese rhubarb (*R. palmatum*)**, dandelion (root), goji, goldenseal, **green tea**, liquorice, **milk thistle**, **nigella**, **saffron**, **saw palmetto (*Serenoa repens*)**, *Salvia miltiorrhiza*, turmeric, wild yam, wormwood, yellow dock
Pancreas, diabetes/hyperglycaemia (high blood glucose). Only add a plant as an adjunct to, or replacement of, diabetic drug therapy after consulting a professional carer.	allspice, **aloe**, artichoke, **ashwagandha**, astragalus, banana, barley, **blueberry**, burdock, cabbage, carrot, lettuce, **cinnamon**, **cardamom**, **cranberry**, fenugreek, **fig (leaf)**, **frankincense**, **garlic**, **ginger**, **ginseng**, goat's rue (*Galega officinalis*), **holy basil**, jambul (*Syzygium cumini*), **maqui (berry) (*Aristotelia chilensis*)**, **milk thistle**, **nettle**, **nigella**, oats, olive, onion, papaya, **passion flower**, **plantain**, **purslane (*Portulaca oleracea*)**, saffron, **sage (*S. officinalis*)**, sunrose, sweet potato, sweet sumach, **walnut (leaf)**, wormwood

Star plant for digestive conditions

Goji (*Lycium barbarum*) features many times in the chart above, taking us outside traditional Western medicinal plants. The name 'goji' is an approximation of the Chinese name for the fruit, 'gǒuqǐ' (枸杞), or wolfberry. It has several other names, including the delightful 'matrimony vine', and also 'The Duke of Argyll's tea tree plant'. (In the 1730s, the Duke received a plant from China labelled as a tea plant, but it was in fact a goji.)

Goji berries have multiple health benefits only recently explored scientifically.

Goji belongs to the Solanaceae plant family, which contains many edible vegetables and fruits, including tomato, potato and physalis. The vine grows well in colder climates, though it doesn't fruit much in the open. The berries taste a bit like cranberries or sour cherries, and are used in cooking and baking, the traditional use of a medicinal food plant to enhance digestive function. Goji berries have multiple health benefits that are just beginning to be explored scientifically. Trials so far suggest antidiabetes function and improving feelings of well-being.

Keeping blood sugar under control

For diabetes (type 2), there are many more traditional herbal medicines than those listed here, possibly due to overlaps between plant-based medicines and foods. Food plants that control blood sugar are an attractive option for preventing type 2 diabetes, as well as for weight-watching and exercise regimes.

Traditional Chinese Medicine

Chinese herbs feature in many controlled clinical trials, especially for liver conditions, diabetes and obesity. They are mostly combined in 'formulations', which consist of many different herbs made up as one prescription. This makes it difficult to understand how the plant medicine works, and means it's almost impossible to pin down actions to any one chemical. Although we don't list them here, the number of Chinese medicinal plants for diabetes is astonishing, and many have proven clinical effectiveness. For Western nations where obesity is becoming endemic, plant medicines or foods can be effective for weight control and diabetes. Even though mainstream Western medicine is not paying much attention, Chinese and Indian medical practitioners certainly are.

Infections and infestations

Condition	Medicinal plant (those in bold are based on controlled clinical trials)
Athlete's foot	Garlic, ginger, neem, olive oil, oregano, **tea tree**
Bronchitis/lower respiratory tract infections	bloodroot, coltsfoot (*Tussilago farfara*), **echinacea**, *Angelica archangelica*, garlic, grindelia, **ivy**, lobelia, mullein, **plantain**, pleurisy root (*Asclepias tuberosa*), thyme, white horehound (*Marrubium vulgare*), wild indigo (*Baptisia*)
Cold sore/Herpes simplex	aloe, coffee, lemon balm, liquorice, peppermint, St John's wort, tea tree
Coughs and colds/upper respiratory tract viral infections	***Andrographis paniculata***, aniseed, cinnamon, coltsfoot, comfrey, cowslip, **cranberry**, **echinacea**, **elder**, elecampane, **garlic**, **green tea**, goldenseal, grindelia, ground ivy (*Glechoma hederacea*), **Malabar nut (*Justicia adhatoda*)**, **mistletoe**, plantain, peppermint, pleurisy root, **sage (*S. officinalis*)**, thyme, white horehound, yarrow
Ear (topical or oral)	chamomile, echinacea, elderflower, garlic, goldenseal, mullein, onion, yarrow
Fungal infections (general)	**bitter orange**, calendula, eucalyptus, goldenseal, greater celandine (*Chelidonium majus*), myrrh, **thyme**, **tea tree**
Headlice	aniseed, garlic, **grapefruit**, lavender, neem, rosemary, thyme
Helicobacter pylori	broccoli, **burdock**, **garlic**, nigella, **walnut**
Influenza	Capsicum, cinnamon, clove, **echinacea**, **elder (berry)**, ginger, **ginseng**, peppermint, sage, yarrow
Insecticides (general)	**basil**, **bay**, bog myrtle (*Myrica gale*), capsicum, chrysanthemum, **garlic**, lavender, **marjoram**, **myrtle**, neem, onion, tobacco, **wormwood**
Intestinal worms	berberis, **bird's-foot trefoil (*Lotus corniculatus*)**, **chicory**, ***Dichrocephala integrifolia***, fig, garlic, ***Hoheria glabrata***, male fern, mustard, neem, **papaya**, pomegranate, **ragweed (*Ambrosia maritima*)**, tansy (*Tanacetum vulgare*), wild carrot, wormwood
MRSA-resistant bacteria	**cranberry**, elecampane, eucalyptus, **garlic**, **liquorice**, myrrh, *Nuphar japonica*, *Polyalthia longifolia*, thyme, turmeric
Shingles/Herpes zoster	berberis, California poppy, **Chilean soapbark tree (*Quillaja saponaria Molina*)**, **Chinese rhubarb (*R. officinale*)**, ***Indigofera suffruticosa***, Jamaican dogwood, lemon balm, meadowsweet, mistletoe, paeonia, passion flower, St John's wort, wild lettuce
Sinusitis	*Angelica dahurica*, echinacea, elder (berry), elm, eucalyptus, eyebright, garlic, ginger, goldenrod, goldenseal, ground ivy, marshmallow, neem, oak (bark), pine, **thyme**, turmeric, wild indigo (*Baptisia*)
Sore throat	***Andrographis paniculata***, agrimony, balm of Gilead (*Populus balsamifera*), **capsicum**, chamomile, garlic, ginger, **liquorice**, mahonia, marshmallow, poke root, **sage (*S. officinalis*)**, silverweed
Thrush/candida	berberis, **devil's fig (*Solanum chrysotrichum*)**, dill, echinacea, neem, olive, oregano, **sage (*S. officinalis*)**, thyme
Ticks	cedar, lemon, lavender, neem, rose geranium, witch hazel

Tonsillitis and laryngitis	bloodroot (*Sanguinaria*), **capsicum**, cat's claw (*Uncaria tomentosa*), echinacea, garlic, goldenseal, myrrh, neem, oak (bark), pau d'arco (*Handroanthus impetiginosus*), **poke root (*Phytolacca decandra*)**, red sage (*S. miltiorrhiza*), **Swertia chirata**, thyme, turmeric, wild indigo, wormwood
Urinary tract	agrimony, **bearberry**, couch grass, **cranberry**, grapeseed, horsetail, juniper, lady's mantle, marshmallow, mustard, plantain, **saw palmetto**, yarrow
Warts and verrucas/papillomavirus (HPV)	aloe, dandelion, greater celandine, lemon balm, **milkweed (*Asclepias curassavica*)**, **myrtle**, *Podophyllum*, tea tree, thuja

Star plants for infections

Going by clinical evidence, the best herb for many infections and infestations is garlic (see Chapter 9), followed by echinacea (which also features in the respiratory chart below) and tea tree. Widespread resistance to chemical antibiotics drives much of this research. For many plants, clinical trial evidence is sparse, but there are hosts of studies on the infecting bacteria or virus, parasite or insect in vitro; if a plant kills an infective agent (bacteria, virus, worm) in the test tube, there is a good chance it will cure the diseases that the infective agent causes in man. So our star plant here should actually be almost any of the plants you will be growing in your physic garden!

Many, if not most, medicinal plants have immune system stimulating effects on top of their specific health benefits.

Immunostimulants

To a greater extent than mainstream medicine, plant medicine relies on our natural immune systems to resist bugs, from the common cold to the potentially deadly cholera or typhoid. The English herbalist Hoffman reminds us that illness is not the bacteria's fault, it is our bodies' condition, though he adds that there is still a need for antibiotics, particularly for the very young or old. The list of immunostimulant plant foods or medicines is so long we did not create a separate chart. Many other plants you grow will have incidental immunostimulant effects.

The discovery of plants' own immune systems has unearthed a fascinating new area of biology. In extraordinary feats of molecular recognition, plants produce cells with receptors that recognise and respond to dangerous pathogenic molecules. In our physic garden we have seen this in practice: medicinal plants seem to strengthen their resistance to invaders over the years, and our Solomon's seal, left untreated for five years, is now hardly damaged by the sawfly larvae that used to strip the plant bare in the past.

Musculoskeletal disorders

Condition	Medicinal plant (those in bold are based on controlled clinical trials)
Arthritis (general)	black cohosh, bog bean (*Menyanthes trifoliata*), celery, devil's claw (*Harpagophytum procumbens*), **frankincense**, meadowsweet, myrrh, nettle, prickly ash, **turmeric**, wild yam
Fibromyalgia	ashwagandha, black cohosh, **cannabis**, capsicum, **comfrey**, devil's claw, ginger, holy basil, horseradish, lavender, mugwort, nettle, pine, ragwort (*Senecio*), rosemary, St John's wort, thyme, **valerian**, willow, wintergreen
Gout	burdock, cherry, cleavers (*Galium aparine*), fennel, ginger, gravel root, lemon, nettle, wild celery, willow
Joint pain and inflammation	dandelion, devil's claw, ginger, meadowsweet, turmeric, willow
Lower back pain/lumbago	aloe, **avocado**, basil, **Brazilian arnica (*Solidago chilensis*)**, **capsicum**, **comfrey**, devil's claw, **dog rose**, **frankincense**, **lavender**, lemongrass, mustard, ragwort (*Jacobaea vulgaris*), rhubarb, **soy**, **willow**, wintergreen
Muscle fatigue/exercise endurance	**ashwagandha**, astragalus, **ginseng** (American, **Chinese**, **Korean** and **Siberian**), liquorice, **peppermint**, rosemary, **roseroot**, *Tribulus terrestris*, wild oats, wild yam
Muscle spasms	Blueberry, **cannabis**, capsicum, chamomile, cherry
Osteoarthritis	**avocado**, **bitter melon**, **blueberry**, *Boswellia serrata*, **comfrey**, **devil's claw**, **dog rose**, **frankincense**, **German chamomile**, **ginger**, **green tea**, **soy**, **turmeric**, **willow bark**
Osteoporosis/bone loss, including menopausal	alfalfa, black cohosh, dong quai (*Angelica sinensis*), ***Epimedium brevicornum***, evening primrose, horsetail, *Ligustri lucidi*, liquorice, marigold, parsley, ***Psoralea corylifolia***, red clover, **soy**, wild yam
Rheumatoid arthritis	ashwagandha, **blackcurrant**, borage (*Borago officinalis*), **cat's claw (*Uncaria tomentosa*)**, **dog rose**, **evening primrose**, **garlic**, **nigella**, ***Podophyllum***
Sciatica	capsicum, clove, eucalyptus, evening primrose, garlic, hop, Jamaican dogwood, juniper, passion flower, rue, St John's wort, turmeric, vervain

For complaints involving muscles, tendons, bones and joints there is no shortage of traditional herbal remedies. A fair proportion of these are now evidence-based, especially for rheumatism and arthritis. As before, for every plant we are familiar with, there is an equal if not greater number of traditional Chinese herbs. For example, for gout there is a host of published papers on positive clinical trial results for Chinese herbs, including a range of formulations like Jiawei simiaosan.

Star plant for joint and muscle pain

Rheumatism and arthritis are all too common conditions, not only for the elderly, and are the most frequent subject of enquiries from our physic garden visitors. We recommend planting a bed of meadowsweet (*Filipendula ulmaria*), also called Queen of the Meadow and Pride of the Meadow, in your physic garden. Apart from its uplifting frothy cream flowers and pleasing scent and flavour as a tea, it has a major but long-forgotten role in plant drug history: the word 'aspirin' comes from *Spiraea ulmaria*, the old Latin name for meadowsweet, which contains salicin from which acetylsalicylic acid (the chemical name for aspirin) was originally synthesised. Meadowsweet and willow bark are still used by herbalists for rheumatism and arthritis (though lacking scientific studies).

Meadowsweet (*Filipendula ulmaria*), Queen of the meadow.

Reproductive system

Condition	Medicinal plants (those in bold are based on controlled clinical trials)
Hot flushes	**black cohosh**, chickweed, **dong quai (*Angelica sinensis*)**, evening primrose, flax, ginseng, **German chamomile**, hops, **liquorice**, red clover, **sage (*S. officinalis*)**, **schisandra**, **soy**, wild yam
Impotence/low libido	ashwagandha, damiana, **Korean red ginseng**, potency wood (*Muira puama*), **saw palmetto**, schisandra, ***Tribulus terrestris***
Labour pain/progress (with professional guidance)	**Bitter orange (*Citrus x aurantium*)**, black cohosh, blue cohosh (*Caulophyllum thalictroides*), cramp bark, **dill**, Jamaican dogwood, motherwort, raspberry (leaf), pasque flower
Lactation: milk stimulation	black cohosh, borage, caraway, dill, fennel, fenugreek, goat's rue, milk thistle
Lactation: milk suppression	chickweed, herb Robert (*Geranium robertianum*), **jasmine**, lemon balm, oregano, parsley, peppermint, walnut
Mastalgia (breast pain)	**chaste tree**, dandelion, evening primrose, **German chamomile**, wild yam
Menopause (general)	**black cohosh**, **chaste tree**, false unicorn root (*Chamaelirium luteum*), ginseng, lady's mantle, **rhubarb**, **schisandra**, snake root (*Aristolochia serpentaria*), **St John's wort**
Menstruation: delayed/amenorrhoea	black cohosh, chaste tree, **dong quai (*Angelica sinensis*)**, false unicorn root, **fennel**, mugwort, parsley, pennyroyal (*Mentha pulegium*), rue, southernwood, tansy, wormwood, yarrow
Menstruation: excessive/heavy periods; painful periods/dysmenorrhoea	beth root (*Trillium erectum*), black cohosh, **celery (seed)**, **chaste tree**, **clary sage**, cramp bark, cranesbill, **ginger**, **guava**, Jamaican dogwood, lady's mantle, **lavender**, motherwort, pasque flower, **rose (oil)**, **saffron**, skullcap, squaw vine (*Mitchella repens*), **thyme**, valerian, wild lettuce, wild yam, yarrow
Morning sickness	chamomile, fennel, **ginger**, peppermint
Premenstrual syndrome/tension (PMT)	black cohosh, black horehound, **chamomile (Roman)**, **chaste tree (berry)**, dong quai (*Angelica sinensis*), **fennel**, **Japanese thistle (*Cirsium japonicum*)**, **lemon balm**, lime, liquorice, motherwort, pasque flower, peony, skullcap, valerian, wild yam
Prostate, benign hyperplasia and lower urinary tract dysfunction	couch grass (*Elymus repens*), damiana, goldenseal, horsetail, hydrangea, **maritime pine (*Pinus pinaster*)**, nettle (root), pumpkin (seed), **saw palmetto**, seaholly (*Eryngium*), **walnut**
Sperm production, quality	**date palm (pollen)**, ginkgo, ginseng, **nigella**, roseroot, **walnut**

Star plants for the reproductive system

Two plants stand out: black cohosh for women and saw palmetto for men, both often used for older people. For men with prostate problems there are dozens of controlled clinical trials supporting the use of saw palmetto for benign prostate hyperplasia. Scientific and clinical research for this is as intensive as for black cohosh for menopausal symptoms. But the plants also relieve problems in the young: menstruation in women, impotence in men. One of the plants has the alternate name 'fairy candle' and the other is a small palm with prickly stems (no prize for guessing which is which! The answer is in Chapter 10).

Aphrodisiacs?

We have not included aphrodisiacs here, despite hundreds of plants reputed to act as sexual stimulants or that improve fertility. The evidence is almost non-existent, with only a few animal studies on plants like ginger and angelica for male potency, and no clinical trials at all. Even though plant 'viagras' are not yet on the research agenda, the web searcher will be overwhelmed by an endless choice of plant products with extravagant claims. (However, the extraordinary claim that drugs such as Sertraline or Sildenafil used for sexual function can restore drooping plants *is* backed by an Israeli scientific study!).

The chaste tree (*Vitex agnus-castus*) also goes by the name of 'monk's pepper'.

One herb in the chart for both menstrual and menopausal symptoms is the chaste tree (*Vitex agnus-castus*). This was sacred to Hestia, the goddess of domesticity, the hearth and family. It is reputed to be an *an*aphrodisiac, i.e. suppresses sexual desire; another name for it is monk's pepper. Nevertheless, it is used as a tonic for both male and female reproductive symptoms and while there is no supporting clinical evidence for it yet, lab research on how it works is focused on the pituitary gland, and hormones like progesterone.

Pregnancy warning

The advice for pregnant women is to avoid medicinal plants during the first trimester (except under supervision). Later, and during breastfeeding, many mothers tend to play safe by avoiding medicinal plants altogether. However, as well as the plants used traditionally (see chart), some have been proven safe: chamomile, cranberry, ginger, nettle and raspberry leaf, for example. Women lactating ought always to seek advice on which herbs to take or avoid.

Respiratory function

Some of these conditions are also listed under Infections and Infestations.

Condition	Medicinal plants (those in bold are based on controlled clinical trials)
Allergies (general)	**Indian ipecac (*Tylophora indica*)**, liquorice, **nettle**
Asthma	butterbur, cocoa, coltsfoot, elecampane, **ginkgo**, grindelia, hyssop, **Indian frankincense (*Boswellia serrata*)**, mullein, **nigella**, **passion flower**, **peppermint**, **pistachio**, thyme, wild cherry, **yellow-fruit nightshade (*Solanum xanthocarpum*)**
Bronchitis/chronic obstructive pulmonary disease	aniseed, **butterbur**, coltsfoot, **dong quai (*Angelica sinensis*)**, elecampane, flax, hyssop, **ivy**, liquorice, lungwort, marshmallow, mullein, **plantain**, slippery elm, **thyme**
Catarrh	**echinacea**, elderflower, garlic, goldenseal, hyssop, lungwort, mullein, onion, thyme
Coughs	coltsfoot, **echinacea**, elecampane, **liquorice**, **Malabar nut (*Justicia adhatoda*)**, marshmallow, mullein, white horehound
Expectorants	bittersweet, cowslip, daisy, **echinacea**, *Angelica archangelica*, soapwort, thuja
Hay fever	ashwagandha, astragalus, chamomile, elder (flower), feverfew, goldenseal, lemon balm, nettle, turmeric, yarrow
Pleurisy	capsicum, garlic, hyssop, mullein
Upper respiratory tract	echinacea, garlic, goldenrod, **green tea**, yarrow

Star plant for respiratory conditions

When asked if they take any herb to fend off colds and flu, many people will tell you echinacea works for them. The echinacea purple coneflower is one of the most beautiful medicinal plants, favoured by gardeners and butterflies alike! (It's also the one exception here of a star that is also in our favourites in Chapter 9). The plant turns up in many of the charts as it boosts the immune system. While we focus on clinical evidence that supports traditional uses, scientific studies can be inconsistent. This is

Echinacea purpurea, a magnet for butterflies.

especially true of medicinal plants where several different parts can be used. For echinacea, the root is traditionally used, but according to a 2006 Cochrane review of clinical trials, 'there is some evidence that preparations based on the aerial parts of *Echinacea purpurea* might be effective for the early treatment of colds in adults'. So maybe you can use your echinacea to make the medicine without having to dig it out and harvest the roots.

Taking the vapours

Asthma and bronchitis are the targets for most herbal options for the respiratory system, with back-up clinical evidence for several European and Indian plants, none of which on its own stands out above the others. We have for many years cleared our heads of colds using inhalations of thyme oil (see Chapter 9), and there are commercial oils containing the likes of camphor, eucalyptus and juniper that work equally well.

A cheering early spring sight in any physic garden is coltsfoot, with its delicate stems and buds that, to our minds, look like the unshod hooves of a young foal. (Other people say it's the leaves that emerge after the buds burst into bright yellow flowers which resemble colt's feet). The flowers are used to make the medicine, usually a decoction, but they can also be dried for smoking. According to Culpepper, 'The dry leaves are best for those who have their rheums and distillations upon their lungs causing a cough, for which also the dried leaves taken as tobacco.' (Perhaps the unpopularity of smoking is one reason why the herb has not yet entered clinical trials.)

Coltsfoot (*Tussilago farfara*), the herb that was smoked to cure asthma!

Amphoteric herbs

The medical herbalist Hoffman refers to 'amphoteric' herbs, applying a word that usually means acting as both acid and alkali, to normalising states of health. By changing their action according to the body environment, these herbs stabilise the function of an organ between extremes (i.e. overactive or underactive). Amphoteric plants for respiration include bloodroot, pleurisy root and white horehound. Pleurisy root (*Asclepias tuberosa*) was once officially part of the United States Pharmacopoeia for pleurisy, but despite long use there is no published clinical trial to date. The amphoteric concept applied to herbs for health awaits scientific investigation, though it wouldn't be surprising if the chemicals that plants evolved for surviving extreme conditions also benefit human health that is out of balance.

Skin

Condition	Medicinal plants (those in bold are based on controlled clinical trials)
Abscesses and boils	blue flag, burdock, calendula, cleavers, coltsfoot, echinacea, fenugreek, flax, garlic, goldenseal, marshmallow, myrrh, plantain, poke root, wild indigo (*Baptisia australis*)
Acne	aloe, blue flag, **berberis**, borage, burdock, cat's claw, cleavers, comfrey, echinacea, garlic, nettle, pokeroot, wild indigo
Bruises	**arnica**, chickweed, **comfrey**, cucumber, elder, lady's mantle, lavender, maple (*Acer*), quince (seed), **St John's wort**, witch hazel
Burns, including sunburn and radiotherapy	**aloe**, **calendula**, chamomile, chickweed, comfrey, cucumber, elder, **golden serpent fern (*Polypodium leucotomos*)**, **lavender**, **Persian silk tree (*Albizia julibrissin*)**, plantain, **sea buckthorn (*Hippophae*)**, **St John's wort**
Eczema	balm of Gilead, blue flag, borage, burdock, chickweed, cleavers, comfrey, figwort (*Scrophularia*), fumitory (*Fumaria officinalis*), **German chamomile**, goldenseal, **mahonia**, nettle, **pennywort**, red clover, skullcap, **turmeric**, **walnut**, yarrow, yellow dock
General skin conditions (anti-ageing, improving elasticity)	**aloe**, chamomile, chrysanthemum, **comfrey**, **dog rose**, ginkgo, ginseng, orchid, pineapple, **rosemary**, **St John's wort**, turmeric, witch hazel, yellow dock
Gingivitis (gum disease, often including dental plaque)	bloodroot, **calendula**, **cinnamon**, clove, echinacea, **ginger**, **holy basil**, neem, **pomegranate**, **rosemary**, *Salvadora persica*, tea tree, thyme, willow, **vervain**
Hair loss/alopecia	aloe, ginkgo, ginseng, nettle, peppermint, **rosemary**, **saw palmetto**
Mouth ulcers	bistort, chamomile, **garlic**, lady's mantle, **liquorice**, marigold, raspberry, red sage (*S. miltiorrhiza*)
Nappy rash/diaper dermatitis	**aloe**, **calendula**, **Roman chamomile**
Psoriasis	**aloe**, angelica, balm of Gilead, blue flag, burdock, **Chinese foxglove**, cleavers, dandelion, figwort, **mahonia**, red clover, **red sage (*S. miltiorrhiza*)**, sarsaparilla, snake needle grass (*Oldenlandia diffusa*), wild carrot, wild celery, yellow dock
Sunscreen/photoprotection	aloe, astragalus, calendula, carrot seed (oil), coconut (oil), **golden serpent fern (*Polypodium leucotomos*)**, **green tea**, marshmallow, olive (oil), **rosemary**, sesame (oil)
Ulcers (general)	**calendula**, chickweed, comfrey, echinacea, goldenseal, marshmallow
Wound-healing	**aloe**, **arnica**, **calendula**, carline thistle (*Carlina*), chamomile, chickweed, **comfrey**, elder, goldenseal, **lavender**, **papaya**, plantain, selfheal, **St John's wort**, woundwort (*Symphytum officinale*)
Wrinkles	apple, chrysanthemum, **cocoa**, gotu kola, green tea, pomegranate, rosemary

Star plant for skin conditions

Comfrey has an illustrious health history: Dioscorides prescribed it for many ailments of the Roman soldiers. Comfrey crops up for nearly half of the skin conditions in the chart. The official comfrey plants can cause confusion since they readily hybridise with each other, producing plants with pink or mauve as opposed to white flowers (these hybrids spring up all around the Dilston garden). But the official comfrey bed is the only herb bed in the whole garden that never needs weeding or feeding. The leaves make an excellent ointment for maintaining skin health, although the FDA has banned their internal use due to risks of liver damage.

One of the many comfrey plants that rampage round our physic garden, cross-breeding and making identification of specific species difficult.

We do defy the general rule by making a delicious soup for ourselves using potato and spring leaves of comfrey (*Symphytum officinale*, rather than Russian comfrey (*Symphytum x uplandicum*) which has much higher levels of the offending alkaloid. You may want to grow this herb to make a comfrey compost or liquid compost 'tea' to nourish other medicinal plants – a blessing for organic gardeners.

Cosmetic concerns

Herbs for the skin help young people who are concerned about blemishes like acne, or who suffer from eczema or psoriasis. Over a third of the medicinal plants used here are evidence-based. But there is no convincing evidence for halting skin ageing through the use of plants. Sunscreen plants do have scientific backing, which is not surprising, since plants generate proteins to protect themselves from harmful ultraviolet rays. We cover cosmetic uses of plants in Chapter 15.

With all these plants for all these health benefits, you are spoilt for choice. Before you decide which you'd like to grow, we can't resist telling you about our favourites. Just some of what we regard to be among the most effective, safest medicinal plants are profiled in the next chapter – from folklore to modern medicine, from growing to using them.

9

Favourite Medicinal Plants

The previous chapter gave you plants listed under the medical condition they treat. This chapter is the other way round. Starting with the plant, we state which conditions it's good for. But more than that, we describe each plant in detail, and give its growing preference and history and our advice for taking it.

Every herbal encyclopaedia or handbook chooses its own selection of the many thousands of medicinal plants. So here is our broad choice of species for your physic garden, species that are:

- clinically verified, with positive effects in one or more controlled trials – possibly not enough results to satisfy pharma-funded drug trial criteria, but enough to set the plant in the context of medical science
- readily grown (depending on climate)
- safe and, for the most part, pleasant to take
- attractive to grow in your physic garden, delighting the senses (aroma, appearance, taste) and/or stirring the imagination with fascinating folklore.

All are widely used for common, often multiple, health issues.

SAFETY FIRST:

- Unless otherwise stated, pregnant mothers, babies and young children, should not take *any* medicines without consulting a health professional first.
- Be aware of possible individual allergies to specific plants.
- If you are on other medication or have any medical condition, consult your health professional or member of the National Institute of Medical Herbalists (in the UK).
- Suggested doses have been chosen to be large enough to produce the required medicinal effect, yet small enough to be safe. Precise doses can vary according to the preparation, your age and health.
- Use of essential oils, which are highly concentrated, is restricted to very small amounts (0.1–0.2 ml; 2-4 drops), inhaled, added to bath water or diluted and applied to skin. Oils are rarely taken orally in more than a drop or two in the UK, but are taken in larger quantities in other countries such as France, where they are often capsulated.

Information on each plant

Each plant is introduced by its common name, followed by its Latin species (scientific) name (in italics), with species synonyms (abbreviated 'syn.') in brackets, and the plant's Latin family name.

If there are multiple medicinal species of the plant (e.g. angelica) we number the Latin names of those species.

SAFFRON

Crocus sativus IRIDACEAE

HERBAL MEDICINE Traditionally for cancer and depression.
SCIENCE Clinically proven for depression, concomitant anxiety, obsesseive compulsive disorder and treatment of Alzheimer's and mild cognitive impairment, land for weight loss and increased satiety.
Neuroprotective *in vitro*. Active chemical crocetin in stamens prevents retinal degeneration in lab models.
FOLKLORE Cleopatra bathed in saffron to enhance lovemaking.

For each plant we give the following information:

Description:	of the plant itself, knowing and growing it, including an illustration.
Special features:	why it's worth adding to your collection.
Folklore:	the stories behind the plant's powers, stories that often match present-day use as evidence-based plant medicines. (This follows up the 'magic to medicine' theme in the Introduction).
What physicians of old said:	traditional uses recorded in old texts, not applicable to, for example, medical plants discovered in the new world by explorers observing Native American practices.
What scientists today say:	we discuss (a) Clinical trials – controlled clinical trials supporting traditional uses (see Chapter 2); and (b) Lab tests – experiments in vitro (test tube) and in vivo (living animals).
Uses still to be tested:	herbal medicine practices today that are not yet subjected to clinical trial testing.
Key chemicals:	a few of the most common or most active ingredients.
Using the herb for health:	ways of using or taking the plant you grow (commercial product specifications are not included).
Dose:	daily dose, generally in terms of the amount of fresh plant material used (or fresh equivalent in dried, tea or tincture preparations, for example) and, where appropriate, other measures such as volume (fruit juice or essential oil). Dose is given in metric units only (grams or mls), although for juices that are safe in large quantities we occasionally give the dose volume in cups. If other sources specify quantities as 'drops', be aware that the size of drops varies with the size of dropper! If self-medicating to treat a condition, you should ideally confirm the dose you plan to take with an a professional herbalist. For commercial extracts, the dose is clearly stated on the label.
Safety:	We have selected plants that are considered safe, but have added any known side effects and contraindications. For example, the plant may not suitable for those suffering from a particular health condition, or may not mix with other medications.
References:	In the reference section at the back of the book we give just two of many articles in peer-reviewed scientific journals on each plant to give you an idea of clinical and lab-based studies supporting the use of the plant's medicinal use. We have selected review or meta-analysis where possible to give the broader picture.

ANGELICA

Species name: 1. *Angelica sinensis* (dong quai); 2. *Angelica archangelica* (syn. *A. officinalis*)

Plant family name: *Apiaceae*

Description
The Apiaceae family has over 60 species of angelica, including the wild *A. sylvestris*. The main ones used medicinally are Chinese *A. sinensis* and European *A. archangelica*.

Chinese angelica, or dong quai (*Angelica sinensis*).

Angelica archangelica.

A. sinensis: perennial; native to cool, mountainous regions in China; it will also grow (to 1m/3.3ft) in cool, moist garden areas. Green stems, white flowers, yellow roots.

A. archangelica: biennial; native of Northern Europe; grows (3m/10ft) in cool, damp soil; readily self-seeds. Its purple marked stems, fragrant divided leaves and large umbelliferous cream flowers make this one of the most beautiful medicinal plants.

Both species: Because of their height they are often positioned at the back of beds.

Special features
A. sinensis's reputation as a virtual panacea is backed by strong scientific evidence for many of its diverse uses.

A. archangelica's 'magic to medicine' story starts as a cure for a medieval plague and ends up with positive antibiotic lab tests.

Folklore
A. sinensis is also known as female ginseng, helping not only menstrual and menopausal problems but also increasing female sexual desire.

A. archangelica was named as a result of an archangel holding out what used to be known as wild celery to a monk who then used it to treat people with the plague in London.

What physicians of old said
A. sinensis, known as dong quai (meaning 'proper order'), is second only to ginseng in Chinese herbal medicine for maintaining perfect health. John Parkinson (1629) proclaimed *A. archangelica* to be at the forefront of all medicinal plants.

What scientists today say

Clinical trials:

A. sinensis treats stroke (cerebral infarction) in combination with other herbs; improves immunity during cancer chemotherapy; normalises platelet function; reduces hot flushes; treats dysmenorrhoea; improves pulmonary function in people with pulmonary hypertension.

A. archangelica improves cognition in people with dementia in the one published clinical trial of the plant extract.

Lab tests:

A. sinensis: the component chemical butylidenephthalide reduces spasmodic activity, and its main chemical, angelica polysaccharide sulphate, is antioxidant.

A. archangelica: insecticide with bactericidal and other antimicrobial activities in vitro; anti-anxiety effects in vivo.

Uses still to be tested

A. sinensis: for amenorrhoea, menopause and enhancing fertility; as a blood tonic, reducing high blood pressure, headaches, infections and fatigue; for healing common skin complaints like eczema; relaxing and calming.

A. archangelica: remedy for colds, coughs, pleurisy, wind, colic, rheumatism, urinary diseases, menopause, poor circulation and digestive complaints.

Key chemicals

A. sinensis: ferulic acid, butylidenephthalide, angelica polysaccharide sulphate.

A. archangelica: valeric and angelic acids.

Using the herb for health

A. sinensis: fresh or dried root and liquid extracts taken orally as a decoction.

A. archangelica: root, leaves or seeds as tea or tincture; ingredient of gins and vermouths; crystallised stems as a confection.

Dose

A. sinensis: 0.5–5g daily

A. archangelica: 2–5g daily

Safety

A. sinensis: various contraindications (it increases the effects of anticoagulants, and is potentially abortive and phytotoxic) suggest it should be used only with professional guidance, as for other Chinese herbal medicine.

A. archangelica: considered safe but not for diabetics or for long-term use. Not to be confused with similar-looking but deadly hemlock, which also grows in damp ground.

ARNICA

Species name: *Arnica montana*
Plant family name: *Asteraceae*

Description
Perennial, yellow-flowering plant, originating in central Europe. Thrives in poor upland soils, where the flower aroma is strongest. Grown from seed or root division.

Special features
Probably best known for its internal use in homeopathy. As a topical (not internal) herbal medicine for osteoarthritis, it is considered to be as safe and effective as anti-inflammatory drugs.

Arnica montana.

Folklore
Known as mountain tobacco as the smoke was once inhaled. People were said to have discovered its uses for the skin as a result of seeing mountain goats rubbing against it when they fell and bruised themselves.

What physicians of old said
Flowers and roots have been used for hundreds of years. The German philosopher Goethe consumed arnica tea to relieve chest pain. Smoking arnica leaves used to be a 'prescribed' pain therapy.

What scientists today say

Clinical trials:
(Relating to use as a herbal rather than homeopathic medicine). A 2013 Cochrane review of topical plant medicines for treating osteoarthritis determined that arnica gel relieves pain as effectively as non-steroidal anti-inflammatory drugs and better than other herbs like comfrey and capsicum. Arnica used topically reduces postoperative swelling (oedema) and laser-induced bruising, improves blood flow, and relieves muscle pain after extreme exercise.

Lab tests:
Immune system stimulant; increases blood flow. Anti-inflammatory action depends on preventing white blood cells from releasing enzymes that break down tissue proteins.

Uses still to be tested
Listed in herbals for internal use as a diuretic for heart disease and for fevers. In homeopathy it's taken internally for sprains, wounds and bruises, and is claimed to treat epilepsy and travel sickness, among other conditions, though most trials of homeopathic preparations show no effect above placebo.

Key chemicals
Sesquiterpene lactones like helenalin, flavonoids, volatile terpenes.

Using the herb for health
Herbalists today do not use arnica internally. Mainly flowers but also roots are used to make lotions and an aromatic essential oil (diluted) for external use. Tinctures, no longer taken internally, can be added to bathing water.

Arnica pain-relieving formulations.

Dose
Gel from the leaf, or lotions containing up to 50% arnica, applied as required to the affected skin area.

Safety
Not for oral use or on broken skin. It contains a toxin, helenalin, which can cause gastritis if taken excessively internally. (This does not apply to the homeopathic dose which is minute.) May cause allergic reaction in those sensitive to helenalin.

BLACK COHOSH

Species name: *Actaea racemosa*
Plant family name: *Ranunculaceae*

Description
Native to NE America and SW Canada. Perennial; growing up to 1m/3 ft, it has deeply serrated leaves and striking long, white, attractively scented flowers that are stamens and stigmas only. Roots are black and knobbly.

Black cohosh (*Actaea racemosa*).

Special features
The original Native American use of this plant for women's (gynaecological) health led to it becoming one of the most popular non-oestrogen menopausal remedies.

Folklore
Also known as squaw root and black snakeroot, North American Indians refer to it as a 'miracle herb' for women due to its many uses, from improving fertility to alleviating hot flushes.

What scientists today say

Clinical trials:
Improves fertility and reduces hot flushes, irritability, depression and anxiety in menopausal women. In one head-to-head trial, cohosh was as effective as oestrogen in alleviating depression. Improves sleep quality in postmenopausal women.

Lab tests:
Acts on dopamine (the reward system in the brain), opioid (pain) as well as oestrogen receptors. Chemical anemonin reduces osteoporosis in vivo.

Uses still to be tested
For psychological premenstrual, postnatal and menopausal symptoms like mood swings and anxiety; promotes milk production; analgesic (e.g. for migraine in the menopause); antispasmodic, sedative and anti-inflammatory.

Key chemicals
Bitter triterpene glycosides; polyphenols like salicylic acid, anemonin, alkaloids, aromatic acids.

Using the herb for health
Use the root dried, as a toxic glucoside ranunculin is converted to key chemical anemonin on drying. The tea, which tastes bitter, is widely taken, although some people prefer the tincture.

Dose
Up to 5g dried root daily in tea or tincture.

Safety
Nausea and dizziness occur rarely at high doses. No contraindications recorded, other than it is not to be used in pregnancy. Possible caution in hormone-sensitive conditions. Do not confuse with blue cohosh (*Caulophyllum thalictroides*) in the barberry family, which is used traditionally as an abortive and contraceptive.

Black cohosh for relief of menopause symptoms has been granted a Traditional Herbal Registration (THR) by the UK government. (THRs are granted to herbal medicines based on long-term traditional, safe use, in a restricted number of medical conditions.)

CALENDULA/POT MARIGOLD

Species name: *Calendula officinalis*
Plant family name: *Asteraceae*

Description
Originating in Southern Europe and Arabia, often hardy in colder countries. Self-seeding annual with pale green leaves and sweet-smelling pale yellow to golden orange daisy-like flowers. Due to its pesticide properties, it can be used for companion planting. Grows well in pots in full sun; its alternate 'pot marigold' name probably relates to its use in cooking.

Special features
Brightening up any physic garden throughout the year, calendula's great skin-healing properties are based more on its age-old medicinal reputation than clinical trial evidence.

Pot marigold (*Calendula officinalis*).

Folklore

Used in rituals since ancient times, the Latin name reflects the fact that it's in flower in every calendar month. Medieval healers considered it so healing that it had to be magical. The name 'marigold' stems from its use as 'Mary's gold' in Catholic Church ceremonies.

What physicians of old said

Dioscorides and Pliny extolled its skin-healing virtues. Culpepper said 'the juice of marigold leaves mixed with vinegar, and any hot swelling bathed with it, instantly gives ease, and assuages it', and that the flowers are 'a comforter of the heart and spirits'. It was used in the American Civil War and World War II to dress wounds and promote healing.

Pot marigold makes a spicy, brightly coloured tea.

What scientists today say

Clinical trials:
Evidence is preliminary, and often in combination with other plants, for treating venous ulcers, diabetic foot ulcers, gingivitis, burns, nappy rash, radiation dermatitis and wounds (including post-caesarean). Treats mouth lesions in one controlled trial.

Lab tests:
Antiviral, antifungal, anti-inflammatory, antispasmodic and antitumour; treats dermatitis in vitro and in vivo.

Uses still to be tested

As an ointment for cuts, bruises, bleeding, acne, skin and eye irritations; internally for cramps, constipation, gastric or duodenal ulcers.

Key chemicals

Activity has not yet been attributed to a single chemical, though ingredients such as calendulin and calendic acid, triterpene glycosides, and flavonoids such as patuletin (used as a dye) and carotenoids may all contribute to biological activity.

Using the herb for health

Taken as a tea (spicy tasting) or tincture. Petals add a tangy, peppery taste to salads and yellow colour to soups or rice dishes (instead of saffron). Used to prepare healing skin lotions and ointments (suitable for children) and for cosmetics.

Dose

Ointments containing 5% plant extract are used as required.

5g petals per teacup, or 2g in a tincture daily.

Safety

Considered safe. Occasional allergies have been reported, but contraindications and side effects not reported.

CHAMOMILE

Species name: 1. *Matricaria chamomilla* (German); 2. *Chamaemelum nobile* (Roman)
Plant family name: *Compositae*

Description

European in origin; grows on poor soil in full sun. Feathery fern-like leaves. Both thrive in pots.

Roman: perennial, creeping and non-flowering with one variety (*C. nobile* 'Treneague') used for lawns.

German: annual or biannual; scented daisy-like white flowers.

Roman chamomile (*Chamaemelum nobile*).

German chamomile (*Matricaria chamomilla*).

Special features

Chamomile is among the oldest recorded medicinal herbs with multiple mind and body health benefits. With characteristic apple-like scents, the German is the most popular for herbal tea, while the Roman is famous for chamomile lawns.

Folklore
Long history of spiritual and medicinal uses includes supporting meditation and sleep. From the Greek for ground apple, it was taken as tea by the Romans. The Roman name, though, came from a botanist in the nineteenth century who found it growing in the Colosseum.

What physicians of old said
Culpepper claimed that 'bathing with a decoction of camomile taketh away weariness, easeth pains to what part of the body soever they be applied'.

What scientists today say
Some uses are common to both species, though the German is more researched.

Clinical trials:
German: sleep-inducing and antidepressant; relieves osteoporosis pain; anti-anxiety (including in intensive and palliative care); treats indigestion and colic; reduces eczema and hot flushes.

Roman: relieves insomnia and anxiety; is a mild sedative and sleep promoter; an anticonvulsant (children); analgesic (teething/earache); digestive and appetite stimulant; soothes nappy rash; treats premenstrual tension.

Lab tests:
Both German and Roman chamomile act on brain GABA (calming) system and are anti-inflammatory, antispasmodic and antibiotic. Decreases stress responses in animal models.

Uses still to be tested
For fear, muscular pain, gastritis, morning sickness, eye and skin inflammation, wounds, burns and allergies.

Key chemicals
Coumarins and flavonoids like apigenin. Essential oil contains the terpenes bisabolol and bisabolol oxide A (German), and pinene, camphene and cineole (Roman).

Using the herb for health
Flowers or leaves used mainly in teas (German is less bitter). Essential oils for aromatherapy. In lotions, creams and other cosmeceuticals.

Dose
5–10g orally daily. Essential oil diluted 100-fold for home use.

Safety
German: reported safe to take during pregnancy and for children.

CRANBERRY

Species name: *Vaccinium oxycoccos* and *V. microcarpus*
Plant family name: *Ericaceae*

Description
From northern hemisphere regions. Evergreen creeping shrub or vine with striking pink flowers and deep red berries. Prefers well-drained but moist sandy soil and is frost-hardy. Closely related to bilberry, blueberry and huckleberry.

Cranberry (*Vaccinium microcarpus*).

Special features
The most famous plant today for urinary tract infections (UTI), entering Western herbalism as a result of sixteenth-century settlers in the US observing Native American healing practices.

Folklore
Used originally by Native North Americans for many conditions, treating bladder disorders, healing wounds and curing tumours. Named by early European settlers in America who thought the stem and opening flower resembled the neck, head and bill of the long-necked crane.

What scientists today say

Clinical trials:

Numerous positive controlled clinical trials indicate that, head to head, UTI effects of cranberry are similar, though not necessarily superior, to antibiotics. Lowers number of infections in women prone to UTI and lowers UTI risk after gynaecological surgery. Helps eradicate *H. pylori* bacteria. Safe and effective prophylactic (protective) against UTI in infants and children. Reduces UTIs in high-risk geriatric patients. Stops bacterial adhesion in urine of treated patients. Reduces marker of prostate cancer in patients and also cystitis during radiation therapy for prostate cancer. Lowers blood glucose, insulin resistance and blood pressure in normal subjects, as well as blood glucose in diabetics. Improves anti-inflammatory and antioxidant blood markers as well as blood lipid profiles. Relieves symptoms of colds and flu.

Lab tests:

Antibiotic, reducing adhesion of microbes (bacteria causing UTI for example); chemicals (e.g. proanthocyanidins) interfere with colonisation of the gut by pathogenic *E. coli* in vitro. Anticancer, inhibiting cell proliferation in a broad range of cancer cell types and in animal models.

Uses still to be tested

Antinausea, wound-healing, laxative, fever-reducing.

Key chemicals

Flavonoids such as proanthocyanidins, stilbenes, terpenes like ursolic acid and phenolic acids.

Using the herb for health

Berries (usually sweetened because they are bitter) are made into juice, sauces and jellies, and can also be infused for teas. Extracted in cognac, the spirit is a delicious addition to the Christmas feast.

Dose

Daily around 300g fruit, though for UTIs up to 1 litre of juice has been recommended.

Safety

Taking warfarin and other anticoagulants is one of very few contraindications reported. Gastric reactions to large quantities may be a risk. Avoid consuming too much sugar in sweetened juice.

Cranberry berries make an excellent Christmas spirit.

DANDELION

Species name: *Taraxacum officinale*
Plant family name: *Compositae*

Description
European and Asian perennial. Its name is derived from its large jagged-tooth leaves looking like 'dents de lion'. Flowers consist of numerous bright yellow florets, the seed head being a classic time-telling device for children. Grown in deep rich soil for larger roots, it was once a commercial crop.

Feature
A wild plant, now growing worldwide, considered a weed until people discover the flavour of the leaves in a spring salad and the caffeine-free 'coffee' ground from its roasted roots (especially if spiced), Both have numerous health benefits that are just beginning to receive scientific attention.

Folklore
The species name derives from the Greek *taraxos* (disorder) and *akos* (remedy), on account of long-recognised health benefits. The alternative name 'pissabed' reflects its diuretic effects.

Dandelion (*Taraxacum officinale*).

What physicians of old said

First recorded for medicinal use by Arabian physicians in the tenth and eleventh centuries. Valued in Chinese herbal medicine where it is known as Pu Gong Ying and is used for the stomach and as a detoxicant. Used in Ayurveda for the liver, and by indigenous Americans for kidney disease. Culpepper said 'It is of an opening and cleansing quality, and therefore very effectual for the obstructions of the liver, gall and spleen'.

What scientists today say

Clinical trials:

Preliminary evidence of treating hepatitis B using the Chinese formulation Jiedu yanggan gao, which contains dandelion. Based on only a few other studies it is diuretic; counters anaemia (with other Chinese medicinal plants) after immunotherapy.

Lab tests:

Many more lab studies than clinical trials provide strong evidence for diuretic and detoxifying activities, as well as anticancer activity which (unlike chemotherapy) leaves normal cells intact.

Uses still to be tested

Spring tonic, stimulating appetite and digestion. Lowers blood pressure and relieves premenstrual fluid retention. Liver stimulant; colon cleansing; treats gall stones and piles. For eczema and wart removal.

Key chemicals

Taraxacin and taraxacerin (an acrid resin), inulin, sesquiterpene lactones, saponins and phenolics.

Using the herb for health

Leaves can be blanched for salads, soups, cooked vegetable (like spinach), sandwiches and beer. Flowers for wine; roots for expressed juice as well as dried, roasted and ground for coffee (often flavoured with spices like cardamom and cinnamon). Also tinctures and teas from roots and leaves.

Dandelion root and coffee.

Dose

Up to 10g root daily. Limit for leaves not set, but obviously restricted by diuretic effects.

Safety

Considered safe, though diuretic effects may affect other medications. While the brown stain caused by the white latex juice is harmless, skin reactions sometimes (but rarely) occur.

ECHINACEA/PURPLE CONEFLOWER

Species name: *Echinacea purpurea* (broad leaved); *E. angustifolia* (narrow leaved)
Plant family name: *Asteraceae*

Description
From North America; perennial up to 60cm/2ft with lanceolate leaves and composite flowers with purple petals. The name derives from Greek *echinos* (hedgehog) on account of the appearance of the orange-yellow prickly seed-cores. Roots (short and fibrous) are used medicinally. Drought and heat resistant, preferring sandy well-drained soil and sun. Grows well in pots.

Special features
Another Native American medicinal plant now renowned internationally as a herbal immunostimulant. An ornamental flower attractive to gardeners as well as bees and butterflies.

Echinacea purpurea.

What Native Americans and European herbalists say

Used as medicine by indigenous Americans for at least 400 years; externally for wounds, burns and insect bites; roots chewed for toothache and throat infections; internal application was for pain, cough, stomach cramps and snake bites. According to *King's American Dispensatory* it could be classified as an antiseptic and restorative but 'strictly speaking, it is practically impossible to classify an agent like echinacea by applying to it one or two words to indicate its virtues ... these qualifying terms will have no place in medicine, for they but inadequately convey to our minds the therapeutic possibilities of our drugs.'

What scientists today say

Clinical tests:
Many controlled trials indicate prevention of upper respiratory infections and reduction of risk and duration of colds and flu. Expectorant; promotes immune function; relieves eczema and reduces anxiety.

Lab studies:
Boosts immune function, with chemicals like polyphenols inhibiting a cell signal protein (TNF alpha) involved in inflammation. Analgesic, antiviral and antioxidant effects, and has cannabinoid activity and reduces anxiety in animal models.

Uses still to be tested

Treats boils, septicaemia and fever.

Key chemicals

Roots contain alkamides such as isobutylamides, caffeic acid derivatives and flavonoids. Essential oil contains anticancer polyacetylenes.

Using the herb for health

Traditionally the root is used to make teas, tinctures, ointments and compresses, though leaves and flowers are also now used. Some people spray the tincture into the throat when they feel a cold coming on.

Dose

1–2g daily; traditionally only the root was used, though aerial parts are also used today.

Preparing dried echinacea roots for teas and tinctures

Safety

Not to be taken on an empty stomach, or by children under 12. May interfere with immunosuppressant drugs.

ELDER

Species name: *Sambucus nigra*
Plant family name: *Adoxaceae*

Description
Native to Europe and North America. Small, fast growing tree (to 9m/30 ft) with pinnate green leaves, creamy fragrant white flowers and juicy purple-black, shiny berries. Closely related to the American elder (*S. canadensis*). Medicinal qualities of other ornamental purple and feather-leaved elder species not known.

Special features
Long reputed to protect against evil, and now confirmed as a treatment for colds and flu, with a wonderful choice of ways to take its fruits and flowers as medicine, from a flavoursome syrup to fine port-like wine and aromatic champagne.

Elder (*Sambucus nigra*).

Folklore

Renowned for keeping away evil and negative influences. Warnings that cutting down the tree incurs the anger of the resident witch may be based on the fact that the burning wood gives off toxic fumes. The English summer is said to start when the tree is in flower and end when it is in fruit.

What physicians of old said

Recorded since ancient Roman times and highly respected by the English herbalists. John Evelyn (1620–1706) said, 'If the medicinal properties of its leaves, bark and berries were fully known, I cannot tell what our countryman could ail for which he might not fetch a remedy from every hedge, either for sickness, or wounds.'

What scientists today say

Clinical trials:

The berry and flower reduce cold duration and symptoms. Clinically safe and cost-effective treatment for influenza. Laxative (with other herbs); improves weight and blood pressure control. Increase in blood proteins (cytokines) involved in its immunostimulating properties.

Lab tests:

Berries are antiviral (neutralising surface proteins); reduce inflammatory response not only in blood but also brain cells. Antioxidant, anti-proliferative and analgesic.

Uses still to be tested

Fever, hay fever, sinusitis and bronchitis, diuretic, antirheumatic and anticonvulsant.

Key chemicals

Flowers contain flavonoids like quercetin and rutin, and glycosides like sambunigrin. Berries contain tannins, anthocyanins and vitamin C.

Using the herb for health

Popular preparation is champagne from the flowers; berries for jelly or jam, and for wine (which improves on keeping for several years). Teas from flowers or berries taste good with honey. Elderberry syrup or 'rob' (juice thickened by heat with sugar and spice) is safe and pleasant for children, but all stems must be removed from flowers and berries.

Different ways of taking elderberries.

Dose

Up to 20g of berries or flowers daily.

Safety

Possible narcotic effects (people are advised not to sleep under the tree). Wood, bark, stems, leaves and unripe berries may be toxic due to the chemical sambucine (a cyanide-inducing glycoside).

FENNEL

Species name: *Foeniculum vulgare*
Plant family name: *Apiaceae*

Description
Mediterranean in origin, up to 1.5m/5ft, elegant, perennial and hardy; aromatic and flavourful feathery leaves; yellow umbelliferous flowers turning to pale green or cream-coloured seeds. Often self-seeding. Not the same species as the cultivar Florence fennel (finocchio, *F. vulgare dolce*) whose swollen bulb is used as a vegetable.

Fennel (*Foeniculum vulgare*).

Special features
Fennel's gracefulness reflects its traditional use as a slimming aid, though relief of gynaecological symptoms has stimulated most scientific research.

Folklore

Named from Latin for 'fragrant hay'. Considered by ancient Greeks and Romans to provide courage, longevity and strength. Roman women used fennel to suppress appetite and control obesity. One of the nine plants invoked in the pagan Anglo-Saxon 'Nine Herbs Charm' (tenth century).

What physicians of old said

According to William Coles, 'both the seeds, leaves and root are much used in drinks and broths for those that are grown fat, to abate their unwieldiness and cause them to grow more gaunt and lank.'

What scientists today say

Clinical trials:

Controls appetite in overweight women. Relieves PMT symptoms, including pain and menstrual problems. Resolves contraceptive-induced amenorrhoea. Decreases hair thickness in women with idiopathic mild to moderate hirsutism; aids recovery of bowel motility and complications after gynaecological laparotomy. Together with lemon balm and chamomile, relieves colic in breastfed infants. Laxative (with other herbs).

Lab tests:

Oestrogenic, antispasmodic, anticancer and memory-enhancing effects in vitro and in vivo. Controls (with other herbs) obesity induced by high fat diet in vivo.

Uses still to be tested

Oestrogenic; facilitates birth; stimulates milk production. Used as slimming aid. Essential oil treats rheumatism and arthritis. Stress-relieving; digestive (treating colic and flatulence); also allegedly aphrodisiac.

Key chemicals

The aroma and sweet flavour are due to anethole (also found in anise) and glycosides such as foeniculoside; essential oil also contains the terpenes limonene and alpha-pinene.

Using the herb for health

Fresh leaves, flowers and seeds (also dried) in teas and culinary dishes, tinctures, spirits (including absinthe), creams and lotions. Aniseed-flavoured seeds are also chewed after meals.

Dose

5–10g leaf; 1–5g seeds daily.

Safety

No known contraindications, though since it used traditionally as a uterine stimulant, avoid in pregnancy.

GARLIC

Species name: *Allium sativum*
Plant family name: *Amaryllidaceae*

Description
From Central Asia; perennial and hardy. Easy to grow in loose, well-drained soil in sunny positions. Bulbs are harvested as leaf tops turn yellow, around the time of summer solstice (northern hemisphere); replant cloves at the winter solstice. Wild garlic (*A. ursinum*) covers woodland floors in springtime.

Garlic (*Allium sativum*).

Special features
One of the most effective and delicious antibiotic plants, which also controls blood cholesterol and relieves fatigue.

Folklore
Egyptian slaves were given daily rations to ward off illnesses. Worn or hung in hallways to protect against werewolves and vampires, possibly related to preventing infections. In Ayurveda, garlic is classified as 'tamasic', meaning increasing passion and ignorance, and so it is avoided by monks of various orders.

What physicians of old said
Ancient Greeks gave it to Olympian athletes to enhance performance. In the *Materia Medica*, Dioscorides wrote that 'it doth clear the arteries'. It was used in World Wars I and II as an antiseptic and to prevent gangrene.

What scientists today say

Clinical trials:
Antibiotic against *Helicobacter*, ear infections, tonsillitis, abscesses, sinusitis, athlete's foot, mouth ulcers. Prevents common cold (limited evidence). Reduces blood cholesterol (total and LDL) if taken for months. Treats arteriosclerosis, angina and arthritis; stimulates immune system. Lowers blood pressure and fasting blood glucose. Reduces fatigue and anxiety in stressed subjects.

Lab tests (including wild garlic):
Hypolipidemic, antiplatelet, pro-circulatory, antibiotic, antioxidant, anticancer and neuroprotective. Against *Streptococcus mutans* (responsible for tooth decay), garlic was more effective than other plant extracts in vitro.

Key chemicals

As well as vitamin C and minerals, sulphur-containing alkaloids like allicin are responsible for antibiotic and other therapeutic effects; saponins, flavonoids and terpenes.

Using the herb for health

Cloves (with skin removed) are mostly used raw, though the flavour is less sharp if pickled or smoked. Added to dips, sauces (famous as aioli) and soups, effective dose levels can readily be reached. Milder-tasting leaves and flowers, especially from wild garlic, are delicious in salads but dose not specified, other than to use 'a handful'.

Dose

1–3 cloves (5–15g) daily.

Safety

No side effects in numerous clinical trials; caution if using antihypertensive, antihyperlipidaemic, antiplatelet or anticoagulant agents.

Wild garlic (*Allium ursinum*).

GINGER

Species name: *Zingiber officinale*
Plant family name: *Zingiberaceae*

Description
From Asia, a perennial with annual stems bearing pink buds and yellow flowers. Can be grown in wide, shallow pots; needs temperatures at or above 20°C/68°F. Grows from rhizomes provided they have not been scalded to stop sprouting.

Ginger (*Zingiber officinale*).

Special features

Greatly valued for many medicinal uses, notably for digestion, as well as being a popular spice and ornamental plant.

Folklore

The root (rhizome) has been used for over 5,000 years. Its digestive and aphrodisiac qualities are valued in many cultures. In ancient (and modern) Asia it is renowned for nurturing the 'fire' element, which manifests in the intestine and heart. The Kama Sutra recommends ginger as a means of arousing sexual energies.

Ginger products, delicious and digestive.

What physicians of old said

Ginger was widely used in Ayurvedic medicine and considered to be an entire medicine chest in itself. An Ayurvedic sutra (verse) mentions eating fresh ginger just before meals to promote digestion.

What scientists today say

Clinical trials:

Reduces nausea and vomiting, including morning and motion sickness, and in chemotherapy. For obesity, weight control and increasing gastric motility. Helps control hyperglycaemia, dysmenorrhoea, osteoarthritis and gingivitis.

Lab tests:

Antispasmodic, antioxidant, antibacterial, antifungal, cytotoxic, anti-allergic, anthelmintic, analgesic, anti-inflammatory, memory-enhancing, neuroprotective and liver-protective.

Uses still to be tested

Analgesic, anticoagulant, appetite stimulant, and circulation boosting (including relieving chilblains). For cholesterol control, fevers, fibromyalgia, flatulence, gout, heartburn and sinusitis.

Key chemicals

Volatile oil contains zingerone and zingiberene. In dried ginger, gingerols decompose to shogaols (both pungent hot components), though the Chinese prefer the fresh rhizome.

Using the herb for health

The rhizome, best collected after flowering, can be eaten as raw slices (and with vinegar, salt and sugar), or used to make tea, cordials, wine, beer, cakes, biscuits, pickles, confectionary and numerous savoury and sweet culinary dishes.

Dose

Up to 3g (in terms of fresh rhizome) daily.

Safety

Other than gastrointestinal effects in some, it's safe within dose limit.

GINKGO

Species name: *Ginkgo biloba*
Plant family name: *Ginkgoaceae*

Description

Originating in China. Deciduous, separate male and female trees grow to 30m/100ft. Thrives in most well-watered and drained areas, though will not fruit in colder climates. Bilobed leaves can be harvested from young (4 or 5-year-old) trees, though full growth takes up to 100 years (grows about 0.3m/1ft a year). Pale green frond-like flowers, apricot-coloured fruit and cream-coloured nuts.

Ginkgo biloba tree.

Special feature

The tree's survival strategies and extended lifespan (oldest recorded is 3,500) is matched by its reputation for longevity and proven benefits for the ageing brain.

Folklore

Reputation for survival is based on it being one of the oldest tree species, dating back almost 300 million years. Also known as maidenhair tree, the name ginkgo is a misspelling of the Japanese for golden apricot. Sacred to Buddhists, and believed in Japanese shinto to house shape-shifting spirits to which spells or mantras were written for health and long life.

What the physicians of old say

In ancient Traditional Chinese Medicine, ginkgo was prescribed as a 'scholar's herb' for concentration and memory. A long history of treating blood disorders led to its introduction, in the 1960s, into Western medicine by German doctors for vascular conditions.

What scientists today say

Clinical trials:

Trials in people with dementia have been inconsistent, possibly due to lack of standardisation, but improved memory is recorded in most studies of people with mild cognitive impairment or dementia at higher dose levels. Older evidence for treating circulation and balance disorders, asthma, tinnitus and glaucoma. Reduces negative symptoms in schizophrenia (as adjunct therapy).

Lab tests:

Circulatory benefits with extracts increasing blood flow, tissue oxygenation and nutrition in vitro and in vivo. Promotes the brain memory signal acetylcholine. Prevents brain damage in stroke models. Contains an inhibitor of the platelet activating factor involved in coagulation and inflammation.

Uses still to be tested

For incontinence and digestive problems in Chinese herbal medicine. In Western herbal medicine, for age-related conditions, varicose veins, post-stroke recovery and macular degeneration.

Key chemicals

Contains phenolic acids, flavonoid glycosides and terpene trilactones (ginkgolides and bilobalides).

Using the herb for health

Fresh or dried leaves as tinctures and teas; nuts used in cooking. Commercial extracts such as EGb 761 are standardised to fixed amounts of ginkgo flavone glycosides and terpene lactones (ginkgolides).

Dose

Not well established; 5g or more for fresh leaves, 50–500mg dried extract daily, depending on use. Take for up to six months for it to take effect.

Safety

Contraindicated with anticoagulants, antidepressants and possibly anticonvulsants. Side effects include increased risk of bleeding, nausea and restlessness. Nuts should not be consumed in large quantities (not more than 5–10 a day).

Ginkgo nuts.

HAWTHORN

Species name: *Crataegus monogyna*
Plant family name: *Rosaceae*

Description
From temperate regions in the northern hemisphere; deciduous tree, fast growing up to 9m/30ft. Often used as hedging in the UK, its small red berries (haws) are named after the old English word for a hedge. Small serrated leaves, sharp thorns and small, white, delicately-scented flowers. Also known as whitethorn (contrasting with earlier-flowering blackthorn which produces sloes). This species is referred to as the common hawthorn, but medical research is also conducted on others such as *C. azarolus*, *C. oxyacantha*, *C. pentagyna* and *C. pinnatifida*.

Special features
A major medicinal tree for the heart, listed in the pharmacopoeias of China and several European countries. Still plays a role in spring festivals on account of its beautiful blossom.

Hawthorn (*Crataegus monogyna*).

Folklore

Used by the Druids to 'open the heart', they apparently gave it to the aged as a tonic against weakness. Other names, May tree or Beltane tree (Beltane is pagan spring festival) reflect its blossom timing. Hawthorn trees were thought to be inhabited by fairies in many folklores. Fruits are called pixie pears in some parts of the UK.

What physicians of old said

Said to have been used by the ancient Greeks and Romans, but not known in the West until 1894 when the daughter of an Irish doctor, Dr Green, discovered from her father's notes that he used it extensively, but secretly, for treating heart disease.

What scientists today say

Clinical trials:
Verified for improving cardiac function, and treating angina, chronic heart disease and high blood pressure; also blood lipid lowering. Proven safe to use for people in heart failure.

Lab tests:
Strengthens the heart muscle force of contraction and blood vessels. Prevents cell death in lab models of myocardial infarction. Inhibits angiotensin-converting enzyme (ACE), as do drugs controlling blood pressure. Has strong phytoestrogen activity.

Uses still to be tested

Reduces atherosclerosis, arrhythmias and phlebitis. Anticoagulant; treats obesity, kidney disease and varicose veins; cures sore throats; diuretic; mild sedative.

Key chemicals

Flavonoids, particularly proanthocyanidins. Haws are rich in vitamin C. Bark contains the alkaloid crataegin.

Using the herb for health

Fresh spring leaves and flowers can be eaten, traditionally called 'bread and cheese' in the UK. Teas and jellies are made from the berries, and tea and wine from the flowers. Is said to take several months to act and can be taken long term. The recommended way to take for heart conditions is as a tincture made from berries.

Dose

1–5g berries daily.

Safety

Long-term safety established, though dizziness and nausea occasionally reported. Opinions differ on using it with digoxin, but no adverse drug interactions are reported in systematic surveys.

LAVENDER

Species name: *Lavandula angustifolia*
Plant family name: *Lamiaceae*

Description

From the Mediterranean and Middle East. Perennial, preferring well-drained soil and sun; pinnate leaves and blue or violet flowers. Best grown from plantlets/plugs rather than from the (slow-growing) seed. Will live in pots. Can be used as bed-dividers. Prune annually to promote new growth and prevent woodiness.

Special features

The most famous of European medicinal plants, with many mind and body benefits. Highly aromatic flowers are spectacular in large beds of dazzling blue and are the source of the most popular essential oil.

Folklore

Used for its perfume and health benefits, especially antiseptic and stress relief. The Romans named the plant after its use in their bathing rituals (*lavare*, to wash). Used by Egyptians in mummification – a faint scent of lavender, which had lasted three thousand years, was detected when King Tutankhamen's tomb was opened in 1923.

Lavender (*Lavandula angustifolia*).

What physicians of old said

According to Dioscorides, lavender cleans wounds and relieves headaches (though it's not clear which species existed then). John Parkinson wrote: 'it is almost wholly spent with us, for to perfume linnen, apparell, gloves and leather and the dryed flowers to comfort and dry up the moisture of a cold braine.' The finding by the French chemist Gattefossé, that it rapidly healed his burns, led to the use of the oil in military hospitals in World War II and then to today's practice of aromatherapy.

What scientists today say

Clinical trials:
Applied topically: treats bruises, burns and wounds. Extensive evidence for nervous system benefits is based mainly on the essential oil. Promotes calm and sleep, relieves anxiety, depression and pain (including lower back pain, dysmenorrhoea and headaches). Treats the peripheral neuropathy in carpal tunnel syndrome.

Lab tests:
Essential oil and its chemicals act on molecules involved in reducing nervous system activity; linalool blocks glutamate (brain-stimulating) signals. Antibacterial and antifungal, promotes protein synthesis relevant to wound-healing. Sedates and relieves pain in animal models.

Uses still to be tested

Digestive; disinfectant; insect repellent.

Key chemicals

The main active calming chemicals in the essential oil are the monoterpenoids, linalool and linalyl acetate.

Using the herb for health

Leaves and flowers (best harvested just before blooming), fresh or dried, in teas, tinctures and lotions and, less readily reaching medicinal dose, in bathing, perfumes and cooking (roasting meat and desserts). Essential oil is unique among essential oils in being used by some on the skin without dilution.

Dose

0.1–0.2ml essential oil; 5–15g fresh or dried herb for tea.

Safety

Approved by the European Medicines Agency as a herbal medicine to relieve stress and anxiety. A safe essential oil which can be applied undiluted, though may cause skin irritation in some. Caution against exacerbating effects of sedative or anticonvulsant drugs. May be oestrogenic. Medicinal value of cultivars not established, but French lavender (*L. stoechas*) may be hazardous taken internally.

LEMON BALM

Species name: *Melissa officinalis*
Plant family name: *Lamiaceae*

Description
Belonging to the dead nettle or mint family, a perennial from Southern Europe. Low-growing with heart-shaped leaves and minute white flowers. Grows almost anywhere temperate and liable to spread widely. Hardy but does not grow well in pots.

Special features
With its enticing lemony aroma and many positive effects on mood and mind, this plant keeps both bees and people calm.

Folklore
The herb was sacred to the temple of Diana where it was referred to as the 'heart's delight'. Also called sweet balm, sweet mary and bee balm (*melissa* is Greek for 'bee').

Lemon balm (*Melissa officinalis*).

What physicians of old said

According to Dioscorides in the *Grete Herball*, lemon balm 'Drunk in wine, it is good against the bitings of venomous beast, comforts the heart, and drives away melancholy'. Pliny said that lemon balm leaves 'being smeared on they well assuage the pains of gout'.

What scientists today say

Clinical trials:
Relieves pain (headaches), colic and palpitations. Calming, reduces anxiety and agitation. Improves memory and treats addiction.

Lab tests:
Increases action of the brain's calming signal (GABA). Acts on other brain signals, including the one for attention and memory (muscarinic and nicotinic receptors for acetylcholine). Antispasmodic and sedative. Antiviral, antibacterial and antifungal.

Uses still to be tested

Antidepressant and uplifting. Reduces fever and toothache; promotes sweating; treats gastrointestinal complaints and insect stings.

Key chemicals

Rosmarinic and caffeic acids, flavonoids such as luteolin, and volatile terpenes such as citronellal, geranial and neral.

Using the herb for health

Use the leaves before flowering. This is our favourite main ingredient of fresh botanical tea (also in all our dried botanical tea blends); left to cool with added lemon and honey it makes a refreshing 'lemonbalmade'. Tinctures are more bitter. The essential oil is one of the most expensive, so beware of adulterated products; it can be skin sensitising. Culinary uses include in soups, sauces, seafoods and salads, adding attractive lemon flavours, though not necessarily at medicinal dose level.

Lemon balm tea is delicious and adds fine flavour to herbal tea blends.

Dose

4–8g fresh herb daily; up to 100mg essential oil for inhalation or diluted a hundred fold in carrier for massage.

Safety

A safe medicinal plant recommended for children. Caution in hypothyroidism.

MILK THISTLE

Species name: *Silybum marianum* (syn. *Carduus marianus*)
Plant family name: *Asteraceae*

Description
From Europe and Asia. A striking annual or perennial growing to 1m/3ft; leaves are shiny green, thorny and lanceolate, with milk-white veins. Purple flowers turn to downy seeds that can survive cold winters to appear as self-seeded plants in late spring.

Milk thistle (*Silybum marianum*).

Special features
This most important medicinal thistle, used primarily for the liver, is popular before a 'night out' to prevent hangovers, or afterwards to cure them.

Folklore
Also called blessed milk thistle, Our Lady's thistle and St Mary's thistle, because the milk-white leaf veins were thought to have originated in the milk of the Virgin which once fell on this thistle plant.

What physicians of old said
Culpepper claimed it treated obstructions of the liver and spleen, as well as the plague. In 1594, herbalist William Westmacott referred to the thistle as 'a friend of the liver and blood'. Dioscorides had previously claimed it cured snake bites, and Gerard that it 'expelled melancholy'.

What scientists today say
Clinical trials:
Reduces symptoms and markers of alcohol and non-alcohol or hepatitis-induced liver disease. Controls blood glucose, and relieves radiotherapy-induced pain and inflammation of mucous membranes.

Lab tests:
A wide range of activities, include regenerating and stabilising membranes of liver cells, anticancer, cardioprotective and cholesterol-controlling.

Uses still to be tested
In Chinese herbal medicine, milk thistle is used to clear toxins, soothe the liver and promote bile flow. In Western herbal medicine, it's used to treat various liver diseases (cirrhosis, jaundice and hepatitis), as well as to promote milk flow and treat cancer.

Key chemicals
Polyphenols, flavonolignans such as silybin and silymarin.

Using the herb for health
The root can be eaten raw or boiled, and unopened flower heads, cooked like artichokes. Leaves, roots, shoots or seeds can be used in teas and tinctures.

Dose
2–4g of roots, seeds and/or leaves.

Safety
Generally considered safe and well tolerated. Can have a laxative effect. May interact with anaesthetics and anti-anxiety drugs.

NETTLE/SMALL STINGING NETTLE

Species name: *Urtica urens*
Plant family name: *Urticaceae*

Description

From Eurasia with heart-shaped leaves and incomplete green flowers (stamens only on male; pistils only on female). Grows in most temperate zones, especially in rich soil. The larger U. dioica is also used medicinally.

Nettle (*Urtica urens*).

Special features
Spring tonic effects, backed by evidence of pain-relieving and antibiotic properties, mean that creating space for this 'weed' in a corner of your physic garden is justified.

Folklore
Urtification was, and still is, a practice of flogging oneself with the fresh nettle plant to treat conditions like chronic rheumatism, lethargy, coma and paralysis. Nettle was regarded as an almost magical plant, protecting people from lightning and increasing fertility, for example. Stem fibres were found in burial cloths from the bronze age. Roman soldiers brought it to Britain to rub on their cold limbs.

What physicians of old said
Nettle beer made by British cottagers, hundreds of years ago, was given to their old folk as a remedy for gouty and rheumatic pains. Dioscorides previously referred to nettle's cleansing qualities.

What scientists today say
Clinical trials:
Topical treatment relieves osteoarthritic pain. Orally treats allergic rhinitis. Relieves nocturia, urinary tract infections and urological symptoms of prostatitis. Provides glycaemic control as well as reducing markers of oxidative stress in diabetics.

Lab tests:
Anti-inflammatory; antibacterial; anticancer; inhibits platelet aggregation and increases insulin secretion. Improves memory and relieves depression in animal models.

Uses still to be tested
Spring tonic (perhaps because it contains minerals like calcium and potassium). Antihistamine (hay fever); anti-asthmatic; blood purifier (reduces uric acid); stimulates hair growth; treats eczema, gout, sore throats, stings and even nettle rash.

Key chemicals
Carotenoids and flavonol glycosides like rutin, histamine and acetylcholine; formic acid in stinging hairs.

Using the herb for health
Pick leaves prior to flowering in spring and use (fresh or dried) to make tea, soup, tinctures, beers and wines. For pain from arthritis, for example, the use is external and stinging is part of the healing. Tea made from the flowers is as tasty as from leaves and they don't sting!

Dose
5–15g leaf; 5g dried root daily.

Safety
If dried or infused to eliminate stinging, it is regarded as free of contraindications, except possibly not to be taken if breastfeeding.

NIGELLA/BLACK CUMIN/KALONJI

Species name: *Nigella sativa*
Plant family name: *Ranunculaceae*

Description
From Southern Europe, Northern Africa and Asia. A sun-loving annual, growing up to 0.3m/1ft, with finely divided leaves, delicate white or pale-blue flowers and black seeds. Grows and flowers readily in colder climates in the summer; also thrives in pots, but needs heat to set seed.

Special features
An Arabian medicinal plant with an exceptional range of health benefits for body and mind, many backed up by clinical evidence.

Nigella sativa.

Folklore
Seeds were found in ancient Egyptian tombs. Cleopatra used the black seeds for skin beauty. It came to be known as a 'cure all' in Arabic culture where it was believed to treat all known diseases. Also referred to in the Bible (Isaiah) as 'curative black cumin' and is used in Ayurvedic practice for restoring harmony.

What physicians of old said
Dioscorides recommended smelling a bag of the seeds to relieve catarrh, and applying as a plaster to relieve headaches.

What scientists today say
Clinical trials:
Positive effects on metabolic, digestive, musculoskeletal and cognitive functions; improves glycaemic control in diabetics, lipid profiles in menopausal women and diabetics, and immune function in arthritic patients; reduces weight and oxidative stress in obese women; relieves arthritic symptoms as an adjunct (add-on) therapy and controls blood pressure; treats asthma, dyspepsia and ear infections; improves memory and cognition in adult males and in the elderly.

Lab tests:
Tests indicate antibacterial, antihistamine, hypoglycaemic, anti-epileptic, memory-enhancing and anticancer among many other effects.

Uses still to be tested
In modern Arabian herbal medicine, nigella is said to treat fever, cough, bronchitis, asthma, chronic headache, migraine, dizziness, chest congestion, dysmenorrhoea, obesity, diabetes, paralysis, hemiplegia, back pain, infection, inflammation, rheumatism, hypertension and gastrointestinal problems such as flatulence, dysentery and diarrhoea (to mention but a few!).

Key chemicals
Rare (indazole) alkaloids such as nigellicine and nigellidine. The oil contains thymoquinone as well as thymol and pinenes.

Using the herb for health
Seeds, dried and roasted to remove bitterness (tasting like oregano) are used in curries and in the spice mix panch phoron (five-spice blend). Also used extracted in oil with the option of added honey.

Dose
2–3g seeds daily.

Safety
Clinical trials do not report significant side effects. Contact dermatitis and lowered blood pressure are rare risks.

PEPPERMINT

Species name: *Mentha x piperita*
Plant family name: *Lamiaceae*

Description
Originating in Europe, this perennial hybrid cross between spearmint and watermint thrives in moist, damp soils. As rhizomes spread widely, it is often grown in pots. Dark-green, purple-veined leaves and purple flowers emit an exhilarating aroma.

Special features
With a long-standing reputation as an antispasmodic, promoting gastric function, peppermint is one of very few medicinal plants incorporated into modern mainstream medical practice.

Peppermint (*Mentha x piperita*).

Folklore

Mint tea has long been, and still is, one of the most popular digestive herbal teas in many cultures. The old herbals make no mention of peppermint since it was only described by Linnaeus in the eighteenth century. Previous references are probably to spearmint, including one in the Bible to mint being of such high value it was used as tithes by the Pharisees.

What physicians of old said

References to mint in the old herbals were not to this species.

What scientists today say

Peppermint is the most studied mint species. The properties of watermint, spearmint and cultivars are less researched, although all contain menthol.

Clinical trials:

Safe and effective short-term treatment for irritable bowel syndrome (IBS) used in mainstream medicine. Anti-emetic for postoperative and chemotherapy nausea. Enhances gastric emptying, thus aiding endoscopy procedures. Anti-asthmatic; prevents migraine progression; reduces perceived mental fatigue; enhances memory and alertness (effects reported for tea and the essential oil).

Lab tests:

Gastrointestinal antispasmodic; increased bile production; activates skin receptors to provide cooling sensations; antifungal; antibacterial; analgesic; anaesthetic; memory-enhancing.

Uses still to be tested

Treats Crohn's disease and nervous disorders; 'clears' the mind. Essential oil relieves depression, improves concentration and reduces apathy.

Key chemicals

The principle active chemicals are the terpenes menthol and menthone. Also contains flavonoids like luteolin, and phenolics like rosmarinic acid.

Using the herb for health

Leaves or flowering tops, better fresh than dried, for teas. Also tinctures and digestive spirits (famously crème de menthe). Essential oil can be inhaled or taken orally (in capsules). Confections (sweets or flavoured chocolates) can provide an active dose for digestive purposes, but are restricted by sugar content.

Dose

Up to 5–10g fresh leaves daily. For IBS, the encapsulated essential oil can be taken orally (up to 1ml daily).

Safety

Caution if taking with antacid or hypotensive drugs. Contraindicated in people with hiatus hernia, kidney stones, gall bladder blockage, reflux or ulcers. Contact with or inhaling undiluted oil should be avoided in children under four years old, but has been used for IBS in children.

RHUBARB

Species name: 1. *Rheum rhaponticum* (English); 2. *R. officinale* or *R. palmatum* (Chinese or Tibetan)
Plant family name: *Polygonaceae*

Description
Perennial. English: widely grown in the West as a vegetable; Chinese: larger and more dramatic leaves and roots which are less liable to rot. All have large leaves, and dramatic tall white flowers; readily grown from root divisions; thrives in well-composted soil (frost-hardy, Chinese to -15°C).

Special features
One of the most widely used plants in Chinese herbal medicine. Chinese rhubarb is more of an antioxidant and English rhubarb more of a digestive aid, especially for infant stomach troubles.

Chinese rhubarb (*Rheum officinale*).

What physicians of old said

Chinese rhubarb is one of the most ancient and best-known plants in Chinese herbal medicine. Its wide range of uses were first documented by Emperor Shen Nung (c. 2700 BC). In a 1923 *Lancet* article, a Dr Burkett claimed, with regard to the treatment of bacillary dysentery, that 'no remedy in medicine has such a magical effect'. The root of the Chinese species is considered superior to the English for herbal medical use, but no head-to-head trial has been conducted for any condition.

What scientists today say

Selecting just some of many studies, mostly on the Chinese species.

Clinical trials:

Treats dysenteric diarrhoea and jaundice in children. Treats pancreatitis and liver disease. Helps detoxify in pesticide poisoning; prophylactic for radiotherapy side effects. Reduces cholesterol; improves arterial function and nitrogen metabolism in renal failure. Relieves menopausal symptoms (including anxiety) and improves memory in the elderly.

Lab tests:

Tannins counter agents promoting diarrhoea in vivo. Antibacterial, anticoagulant (antiplatelet aggregation), anticancer and antispasmodic. Tannins such as gallic acid and catechin are as strong anti-inflammatories as aspirin.

Uses still to be tested

Digestive, mildly laxative (large doses), antispasmodic, treats burns and sores.

Key chemicals

Anthraquinones (rhein and physcion), anthocyanins and stilbenes. Astringency due to rheotannic acid. Very low levels of oxalates (also occurring in other edible plants) in stems compared to leaves.

English rhubarb (*Rheum rhaponticum*) root.

Using the herb for health

Root, which is bitter, is usually dried, powdered and taken as teas or tinctures. Culinary use of stems (also testing positive in clinical trials) includes syrups, desserts, wines, chutneys and pickles.

Dose

1–2g root daily. No limits set for stem as it's a foodstuff, though if you eat too much, it may act as a laxative.

Safety

Leaves toxic due to high levels of oxalic acid. Stems to be avoided by sufferers of intestinal inflammation, gout, rheumatism or epilepsy.

ROSEMARY

Species name: *Rosmarinus officinalis*
Plant family name: *Lamiaceae*

Description
Mediterranean origin. Perennial, woody herb, grows to 1.5m/5ft. Fragrant, evergreen leaves (needles) and pink, blue or white flowers. Flourishes in full sun and well-drained ground; can be pot-grown. Frost-hardy most winters, but best to protect in case. Prune regularly to prevent woody growth and encourage new leaf growth. Pest-resistant and may protect nearby plants from insect invasion.

Rosemary (*Rosmarinus officinalis*).

Special features

The herb with a reputation, not only for improving memory but as a symbol of fidelity and remembrance of the departed.

Folklore

Greek scholars braided it into their hair to improve their memory, and it was later laid on bed linen to ensure faithfulness. Many magical beliefs include the notion it took its colour from the Virgin Mary's cloak (hence the rosemary name) and that it grows to the height of Christ when he died.

What physicians of old said

From the *Grete Herball*: 'Against weyknesse of the brayne and coldenesse thereof, sethe rosemaria in wyne and lete the pacyent receye the smoke at his nose and keep his heed warme.' According to Culpepper, rosemary 'helps the cold distillations of rheum into the eyes, and all other cold diseases of the head and brain, as the giddiness or swimmings therein, drowsiness or dullness of the mind and senses like a stupidness.'

What scientists today say

Clinical trials:
Improves attention and memory (in young and old). Relieves anxiety, helps with addictive-drug withdrawal. Promotes hair growth and improves skin conditions (including sun protection). Treats gingivitis and controls blood pressure.

Lab tests:
Acts on (nicotinic receptors for) the memory signal acetylcholine. Increases blood flow, which may also explain beneficial effects on brain. Neuroprotective, antioxidant and antifungal. Other antibiotic effects include inhibition of MRSA (methicillin-resistant *Staphylococcus aureus*) in vitro.

Uses still to be tested

Tonic, improving mood and digestion; treats palpitations, headaches, muscular pain and neuralgia; relieves cold symptoms. Essential oil as an analgesic, disinfectant and stimulant.

Key chemicals

Phenolic diterpenes like carnosol; rosmarinic acid acting as an antioxidant; volatile oil containing camphor and borneol.

Using the herb for health

Leaves and flowers in teas and tinctures. Essential oil approved as a food preservative and added to cosmeceuticals like shampoos.

Dose

10-15g fresh herb daily. Usual restrictions apply to use of the essential oil.

Safety

Not in epilepsy.

ROSEROOT

Species name: *Rhodiola rosea*
Plant family name: *Crassulaceae*

Description

Perennial; may have originated in south-west China. Thrives in cold regions, especially mountains and seacliffs. Grows up to 30cm/1ft tall, with fleshy pale green leaves, yellow flowers and long, thick, rose-scented roots. Slow-growing; can be grown in deep pots.

Buds of roseroot (*Rhodiola rosea*).

Special features

Extensively used for enhancing physical performance and relieving stress, backed by evidence on endurance performance.

Folklore

An ancient remedy for fatigue; important to ancient Greeks, Vikings and Siberians for health and vitality. One alternate name, Aaron's rod, implies magical powers. In Siberia, bouquets of roots have long been given to couples to enhance fertility, and roots are used in all-night rituals with shamans (healers).

What physicians of old said

In his *Materia Medica*, Dioscorides said it could be bruised and applied to the head for headaches.

What scientists today say

Roseroot differs from most of our other chosen plants in that its clinical trial evidence shows more inconsistent findings. Even so, we focus on positive results than confirm traditional uses and on lab tests.

Clinical trials:
Reduces fatigue (including stress-related and muscle fatigue); increases stamina for high-altitude training in athletes and in those with 'burn out' or chronic fatigue syndromes. Reduces mountain sickness. Limited evidence for use in anxiety, depression and for memory. Helps with heart disease (angina).

Lab tests:
Improves breathing and ventilation (blood oxygen) efficiency. Chemicals (rosavin and salidroside) have antidepressant, antistress and memory-enhancing effects in vivo.

Uses still to be tested

Mood-enhancing; helps in coping with stress; immunostimulant; stabilises blood pressure; treats cancer; improves libido.

Key chemicals

Rosin and rosarin and other cinnamic glycosides, phenols and terpenes like geraniol and citronellal.

Using the herb for health

Root is best used fresh but can be dried, and taken as a tea or tincture. Alcoholic extracts may be more effective than water extracts due to higher rosavin content.

Roseroot root.

Dose

Up to 5g daily.

Safety

On the basis of clinical trials it's considered to be safe and non-addictive. May increase anxiety and agitation, common to other stimulants.

SAGE

Species names: *Salvia officinalis* (common, or garden); *S. lavandulaefolia* (Spanish)
Plant family name: *Lamiaceae* or *Labiatae*

Description
Mediterranean. Woody perennial shrub with green-silvery leaves (Spanish leaves are lighter in colour and narrower), and purple, pink or blue flowers. Likes well-drained soil and grows quite well in containers. Usually frost-hardy unless very wet (Spanish sage less so). Leaves are harvested before flowering and stems cut back annually to promote new leaf growth. Do not confuse with ornamental garden Salvias or clary sage (*S. sclarea*) used in aromatherapy.

Special features
Among many benefits for mind and body, its reputation for enhancing memory prompted our creation of Dilston Physic Garden.

Salvia officinalis.

Folklore
The *salvia* name comes from the Latin 'salvere', which means 'to be healthy/well' – hence the greeting 'salvere!', to wish someone good health. Valued in China and Arabic countries and by gypsies as the key to a long life.

What physicians of old said

Gerard said, 'Sage is singularly good for the head and brain. It quickeneth the senses and memory, strengtheneth the sinews.' According to Grieve, there is an old French saying which translates as: 'Sage helps the nerves and by it palsy is cured and fever put to flight' (*A Modern Herbal*, 1931).

What scientists today say (referring to either or both species)

Clinical trials:

Enhances memory, alertness and mood, and is antifatigue. Treats coughs and acute pharyngitis, and reduces bacteria in dental plaque in the young. Lowers blood sugar and cholesterol in diabetics, and reduces hot flushes in menopausal women.

Lab tests:

Strengthens the action of the brain's memory and awareness signal (acetylcholine). Blood glucose reducer; anti-inflammatory; antioxidant; antibiotic; anticancer; oestrogenic.

Uses still to be tested

Nerve tonic; antiseptic for throat infections and catarrh; stimulates milk flow; reduces salivation in Parkinson's disease.

Key chemicals

Thujone and camphor are the main terpenes in *S. officinalis*; *S. lavandulaefolia* contains trace amounts of thujone and is higher in cineole and camphor. Both contain a variety of polyphenols such as rosmarinic acid and luteolin.

Using the herb for health

Leaves, fresh or dried, in teas sweetened with honey; particularly delicious in wintertime when leaves are less bitter. Also available as a tincture, capsules/tablets and lozenges. A favourite recipe of ours is leaves of common sage fried in oil or butter, lightly salted, sprinkled with sugar and eaten as crisps. Sprays (water extracts) used in the mouth for throat sores/ infections.

Spanish sage (*Salvia lavandulaefolia*).

Dose

10–20 fresh leaves daily.

Safety

Caution in high blood pressure. Not in epilepsy. Not for children, or pregnant women at medicinal dose (due to thujone in *S. officinalis*); *S. lavandulaefolia* does not carry this risk, though contraindicated in epilepsy due to camphor. Do not confuse with the hallucinogenic divine sage (*S. divinorum*) often referred to as 'Salvia'.

SAW PALMETTO

Species name: *Serenoa repens*
Plant family name: *Arecaceae*

Description

From southeastern USA. Small palm (max 3m/10ft), slow-growing in sandy soil, hardy and long-lived (over 500 years). The stem below the leaf fan is sharply saw-edged; flowers are pale yellow; fruit is reddish black and contained in a panicle that can weigh up to 5kg/11lb. A striking ornamental palm that thrives indoors in large pots but only flowers at higher temperatures.

Saw palmetto (*Serenoa repens*).

Special features
One of the best-known Western herbal medicines for men, renowned for treating benign prostate hyperplasia (BPH), with the added bonus of improving sex life. Included as one of the few plants specifically for men, even though it only fruits in hot dry areas, doesn't taste so good, and, in the opinion of some medical practitioners, should be used only under medical supervision (even for benign conditions).

Folklore
Native American medicine men kept a bag of saw palmetto for a wide range of health benefits, including as an antiseptic and for fertility. Also used to make hair shine.

What physicians of old said
The first report by a physician in Georgia (Dr J. B. Read, 1879) read: 'By its peculiar soothing power on the mucous membrane it induces sleep, relieves the most troublesome coughs, promotes expectoration … its sedative and diuretic properties are remarkable'.

What scientists today say
Clinical trials:
Reduces BPH symptoms such as frequency and nocturia, though not all trials are positive; some show effects similar to drugs, but the herb has fewer side effects. Improves sexual function and quality of life in middle-aged men. Helps recovery from BPH surgery and treats urinary tract infections associated with prostatitis. Long-term use reduces BPH risk. Improved hair growth in pilot studies.

Lab tests:
Anticancer, reducing activity of the enzyme that promotes growth of prostate cells. Anti-inflammatory and inhibits prostatic muscle contractions.

Uses still to be tested
For testicular inflammation, urinary tract infection; used as a diuretic, a tonic and for clearing catarrh.

Key chemicals
Lauric and oleic acids, myristic, palmitic and linoleic fatty acids.

Using the herb for health
Berries are not so pleasant-tasting; teas often have other added ingredients like lemon, honey or vanilla for flavour. Compared with teas, tinctures may not extract all of the active ingredients, which may account for clinical trial inconsistencies.

Dose
0.5–1g daily, effects taking weeks to appear.

Safety
For anyone already affected by prostate problems it is advisable to consider using this herb after professional consultation. Safe when used at correct dose. May interact with anticoagulants and hormone treatments. Teeth of spines on stem can tear the skin if you handle the plant.

ST JOHN'S WORT

Species name: *Hypericum perforatum*
Plant family name: *Hypericaceae*

Description

Originating in Europe, this plant thrives in poor soil. Although perennial, it often doesn't survive more than a year or two in one place, seeding elsewhere. Small oval leaves are distinguished by holes (perforations). It has bright yellow flowers; buds or seed pods produce a reddish liquid if crushed. Can be confused with several closely related *Hypericum* species, some hybrids.

Special features

Medicinal plant renowned for its antidepressive and powerful anti-inflammatory (e.g. for wound-healing) effects. The two properties may be linked, since depression is now considered to be an inflammatory condition of the brain.

St John's wort (*Hypericum perforatum*).

Folklore

Originally thought to drive away demons and devils in the days when spirit-possession was one explanation for feeling low or hopeless or depressed; it's still called 'chase devil' today. It's named St John's wort because it flowers in midsummer on St John's day.

What physicians of old said

Culpepper: 'It is a singular wound herb; boiled in wine and drank, it heals inward hurts or bruises; made into an ointment, it opens obstructions, dissolves swellings, and closes up the lips of wounds.'

What scientists today say

Clinical trials:
Heals wounds, including bruises and burns, and improves general skin condition. Numerous trials support its use for mild to moderate depression, being as effective as selective serotonin reuptake inhibitors (SSRI) antidepressants such as sertraline and paroxetine, but with fewer, if any, side effects. Treats anxiety, including for menopausal women.

Lab tests:
Anti-inflammatory and neuroprotective. Acts on more brain signals (GABA, glutamate, cholinergic, opioid and melatonin, as well as serotonin) than SSRI drugs.

Uses still to be tested

For herpes, pulmonary complaints, bladder conditions, diarrhoea, hysteria, neuralgia, sciatica, menopause (including fatigue) and nocturnal urinary incontinence in children.

Key chemicals

Contains a broad range of flavones, tannins and phenolics. The hyperforin, adhyperforin and hypericin combination may be responsible for antidepressant effects, though extracts for research or commercial production are often standardised to one of these chemicals.

Using the herb for health

Leaves and flowers taken orally as teas (not so pleasant-tasting – it's woody and bitter) or tinctures. Infused oils or diluted essential oil are used for topical applications.

Dose

Up to 15g, though dose for fresh leaves and flowers is not well defined since most people use extracts (1g daily) for mild to moderate depression.

Safety

As safe as the placebo in trials, though nausea and phototoxicity are occasionally reported. Interferes with metabolism of drugs like immunosuppressants, chemotherapeutic agents and contraceptives so is contraindicated with certain medications. May alter effects of synthetic antidepressants. Not enough information to predict safety in pregnancy.

THYME

Species name: *Thymus vulgaris*
Plant family name: *Lamiaceae*

Description
From Mediterranean regions. Low-growing woody perennial with numerous branched stems; tiny shiny leaves and purple flowers which smell sharp and peppery. It does not thrive in wet conditions but will survive in containers. Readily available forms are cultivars of the wild thyme (*T. serpyllum*) with various stronger and different aromas. Needs to be cut back regularly to encourage new, non-woody growth.

Special features
A herb with an age-old reputation for its strengthening properties, now backed up by proven, powerful antiseptic effects.

Thyme cultivar similar in appearance to common thyme, *Thymus vulgaris*.

Folklore

Believed to instil courage and strength, Roman soldiers would bathe in thyme before going into battle. In the Middle Ages, English ladies commonly embroidered an emblem of a bee hovering over a sprig of thyme onto the scarves they gave their knights. Scottish highlanders also used the herb to prepare for battle and prevent nightmares.

What physicians of old said

Gerard said it would cure 'pains in the head', and Culpepper, that 'It purgeth the body of phlegm and is an excellent remedy for shortness of breath. It is so harmless you need not fear the use of it.'

What scientists today say

Clinical trials:

Is as effective as ibuprofen in reducing the severity of pain and spasm in dysmenorrhoea. Thyme (with honey) reduces inflammation and polyp formation and promotes mucosal healing in chronic rhinosinusitis. Together with primrose or ivy, it treats acute bronchitis. Immunostimulant in cancer patients.

Lab tests:

Antibacterial activity against numerous different types of bacteria, including methicillin-resistant *Staphylococcus aureus* (MRSA). Antifungal, antispasmodic, expectorant and mucociliary clearing (helping bronchial cilia to clear away mucous). Thymol acts on brain inhibitory (GABA) receptors, and acts positively on brain and liver functions in models of alcoholism.

Uses still to be tested

Decongestant and expectorant for coughs; mild sedative; for epilepsy and migraine; treats hangovers; reduces nightmares. Widely reported to improve respiratory and gastric functions in farm animals (sheep, goats, and chickens) and horses.

Key chemicals

Essential oil is rich in thymol, borneol, linalool, carnosol and carvacrol.

Using the herb for health

Leaves are used to prepare steam inhalations, nasal sprays, gargles, teas (lemon thyme, *T. citriodorus*, being particularly fragrant), syrups and tinctures. Inhalation of steam from a few drops of essential oil added to hot water for colds. Used in cooking, soups, roasts and many Italian dishes.

Dose

Not well defined for ingesting the whole herb, but in teas 5–15g daily.

Safety

Human trials refer to excellent safety profile and tolerance. Safe for children in moderation, for example: cooled tea added to babies' baths.

VALERIAN/GARDEN HELIOTROPE

Species name: *Valeriana officinalis*
Plant family name: *Valerianaceae*

Description
From Europe and Northern Asia. Tall (up to 1.2m/4ft); perennial thriving in damp areas. Spear-shaped, segmented leaves, small white or pinkish sweet-scented flowers and a highly branched root (the medicinal part) that develops a pungent (for some unpleasant) smell when dried. Vigorous self-seeder, the flowers follow the sun, as does the separate heliotrope species.

Special features
Despite the rather offensive smell of its dried root, this is the most widely used sleep-inducing herb, which acts to calm the central nervous system.

Folklore
Used as a medicine, spice and perfume (from flowers) in the Middle Ages. Its name, from the Latin *valere* ('to be strong and healthy'), may relate to the root's smell or powerful healing. Attractive to cats and rats, it may have been used by the Pied Piper of Hamelin to lure away rodents.

Valerian (*Valeriana officinalis*).

What the physicians of old said

Galen referred to it as a cure for insomnia. John Cooke said, in his 1793 Dublin lectures on *materia medica*, that 'valerian was formerly much celebrated as a medicine adapted to the cure of epilepsy; indeed, by some it was considered as a specific' (specific is a remedy indicated for a particular disease). In World War II it was used to relieve shell shock and the stress of air raids.

What scientists today say

Clinical trials:
Enhances sleep, treating insomnia by reducing periods of wakefulness. It interferes less with coordination than the anti-psychotic drug chlorpromazine. Reduces agitation in depressed children; calms during tooth extraction and helps withdrawal from benzodiazepine tranquillisers. Reduces compulsive behaviours in obsessive compulsive disorder and treats fibromyalgia.

Lab tests:
Prevents the breakdown of brain calming signal (GABA). Enhances the sleep signal adenosine. Anticonvulsant, antispasmodic and neuroprotective.

Uses still to be tested

According to present-day medical herbalists it is anti-epileptic, antidepressant and hypotensive. Used for premenstrual tension, acid reflux and palpitations.

Key chemicals

Sedative activity is associated with a combination of valepotriates and valerenic acid (a volatile sesquiterpene).

Using the herb for health

Roots are used in teas and tinctures. Young leaves (medicinal value unknown) are delicious in salads. The old herbalists refer to the use of the leaves which are delicious in salads, Culpepper stating that 'The green herb being bruised and applied to the head taketh away pain and pricking thereof'.

Dose

5–10g daily; dose for tinctures (more commonly used than fresh root) depends on original herb concentration.

Valerian root.

Safety

Contraindicated with other tranquillising drugs, anaesthetics or alcohol; may be associated with 'hangover' effects; may provoke headache. Rare liver toxicity reported is likely due to adulteration of commercial preparations. Identification caution: hemlock has umbelliferous flowers and a foetid root similar to valerian, but hemlock is deadly.

WHITE WILLOW

Species name: *Salix alba*
Plant family name: *Salicaceae*

Description
Deciduous tree from Europe and Central Asia. Grows to 15m/50ft. Flourishes near water; its short lifespan under 100 year is doubled by coppicing. Readily propagated from cut stems (whips). Slender leaves, silvery due to silky white hairs, give the tree its *alba* (Latin for 'white') name. Male and female plants are separate, the pale green catkins of the male being longer. The bark on young trees is pale yellow, turning grey-brown with deep fissures in older trees.

Special features
Famous because aspirin, the most widely used drug in the world, is based on the structure of salicin, the chemical derived from willow. The bark itself may be a safer treatment for pain and inflammation than aspirin.

Bark of the white willow (*Salix alba*) tree.

Folklore
Used as medicine for thousands of years, the willow is associated with vitality, fertility and immortality because of its vigour. It's part of the mythology of many cultures. For the Celts it was the first tree of creation and for Taoists it stood for strength that lies in a yielding nature, just as the tree that bends in the wind.

What physicians of old said
Recorded as far back as the ancient Greeks and Romans by Hippocrates, Pliny and Galen, for its fever-reducing and analgesic properties.

What scientists today say
Compared with aspirin and common medications containing aspirin, there are only a limited number of studies on willow bark extracts as the herbal medicine was superseded by the drug.

Clinical trials:
Reduces joint and rheumatic pain, and treats osteoarthritis. According to a Cochrane review of clinical trials, the bark reduces back pain more than placebo with no significant side effects (whereas aspirin increases the risk of gastrointestinal bleeding).

Lab tests:
Reduces inflammation, acting in the same way as its derived aspirin and other non-steroidal anti-inflammatory drugs (NSAIDs), associated with prostaglandin regulation. Antioxidant; halts proliferation of colon cancer cells.

Uses still to be tested
For many other kinds of pain, including headaches, gout, lumbago and sciatica, and reduces skin ageing.

Key chemicals
Salicin (from which aspirin is derived) is the main active chemical. However, other ingredients, salicylates as well as polyphenols (tannins and flavonoids) are also implicated in therapeutic pain-relieving effects.

Using the herb for health
Fresh or dried bark can made into teas, decoctions and tinctures or chewed (for toothache and inflamed gums). Leaves and bark from other willow species are also said to be medicinal. Willow schnapps is made from male-catkins (mainly from the 'pussy' or goat willow) infused in vodka. Bark is said to be best from young trees in the spring but chemical comparisons have not been made. (NB: don't remove bark all round the trunk or the tree will die.)

Dose
1–3g bark (usually dried) daily (approximately 100mg salicin content); takes longer than aspirin to act but with lasting effects.

Safety
Adverse effects (such as gastrointestinal irritation) are minimal compared to NSAIDs, though tannin content is high. May interact with anticoagulants. Allergic reactions to salicylates can occur in sensitive individuals. Some say that, like aspirin, it is not for children.

ABSENT FRIENDS

If your favourite isn't here, that's only because space doesn't allow us to include all favourites! Other evidence-based favourites of ours include:

Trees

apple, chaste, cinnamon, clove, cocoa, frankincense, horse chestnut, olive, Scots pine, tea tree, walnut and witch hazel.

Horse chestnut (*Aesculus hippocastanum*), clinically verified for venous insufficiency with anti-ageing effects on skin fibroblasts in lab tests.

Perennial plants/shrubs

aloe, ashwagandha, astralagus, blueberry, comfrey, dog rose, evening primrose, feverfew, ginseng, gotu kola, hop, liquorice, meadowsweet, passion flower, plantain, rose, saffron, turmeric and yarrow.

Feverfew (*Chrysanthemum parthenium*), clinically proven for migraine relief in numerous controlled trials.

Annuals

bacopa, basil, cayenne, chervil, dill, flax, nasturtium, spinach, sunflower.

Then there is an annual that has gained a high profile medically on account of the newly discovered properties of one its key chemicals. But the plant remains illegal in the UK and many other countries. Cannabis, rich in the psychoactive cannabinoid (THC) requires strong light and heat to flourish. Hemp, from which rope and clothing materials are made and the source of edlible hemp seed, grows readily in cooler climes though it may not seed at lower temperatures. Hemp is low in THV and rich in the non-psychoactive cannabidiol. Either as cannabis or as a hemp oil, rich in the cannabidiol, the plant has gained an ever-expanding reputation (evidence-based) for its value for treating epilepsy, pain, and sleep disorders, as well as positive sedative, protective and immuno-modulatory effects.

Hemp (*Cannabis sativa* L. subsp. *sativa* var. *Sativa*), anti-epileptic, antipsychotic and analgesic effects proven in controlled clinical trials.

There are thousands more for you to explore as you become ever more experienced in knowing and growing medicinal plants!

Now we can move on to explain how to source plants for your collection, and cultivate and maintain them.

10

Cultivating Medicinal Plants

Now that we've given you some ideas about which plants to add to your physic garden, here are some tips on how to find and grow medicinal plants. Medicinal plants are just plants, so don't be put off or think they need specialised care. And looking after plants that look after us is a joy for new and practised gardeners!

Benign neglect is our ideal. You're aiming not so much for a neat botanic garden but for more a natural medicine chest in which some remedies decide where to go and then move on. While a manicured physic garden may look better than one grown more naturally, the quality of its medicinal plants is not necessarily better; many are wild plants.

Our physic gardening strategies evolved to maintain healthy plants, and you, in turn, will find what works best for you and your plants. The key criterion is that the plants should contain appropriate levels of the active chemicals involved in human health. Vegetables untreated by pesticides may not look perfect but they have higher levels of salicylate defensive chemicals, which protect us against types of cancer.

Growing
Growing medicinal plants is the same as growing any other plant: we nurture newcomers until nature takes over. For medicinal annuals, shrubs and woody perennials, there is no one rule on planting, though well-drained poor soil works for many herbs. For each of the hundreds of plants in those charts in Chapter 8 to help you choose plants to grow there are

specific growing instructions in the sources listed at the end of the book (copious detail from Mrs Grieve and near poetic prose from Nicholas Culpepper, for example). Instructions on sun or shade, damp or dry, maximum and minimum temperatures, height and spread, are also given on seed packets and pots (for bought-in plants), and advice on growing conditions is widely available in horticultural books or websites.

For plants that don't thrive at first, try obtaining new plants from different sources and/ or growing them in a different part of the garden. We give up on newcomers if, after three years, they have not established themselves. Your particular soil, climate or local predators will mean that certain plants won't flourish, but the joy of finding and growing those that thrive is ample compensation.

Species that grow in the wild locally are easiest to establish, provided you can identify them. These are the ones used in the days of home herbal remedies that people near you made from the plants they grew or gathered from hedgerows and fields. When local 'weeds' like nettle, thistle, dandelion, dog rose and plantain invade our garden, we let them rampage – but only in allocated areas. When you have planted seeds and they have started to grow, select the strongest seedlings as you thin them out.

Managing your plants

Maintenance of physic gardens involves managing alien invasions and height hierarchies! Our general approach is to provide the plants with as natural a life as possible, as if they were growing in the wild. Leave plants to complete their seasonal cycle – from spring growth, flowering, seeding, to dying back. Leaving dying plant parts in place, rather than throwing them on the compost heap, returns goodness to the soil, and letting plants spread naturally to new beds prevents exhausting an essential mineral or nutrient from the soil. In situ weed piles and fallen leaves compost over winter and provide materials for wildlife (nest building in spring, feed in winter). Stems and seed heads add visual interest in winter. Seed heads of teasel (for 'warts and wens') and honesty (as moonwort, according

to the doctrine of signatures, for curing moon madness) make for the most magical images on a frosty morning.

When plants self-seed, try to keep them where they landed. They will be superior to any you have planted yourself as they will have found the spot that suits them. They will positively vibrate with vitality. As for labelling, you can move the

One plant worth leaving over winter for its frost-covered beauty is teasel (*Dipsacus*), which has antifungal activity in lab tests.

labels for these wanderers around – for example, our St John's wort bed moves every year and we never know where it will be next! Letting plants spread naturally to new beds also prevents exhausting an essential mineral or nutrient from the soil.

Weeding

Hand-weeding or hoeing is best for plants that are woody or that you want to self-seed naturally. But for some, keeping beds weed-free by covering the ground with a mulch is a great time-saving option (and saves plants in drought). We often use weed-suppressing fabric, a lightweight, dark artificial membrane that allows water through but prevents weeds growing up, when establishing new plants.

Feeding and fertilising

Your physic garden itself can provide extra nutrients for your plants. Comfrey and nettle make excellent liquid fertilisers. A new trend is making 'compost tea' by soaking leaves in water and straining it. This avoids the uncontrolled spread of seeds that you can get if you use composted whole plants.

Self-seeded mullein (*Verbascum*), proven (in combination with other herbs) to ease pain.

Growing nitrogen-fixing species like mustard, clover and fenugreek – all part of the herbarium – is another option. You can use animal manure, though it has its own problems. We gave up using free local supplies of horse manure because it contained seeds from pasture grasses, which sprang up after we'd spent many years removing grass weeds. Hen manure solves that problem as chickens don't graze on long seeding grass (because it gets stuck in their crops). For human waste, like the contents of our 'long drop' loo, only urine can safely be used because it is sterile. Some people swear that lemon and tomato plants do better if 'sprayed' regularly with urine, but others find the use of human waste on physic garden produce off-putting.

Perennials usually thrive even if you regularly harvest their leaves or flowers. You may be surprised how little added nourishment many medicinal plants need. Our lemon balm bed has supplied leaves for herbal teas for over ten years without a drop of fertiliser.

Pruning

There are no pruning requirements specific to the physic garden, other than cutting back woody perennials (lavender, thyme, savory, germander) each year to encourage new growth. Coppicing is a wonderful way of keeping deciduous trees (oaks, ash, hawthorn, willow) from growing too tall: it benefits the tree, keeping it in a prolonged juvenile state, a source of inspiration in a physic garden!

Toxic seeds and plants

Natural seeding from toxic species is a particular problem in a physic garden. At Dilston, belladonna springs up in unexpected, and therefore unlabelled, places because of seeds spread in pigeon droppings. Birds are mostly immune to poisonous berries like belladonna and yew because the seeds that contain the toxins pass undigested through their intestines. However, not all berries are harmless to birds; the ornamental sacred or heavenly bamboo (*Nandina domestica*) originates in Asia where it has medicinal uses, but in the USA it has killed waxwings due to cyanide in its red berries.

Ideally you should exclude from your physic garden plants that are toxic to your local animals. While none of our resident cats or visiting dogs has come to grief after eating plants – seeming instinctively to avoid lily bulbs, cyclamen roots, bane berries or buttercups – we did hear of someone else's cat that died after eating foxglove leaves.

Pests and predators

Many medicinal plants can win their war against insects unaided. We have never used insecticides at Dilston, though a few species are occasionally afflicted by insects. Wormwood leaves sometimes turn black with tiny flies, but we just wait a few weeks until the silvery leaves clear and the plant seems none the worse for wear. Because of wormwood's pest-killing properties, you can use a wormwood spray to kill pests like caterpillars on other plants.

To make a wormwood spray, blend a cup of wormwood leaves in a processor with a little water. Pour into a saucepan, add five cups of water, bring to the boil to sterilise, stand for a few hours, strain and bottle. You can add other plants (in equal amounts) like chilli, eucalyptus and of course pyrethrum (*Tanacetum cinerariifolium*), which was once used as a vermifuge. Keep the spray off your person (especially away from eyes), and wash the target plant parts before harvesting.

There is one exception to our ban on artificial chemicals. Culinary herbs with health-giving properties, like basil and dill, and psychogenic species like mandrake and opium poppies, need help when their tender spring leaves are ravaged by slugs and snails. We tried every strategy to no avail and found that the only way to deal with them, other than removing them by hand, is to use ferric phosphate pellets. These don't harm other animals like birds, frogs or even us, and are accepted for organic horticulture.

Pest control is part of all garden maintenance. You will no doubt work out strategies for your local hole-diggers (from bandicoots to badgers), for animals that destroy plants seemingly out of pure mischief (from squirrels to racoons) and for poisonous visitors (from snakes to spiders). Our way of controlling greedy rabbits and pigeons adds pleasure to our physic garden: visitors enjoy our cluster of cats and romping kittens as much as our plants, reminding us of the benefits of pet therapy.

Dilston cats save many medicinal plants from rabbit demolition.

Soil type

Is your soil chalky, clay, acid, alkali, stony, boggy? Ours is acid, which angelica, calendula and even belladonna prefer. Many small-leaved aromatic Mediterranean herbs such as lavender, thyme, bergamot and sage thrive in thin, dry stony soil. Our terrain, a glacial riverbed, suits them perfectly, because dryness and heat enhance production of essential oils. Plants such as valerian, meadowsweet and mint prefer damp conditions. You have a bed that slopes? No problem: put the dry-loving plants at the top, and put the damp-loving ones at the bottom where the water and nutrients will run down to them. Many strategies for adjusting or working around your soil type can be found on horticultural websites and new gardeners can benefit from the years of experience of others.

Hazards

Take care to prevent falling trees, branches or even fruit from posing a hazard. We keep an eye on all older trees, removing them or their larger branches if they sway ominously in strong winds, and prune new trees to hand height (this cuts tree surgeon costs and provides our volunteers with topiary tasks they enjoy, since they're deprived of cutting back the plants). One extreme case is the Bunya nut from the *Araucaria bidwillii* tree. The nuts are used in Australian aboriginal feasting ceremonies, and have antimicrobial benefits. However, they can weigh as much as 10kg (22lb), and can be fatal if they fall on your head.

Rue (*Ruta graveolens*) can cause severe skin lesions due to light-activated chemicals (psoralens).

More common physic gardening hazards include skin lesions from contact with some species, especially in sunlight. This can be severe for medicinal plants like rue (*Ruta graveolens*) – this blue-leaved, enticingly scented antispasmodic herb once landed one unsuspecting team member in hospital with blistering. Do check out websites regarding 'contact dermatitis' from plants (see the notes at the end of this book). Some writers overzealously include the likes of parsnips and parsley, lemon and lavender! Wearing gloves when dealing with notorious culprits like hogweed and euphorbia is common sense, but in the physic garden gloves are also necessary when dealing with strongly toxic species like wolfsbane and belladonna where chemicals can be absorbed through the skin, especially broken skin. The herbal first aid section in Chapter 13 will help with other hazards.

Sourcing seeds and seedlings

If you have a garden, you may find that some of your plants are medicinal. For example, lily of the valley (heart), Solomon's seal (lung), eucalyptus (antibiotic) and myrtle (bronchitis) are all health promoting. And you'll almost certainly have weeds with mighty healing powers like dandelion and nettle.

Seeds that you have in the kitchen for culinary purposes, like fenugreek, coriander and linseed, can be used to grow plants (assuming the seeds have not been irradiated to prevent germination). You can buy suitable plants in ordinary garden centres (marigold, echinacea or passion flower), as well as in specialist tree nurseries (hawthorn, witch hazel, eucalyptus), or native plant nurseries (lemon balm, feverfew, fennel). Medicinal plants native to your area will be the ones used by local people in the past and will be easy to grow: nurseries in Australia stock aboriginal species, while the North Carolina Native Flower Society links to outlets for North American Indian medicinal plants.

But there will still be some plants on your wish list (like saw palmetto, chaste tree) that you can only obtain from specialist suppliers like Crimson Sage in California (which sells organic Chinese, Ayurvedic, European and Native American plants). The owner of Poyntzfield Nursery in Scotland travels to Japan and India for rare medicinal plants, which they then grow and sell.

Gardeners often swap plants, and when your friends hear about your new physic garden, you will probably be offered some. Marie Addyman, a plant historian associated with our local William Turner garden, regularly arrives at Dilston with rare species like false helleborine (*Veratrum album*), a toxic member of the lily family reputed to treat hypertension.

False helleborine (*Veratrum album*), a dramatic but toxic medicinal plant gifted to our physic garden.

Foraging for fruits of nature

If you are rambling in the autumn look out for ripe seeds to sow. You can gather seeds and fruits from local plants growing wild. This is usually legal (as long as you don't remove the whole plant), though do check regulations in your area. For example, in New Zealand you need permission for seed gathering in reserves, whereas in Finland collecting wild plants in the woods is widely practised. There will be 'garden escapes' (plants introduced from elsewhere that have seeded and spread from local gardens) in the wild too, some of which are medicinal: milk thistle, a great liver tonic originating in Southern Europe, is considered a pest in parts of Australia where it is spread by the wheels of grass cutters. It's often the 'weeds' with medicinal properties that have a place in a physic garden. (The difference between 'wild plant' and 'weed' is only a matter of whether you want the plant or not.)

Identifying plants

If you are not a botanist or expert at identifying species, and you want to identify a plant you have obtained, compare it with pictures and descriptions in illustrated herbals. Then, to be sure you have the correct medicinal variety of the species, often with *'officinalis'* (the medieval Latin term denoting medicinal use) in its name, you will need a knowledgeable friend or a botanical society. We depend on members of the local Natural History Society of Northumbria who regularly check that the plants in our physic garden match the labels we have put on them. These experts spot mistaken identities, once noticing, for example, that a white star-shaped flower that we had labelled eyebright (*Euphrasia*) was in fact lesser stitchwort (*Stellaria graminea*). And do be careful about varieties bought from plant nurseries – we've had some that were wrongly labelled.

Our physic gardening tips

1. Wear gloves, at least when handling irritant species.
2. Ensure each plant or bed of plants is clearly and accurately labelled. Precise labelling and continual weeding will prevent any cases of mistaken identity, so you can be confident that you really are using the correct plant and won't poison yourself!
3. Add warnings on labels for toxic species. Exclude plants that are toxic to animals in your area, or exclude *all* toxic plants if you are worried about them.
4. Weed regularly to ensure no other plant can be confused with the main medicinal plant.
5. Leave the plant to run through its complete growing cycle. Leave stems and seed heads for winter insects.
6. Leave autumn leaves to compost. Allow plants to spread naturally as a way of invigorating stock.
7. Retain weeded materials in discrete piles to recycle into the soil.
8. Use natural fertilisers only sparingly, if at all.
9. Don't use *any* artificial chemicals, especially not insecticides.

Harvesting

Finally, how do you know when to collect your physic garden plant parts? There are a few simple rules that, for most species, mean you gather the plant part when active chemicals are at their highest: roots before or after aerial growth; leaves before flowering; flowers newly opened; and fruits, nuts or seeds when ripe. Best used freshly gathered, all can be dried (with care – see the next chapter on safety), though some volatiles may escape.

Any garden takes time to develop. Getting to know the healing herbs that flourish in yours will be an endless pleasure. Now, with more delight in store, we move on to the marvellous ways you can prepare and use your medicinal plants.

PART THREE
USE
Using Your Physic Garden Plants

11

Safety First

Ignorance is *not* bliss in the physic garden. For safety, before harvesting, you need to know:

- the plant's identity
- which part of the plant to use
- how to prepare and store it
- the dose, which has to be large enough to be effective but small enough to be safe.

If you are buying from elsewhere, you will also want to know safe reputable sources of plants or preparations. In any case you will want reliable sources of advice and information, and how to use them.

Identifying plants correctly, and avoiding dangerous lookalikes

You can find poisonous plants in most gardens – yew trees, rhubarb (leaves), foxgloves, snowdrops, lily of the valley, aconitum – just a few digitalis leaves or yew berries can be lethal. In your physic garden, even greater care is needed because you are growing plants for consumption and for medicinal use. Fortunately, most toxic plants are easily identified and you will not be using those as medicines. In hotter zones, the strychnine tree (*Strychnos nux-vomica*) has red berries so toxic to humans that convulsions and asphyxia can result in death before reaching hospital. It is never used medicinally now, except in homeopathy where the level of strychnine in nux vomica is so low it cannot be detected.

In the previous chapter, on cultivating, we explained how to be sure of medicinal plant identity: strict weed control, and botanical back-up for identification. (Other options, especially for the professional grower, are genetic, microscopic and chemical analysis.) And always be on the lookout for toxic lookalikes. Some poisonous plants masquerade as harmless. The lush, shiny black berries of belladonna (*Atropa belladonna*) look like blackcurrants or blueberries and even taste sweet but they are highly toxic: belladonna-berry pies have landed unsuspecting foragers in hospital. The symptoms are dry mouth, dizziness and drowsiness, followed by kidney failure and seizures – typical of poisoning by atropine, which is the alkaloid chemical in belladonna. Even a small number of berries can be fatal for the very young or old. Other lookalikes with dire consequences for uninitiated foragers are:

- The young leaves of poisonous foxglove and beneficial comfrey, which look remarkably similar. A notorious outbreak of foxglove poisoning caused by supposed 'comfrey tea' was reported in Singapore in 2010.

- Wolfsbane (*Aconitum lycoctonum*) and monkshood (*Aconitum napellus*) are both highly toxic, but their bright green rosettes of young leaves have been mistaken for parsley.

- Poisonous hemlock (*Conium maculatum*) closely resembles beneficial valerian. Both are umbelliferous (umbrella-like flowers in hollow stems) with stinking roots.

- Poisonous 'lords and ladies' (*Arum maculatum*) is easily mistaken for beneficial wild garlic, as both have shiny, pointed leaves in the spring and grow in woodlands.

Make sure that any toxic plants you've deliberately planted in your garden are labelled very clearly. Remove potentially dangerous unlabelled invaders from beds of other plants. You might decide to exclude potentially deadly plants altogether from your physic garden, leaving them to well-policed poison gardens such as at Alnwick Castle (Northumberland, UK), especially if you have young children around. However the magic and medicinal uses of these plants are intriguing, and being able to identify poisonous plants can be a useful (even life-saving) skill.

Fatal mistakes have been made because of the similarity of young comfrey to the foxglove leaf.

The young leaves of wolfsbane (*Aconitum*) look deceptively like some culinary herbs.

Can you distinguish the toxic *Arum* leaves among the wild garlic?

Legal issues

Legal restrictions on growing some poisonous plants may provide peace of mind for new physic gardeners, because you can't buy some of the forbidden plants. Even so, the self-seeding of illegal plants is still a potential hazard: plants such as cannabis or magic mushrooms, that may be forbidden by law, could self-seed in your garden. Birds have been blamed for unexpected cannabis plants because some birdfood contains cannabis/hemp seeds. On one occasion, magic mushrooms (*Psilocybe*) sprang up in the compost we obtained from our local town council! Any time an unknown or unexpected species appears in your physic garden, identification and safety checks are essential.

Using the correct part of the plant

The active ingredients of a plant are normally to be found in all its parts. Usually the leaves are the most potent part, although in some cases the roots, fruit, flower, seed or bark are traditionally the most used parts, as with angelica root, rowan berries, lavender flowers, sunflower seeds and willow (inner) bark.

But for some fruit and vegetables that provide health benefits, there are parts of the plant that you must not eat: tomato and rhubarb leaves, apple and cherry pips, mango peel and any green part or shoot of the potato spring to mind. For others, there are essential preparation procedures to avoid toxicity. Red kidney beans, a great source of folate and proven to reduce blood glucose, can give rise to symptoms of food poisoning if not thoroughly cooked. The tropical food plant cassava (*Manihot esculenta*) has healing properties and lots of calories, and is used for prostate cancer; however, the leaves are toxic, unless treated to remove the naturally occurring cyanide.

Before harvesting always check which part of each medicinal plant is to be used. This is clearly stated in the authoritative herbal texts and websites in the resources section of Chapter 9. For the specially selected safe favourites to choose from (Chapter 10), there is information on the most effective part of each plant to use, but no other parts are recorded as toxic.

Care in preserving plant materials

To make a poultice, ointment, tea or tincture, the best time to harvest depends on when medicinal chemicals are most active. (While this is known for most medicinal plants, guidelines are provided at the end of Chapter 10). You then have to preserve the plant material until you want to use it.

If you dry medicinal plants inefficiently and then store them, you risk not only losing the active chemicals but also harbouring fungi. An extreme example is the ergot fungus (*Claviceps purpurea*) which infects rye and other cereal crops. Rye bread is proven to control blood sugar, but the fungus was responsible for poisonous bread causing burning sensations, hallucinations and convulsions, called St Anthony's fire (after the medieval monks who treated the symptoms).

While ergot fungus is fortunately conspicuous as a black growth on seeds, inadequately dried herbs can be infested with other less obvious, though much less toxic, fungi.

The Salem witches

Convulsive symptoms, hallucinations, mania and melancholia induced by ergot-tainted rye may have led to the accusations of bewitchment that resulted in the 1692/3 witch trials in Salem, Massachusetts. It's an intriguing explanation of the unfortunate victims' behaviour, although if the food supply was widely contaminated, it's not clear why only a few of the population were affected.

Ergot-infected rye grass (*Lolium perenne*).

Using drying ovens is one option; another, which we find works well, is drying at room temperature in a well-ventilated room out of the sunlight for two weeks, and storing in loosely sealed brown-paper bags. One of our volunteers swears by the airing cupboard. But without heat treatment, which unfortunately reduces essential volatile ingredients in some herbs, you must check the contents regularly for any developing fungus or other invasion (the hatching of tiny black flies from microscopic eggs on dried nettle leaves is one we heard of!). For further guidance on preparing and preserving your medicinal plants refer to the next chapter on formulations. You'll notice that teas and tinctures feature high on our list of ways to take the plant medicine; now you know some of the reasons why! Alcohol (over 10%) or boiling water will prevent the growth of any microbes or fungi, though they won't destroy any toxins already infecting the plant.

Using the correct dose

Paracelsus, the sixteenth-century physician and alchemist, remarked: 'Poison is in everything, and nothing is without poison. The dosage makes it either a poison or a remedy.' This observation is as valid now as it was then. Anything can be harmful in excess: Vitamin A (in carrots, for example), sodium chloride (salt) or caffeine (tea, coffee) – even water! Finding the right dose is vital. If, like most of us, you don't have a medical herbalist degree or a diploma in medicinal plants, information on safe preparation and dosage can be gleaned from authoritative herbal websites, handbooks and encyclopaedias or, best of all, by seeking guidance from an affiliated medical herbalist.

For any drug or food there is also the issue of allergy. Just as with everyday foods like peanuts (and even oats), individual allergic reactions to herbs such as mustard, celery, chamomile and garlic do sometimes occur and can be serious, although they are usually rare. Reaction to medicines of any type depend on the individual, so if you're taking a plant medicine you haven't used before, it's wise to start off with a lower trial dose at first. Allergic and other reactions to plants can sometimes be due to deliberate or accidental adulteration of the plant material, so growing your own, or obtaining your plant medications from a reliable source, will minimise the risk.

Safe sources of plants and preparations

Medicinal plant products can be contaminated, adulterated or even deliberately spiked with an active chemical to cut costs. A quick search of scientific reports on contamination of herbal medicines (PubMed) highlights hundreds of papers on toxic metals, microbes including fungal, toxic alkaloids, pesticides and even drug additives in herbal medicines (some outrageous examples include St John's wort tablets found to contain only a laxative, Viagra added to plant remedies for erectile dysfunction, and deadly aconitum in Hong Kong herbal medicines). Ideally the label on commercial plant extracts includes the chemical content of bioactive ingredients. Even so, unless they're from a reputable company, you don't know what else is in there.

There may be some herbs that just won't grow in your garden, or that won't produce enough for your needs, or that you simply want to use before your own physic garden is established. You will then have to source them from elsewhere, and you want to be sure they are safe and pure. At one meeting we attended on Alzheimer's and prospects for medicinal plants, one speaker declared that there are more ginkgo leaves in health shops than there ever were on ginkgo trees worldwide, highlighting a problem with commercial herbal medicines: lacking exhaustive regulation, these products are more vulnerable to 'forgery' and adulteration than processed foods, and incorrect or missing ingredients in a health product are potentially harmful. It is better to always buy from sources recommended by a registered medical herbalist.

For example, in the UK there is the Traditional Herbal Registration (THR) scheme, overseen by the Medicines and Healthcare Products Regulatory Agency (MHRA). Medicines are registered based on 'a tradition of use' for at least 30 years. A THR marking on the packaging guarantees they comply with quality standards, with directions for use. THR products can be bought over the counter so you can find them in your local health shop, pharmacy or supermarket. However, the THR markings are based on traditional usage and not on any scientific evidence of efficacy. Thus, using them as first choice for serious conditions is more of a risk, especially if this delays other effective treatment. It's worth repeating – consult a qualified herbalist to establish which medicinal herbs to try to treat a condition.

Seek out 'pharmacopoeia grade', for the highest quality commercial medicinal plant products, essential for clinical and scientific research and sold by companies such as Statfold Seeds in the UK or MediHerb in Australia. The identity of the species is verified using microscopy, chromatography or genetics, and the quality is checked to ensure it has the standard level of (for example) essential oil constituents, polyphenols or flavonoids to be effective. But you won't get fresh, or even local herbs from commercial companies! So growing your own still wins.

Reliable advice and information

When you are armed with reliable information, self-medication with safe foodstuff botanicals like lavender, lemon balm, peppermint and fennel is as risk-free as can be: self-medication with plants was the norm before chemical drugs, giving us a long-standing legacy of safety and efficacy, and in any case, many of these plants are everyday foods. But more generally, and certainly for some stronger plant medicines, it's prudent to approach them with care and wise to arm yourself with good advice and information.

If you intend trying plant-based medicine (i.e. taking a plant at a medicinal level) straight away, seek out an affiliated medical herbalist. They will give you safe, effective prescriptions personalised to your specific needs with few or no side effects, for both acute treatment and long-term management of chronic conditions. Do check your medical herbalist is professionally affiliated – check with the herbalist association in your region (some of which are listed in this chapter's resources). Some medical herbalists make it clear which plants they use and which conditions they specialise in, making your search a little easier. Moreoever, with so many effective diagnostic tools and therapy options in mainstream medicine today, it is only sensible to raise any new health issue with your mainstream health practitioner and always let them know you are taking, or thinking of taking, a plant medicine, especially if you are already on medication.

Much detailed information on medicinal plants of interest is available on the web. However, there is no one-stop authoritative site that covers all the world's medicinal plants, what they treat, the scientific and clinical evidence behind them, how to take them and whether there are any contraindications or side effects. Of course, some web sources are more authoritative than others. The World Health Organisation Monographs provide scientific information on the safety, efficacy and quality control of a number of widely used medicinal plants. Others, such as the Herb Society of America and British Herb Society, provide reliable practical information.

If you are simply looking for general information on what herbs can do to maintain your health or for common first-aid treatments, then books by professional registered herbalists are a good starting point. To dig deeper, there are monthly academic journals that publish reputable scientific evidence based on research on medicinal plants. Alternatively, you can take courses, from introductory to diploma-level, in using herbs for health. Your nearest physic garden or medical herbalist may run these, as we do at Dilston. Although these courses do not qualify you to prescribe, they teach you how to maintain health and treat common conditions before they become chronic.

If you sell your medicinal plants

If you intend to market your physic garden produce commercially, it is worth enlisting in training sessions on how to prepare cosmeceuticals, for example (Chapter 13). But with or without expert tuition you are legally required to have preparations like balms and lotions approved for safety and stability. The same applies to marketing herbal food products. Statutory regulations vary internationally, so be sure to check your local situation. In the UK, for example, regulations on marketing a product as a medicine, even a plant-derived foodstuff, are *very* complex.

Whether herbal produce from your physic garden is for commercial or home use, the next step is to find out about the many different ways you can safely prepare or 'formulate' your herbal medicines.

12

Making Medicine: Formulating Your Physic Garden Plants

There are so many wonderful ways of taking plants for health and healing beyond tablets and tinctures. You can inhale the volatile oils, drink herbal teas, eat plants as food, rub in balms or bathe in oils, slap on a patch or poultice, even smoke or 'smudge' with the dried leaves. In order to be medicinal, the dose recommended by medical herbalists for a particular plant is readily obtained using infusions (water extracts), tinctures (alcohol extracts), tablets (dried extracts) or lotions. Whether taken orally, inhaled or applied topically, medicinal plant chemicals enter the bloodstream and other tissues. But it's worth remembering that what gets into the body depends on how the plant is extracted – alcohol (tincture), glycerine (glycerites) and water (teas) pull out different chemicals.

For most alternatives to the likes of tinctures and tablets, dosage is not so precise and scientific research has not been done. We include these others because most are based on long-standing traditional use and people like to use herbs in these ways; bathing in or strewing herbs may well be subjected to scientific research in the future. There was a time when the idea of doing serious research on drinking herbal teas or inhaling aromatic plant oils would have been dismissed!

Left: Sage leaf pills professionally made for our clinical trial, but you could roll your own!

In the table below, we identify the many medicinal 'formulations', i.e. ways to prepare and keep remedies, and how to take or apply them. (For more about taking the plants for health as teas, food, oils and cosmetics see Chapters 14 and 15.)

Medicinal plant formulations

- An asterisk (*) in the 'Application' column indicates that when you use the formulation in this way, you can obtain enough of the active ingredients to reach the medicinal dose recommended by herbalists for this plant.
- A 'teaspoonful' means a standard 5 ml teaspoonful.
- The doses for our chosen portfolio of plants are given in Chapter 9.
- Details for other herbs are provided in classic herbal reference sources.
- About the alcohol in tinctures: vodka is more or less 40% pure alcohol, the rest water; unlike other spirits, plain vodkas contain no flavouring. Pure (100%) ethanol can only be obtained under licence and other alcohols like methylated spirits (denatured) are toxic and should never be used.

FORMULATION	PREPARATION Methods	APPLICATION How to Use
Alcoholic tincture	Ethanol (content 20–80%, usually 40% in water) extract of plant material. For medical herbalist tinctures, plant proportion, per cent alcohol and extraction period can vary, but our own standard recipe is to add an equal volume of vodka to freshly picked herb material, store in a dark jar for six weeks, agitating regularly, strain and bottle the liquid (which keeps for years).	*1–2 teaspoon, 2–3 times per day, neat or diluted in water, to taste.
Balm, lotion or ointment	Herb infused in hot oil, strained and made up with beeswax; may also include essential oils.	*Apply to skin, e.g. hands, face, feet.
Bathing – additives	Bath salts, shower gels and bath 'bombs' containing herb extracts or essential oils.	Add to warm water and soak.
Capsules, pills or tablets	Dried finely chopped or ground plant material and/or essential oil inserted in gelatine capsule, or compounded with a binding agent into a round pill or flat tablet.	*Dose ranging from 100–500mg, 2–3 per day, with water.
Cooking ingredients	Dish prepared from medicinal food plant, or with medicinal herb or spice added primarily for flavouring.	*Consume regularly in soups or smoothies.
Decoctions	For tougher plant materials (such as berries, bark and root) simmered (for at least 15 minutes, depending on the plant) to extract the active constituents.	*Drink as tea, hot or cold, or add to food.

FORMULATION	PREPARATION Methods	APPLICATION How to Use
Essential oils	Fresh plant material usually steam-distilled (less often cold-pressed or chemically extracted) to produce the pure aromatic/ volatile plant oil.	*Add to carrier oil for massaging and roll-on bottle application, to perfumers alcohol for sprays, to vaporisers for vaping (concentation for each is 10–30%, depending on volume delivered).
Flower essences	Flowers are infused in water to produce a 'mother essence' which is then diluted further with water (several fold, so chemicals are extremely dilute) and preserved in alcohol.	Drops taken orally in water as required or for a prescribed period.
Glycerites	Approximately half-and-half fresh herb and vegetable glycerine (itself diluted to around 75% with water), infused for up to 3 months before straining and storage.	*Use as for alcohol tincture, above.
Homeopathic remedies	Plant material extracted in water or alcohol, serially diluted to extremely low or negligible concentrations and made into pellets with sucrose.	Pellet dissolved under the tongue (dose frequency varies).
House cleaning	Water or vinegar infusions of herbs, which can be mixed with washing soda or soap, for disinfectants or air fresheners.	Spray or apply directly to kitchen and bathroom surfaces and floors.
Hydrosols	Plant heated in water to produce a distillate that contains water-soluble ingredients and essential oils. Considered safer than essential oils.	*Consume undiluted or use in sprays and skin lotions. Store in fridge.
Lotions or ointments	Plant infused in hot vegetable oil, strained and made up with melted beeswax, often adding a trace of an essential oil.	*Applied externally.
Oil infusion	Washed and dried herb infused in a cooking oil for a week or more. Caution: first sterilise herb using heat to exclude toxic bacteria.	Used for flavouring in cooking or dressings.
Pastes	Fresh parts ground to a paste.	*Applied externally.
Poultices, compresses and patches	Paste of fresh or moistened dried herb or essential oil plasters applied to skin.	*Applied regularly, several hours at a time.
Smoking	Dried herb burned on a charcoal disc or in a vaporiser.	*Inhale directly.
Spirits	Distilled from wines made from the plant, or made by infusing the plant in other spirits with similar chemical content to tinctures – the difference being tinctures are made using specific concentrations of plant material.	*Imbibe in moderation.
Strewing	Fresh aromatic herbs, often mixed with straw.	Spread over floors for fragrance, and as disinfectants or insecticides.

FORMULATION	PREPARATION Methods	APPLICATION How to Use
Suppositories and douches	Ground fresh or dried herb in capsules or added to a butter (e.g. coconut) for suppositories, or added to water or vinegar for a douche.	*Apply regularly.
Sweets and candies	Combine fresh or dried herb or essential oil (2–5% max, depending on the essential oil) with sugar, honey or natural sugar in pastelles or truffles.	*Consume with caution (due to sugar).
Syrups	Herbs boiled in water and sugar and strained, or infuse herb in plant syrup or honey.	Use for flavouring foods and drink.
Teas or infusions	Infuse fresh or dried herb (generally 5g, less if dried, per cup) in near-boiling water (though cold water can be used) and strain.	*Drink 2–3 cups per day to achieve dose.
Wines	Recipes for individual medicinal fruit and flower winemaking usually involve extraction in water at high concentrations (up to 1:1).	*A glass or two daily.

Few conventional doctors tell you to have fun deciding which way you prefer to take your medicine, but with physic garden plants you can do just that. For formulations like bath oils and flower essences, the level of the original plant material entering the body may be below the recommended herbalist dose, but it may still aid well-being, perhaps with long-term cumulative effects. For treating disorders though, use one of the formulations where the dose is easily and precisely controlled.

As you probably won't be rolling pills or packing capsules as a first choice way of getting the right dose, a word on glycerites versus tinctures. Both are easy to make and a fun way to try and taste your favourite herbs. The glycerite obviously has no alcohol (one teaspoon of tincture is about a fifth of a unit of alcohol), but it does taste very sweet even though glycerine does not affect blood sugar in the same way as sugar.

Many formulations start with grinding the plant in an old-fashioned pestle and mortar.

Homegrown health

Knowing, growing and using your physic garden plants is both empowering and reassuring, quality- and safety-wise. It allows you to take control of personal and family health, especially for prevention and protection. If you were to employ a traditional Chinese doctor in past times you would only pay for services if you were kept healthy. (This is the opposite of

Western medicine where the doctor, drugs or other treatments are involved mainly when something goes wrong.) Having a physic garden is in some ways like having your own traditional Chinese doctor as you find out which plants are going to keep you healthy.

Our favourite formulations are teas and tinctures. They capture ingredients from the fresh plant in its prime, are readily made, safely stored (dried herbs for teas), sterility is guaranteed (using boiling water or alcohol) and they usually taste good. Our other top choice is nutraceuticals, i.e. plant food with health benefits over and above sustenance (see Chapter 14). Enjoying

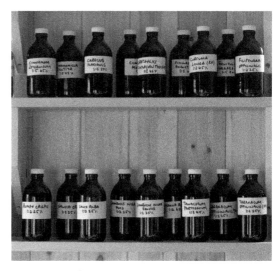

Examples of medicinal plant products in the Dilston Physic Garden shop.

using what you grow for health and healing encourages you to take the medicine regularly, paving the way to protection and prevention.

You could try out your herb of choice in a variety of ways to see which suits you best. But your choice of preparation for proven health benefits will depend on the evidence on the formulas that work in trials. In our trials of sage tested on memory, the pure essential oil and the dried herb worked well in oral capsules, but an extract processed into pills did not. And for the lemon balm we tested on mood (for calming effects), capsules (containing the dried herb) taken orally worked better than applying a lotion containing the essential oil to the skin. This is not so surprising: different plant ingredients are extracted according to what you use. Water is a poor solvent of resins, but a great solvent for carbohydrates and mucilage; alcohol is great for many medicinal constituents (terpenoids, carotenoids, alkaloids), but poor for mucilage; and glycerine by itself (without heat or water) is a poor solvent of most constituents except volatile oils.

In the next chapters, we explore how to use health-providing herbs from your physic garden in specific ways and for particular purposes beyond taking care of personal health – from first aid and treating child and animal ailments to cosmeceuticals and aromatics. They all depend on understanding how to choose, create and control your plant formula.

herbal
first
aid

(assembling
a natural first
aid kit)

13

Caring for Your Family, Animals and Home

Like home herbalists of old, you can explore herbal healthcare not just for yourself but for the whole family. Herbal first aid, safe remedies for children, and even for pets and farm animals, fall into this broad category, as does keeping the home itself healthy with disinfectants and air purifiers.

First aid
Common healing herbs can deal with minor injuries normally treated at home. The botanic first-aid kit also covers you where immediate or familiar healthcare is not available, such as when travelling or on holiday. But note that obviously this section excludes immediately life-threatening conditions, heart problems, poisonous bites, serious injuries and anything requiring urgent assistance from medical professionals.

Different people have different needs, so herbal first-aid kits are usually assembled to suit specific individual or group needs. For example, a page on the *Ann Arbor News* website (US) advocates the following core herbs:

plantain as a poultice for bug bites
yarrow to stop minor bleeding
catnip as a natural mosquito repellent
jewelweed (*Impatiens capensis*) for poison ivy

burdock (*Arctium lappa*) for burns and scalds

St John's wort as a salve for nerve pain, bruising, and sore muscles.

A page on the *Mother Earth Living* site (US) suggests a different kit:

aloe vera gel for burns and sunburn

arnica for anti-inflammatory and circulation-stimulating properties, sore muscles, sprains, strains and bruises

calendula as an astringent, antibacterial, antifungal, anti-inflammatory and wound-healer

comfrey containing allantoin for stimulating tissue growth and healing wounds

German chamomile, safe for children, with mild sedative and antispasmodic properties, also promotes relaxation, relieves indigestion and soothes skin irritations.

One of our visitors recalled her grandmother using chamomile leaves inside nappies to prevent rash, and most of us recall being told that dock leaves cure nettle stings.

Your own garden's first-aid kit may include plants used traditionally and easy to source in your locality, ideally backed up by scientific evidence. While species suggested for common acute conditions are not all evidence-based, some versatile herbs like aloe vera, chamomile, lavender and St John's wort are associated with convincing clinical and scientific evidence for anti-inflammatory, antibiotic and/or nerve-soothing or analgesic effects. We always have to hand aloe (using gel from the fresh plant leaves), capsaicin cream, chamomile as fresh herb paste or tea and, of course, the all-embracing lavender as essential oil, which for many works rapidly for stings. Options for specific needs (see the table) will let you check which plants suit you (consult the previous chapter for how to prepare them).

Does local folklore always get it right?

British children are told to rub dock leaves on nettle stings. The stinging is caused by formic acid in the nettle, which is *not* neutralised by any chemical in the dock (*Rumex*). Instead, the acid is easily washed away with water. Perhaps the story survives due to the placebo effect of a parent attending the child's injury. But then there is evidence that the plant extracts can reduce the size of wheals induced by histamine (also contained in nettles).

Soothing gel straight from a fresh aloe leaf.

Botanical first-aid treatments

Condition	Medicinal plant
Antiseptic	garlic, echinacea, marigold, tea tree, thyme, witch hazel
Bee stings	chickweed (*Stellaria media*), garlic, lavender, plantain
Bruises	aloe vera, arnica, calendula, hyssop, St John's wort
Burns	aloe vera, chamomile, comfrey, lavender, St John's wort
Diarrhoea	Agrimony, bramble, lady's mantle, nettle, raspberry leaf, tormentil
Feeling faint	Ginger, *Ginkgo biloba*, lavender, lemon balm, rosemary
Frostbite	*Angelica archangelica*, capsaicin (active component of capsicum), ginger, rosemary, schisandra, yarrow
Hangover	ginger, milk thistle
Headache	bay, feverfew, ginger, lavender, lime, meadowsweet, peppermint, rosemary, white willow, wood betony
Hiccups	cardamom, lemon, mint
Indigestion	cardamom, chamomile, fennel, ginger, meadowsweet, peppermint
Muscle sprains and strains	cabbage, capsaicin, comfrey, elder leaf, peppermint, St John's wort
Nausea	fennel, ginger, peppermint
Pain, general	feverfew, meadowsweet, St John's wort, valerian, white willow
Panic attack/anxiety	chamomile, lavender, lemon balm, passion flower
Sleep aids	chamomile, hops, lavender, valerian
Spider bites	echinacea, basil, lavender, plantain
Styptic, stopping bleeding	agrimony, horsetail, mahonia, oak, plantain, shepherd's purse (*Capsella bursa-pastoris*), witch hazel, yarrow
Sunburn	aloe, chamomile, chickweed, cleavers, lavender, peppermint, potato, witch hazel
Toothache	chamomile, clove, feverfew, ginger, tea tree, thyme
Wasp stings	aloe vera, garlic, lavender, plantain

The table above was compiled together with our Dilston Physic Garden herbalist, Davina Hopkinson. Most of these traditionally used plants are backed by scientific evidence (see Chapter 8).

Herbs for child health

If you have doubts about alternative medicine in child healthcare, consider the example of ADHD (attention deficit hyperactivity disorder). Amphetamine-related drugs are increasingly prescribed for this condition, but their side effects, such as weight loss, headache and sleep disturbance, can be problematic. In contrast, results of controlled clinical trials showed that valerian and lemon balm improve symptoms of hyperactivity, attention deficits and impulsivity in children without significant side effects, and that saffron is as effective as ritalin for ADHD.

Herbs for most everyday problems for children are based on traditional use because clinical and scientific evidence is mostly derived from adult populations; controlled clinical trials in children are rare because of risk assessment and consent issues. But some traditional plant medicines *are* backed by controlled clinical evidence: lavender oil reduces anxiety in diabetic children as they test themselves for sugar levels to see how much insulin they may need. Lavender also cuts the need for analgesics in tonsillectomy paediatric patients. Dill controls giardia parasite intestinal infections in under one-year-olds in India. Comfrey cream speeds up the healing of abrasions in 3 to 12-year-olds. And apple pectin and chamomile combination reduces diarrhoea in 6-month to 6-year-olds.

Safety is vitally important, both in choice of herb and in dosage. Children are more sensitive than adults; children respond vigorously to even mild herbs, and stronger herbs can potentially cause unwanted reactions. Although the plants listed below are recognised as safe for children, appropriate dosage is essential. Herbalists, like other medical practitioners, use formulas such as 'Clark's rule' to calculate dosage. In effect, this considers a 'standard adult' to weigh 70kg/150lbs, and then scales down the dose pro-rata for each child according to their weight.

Traditional herbal remedies for children

Recommendations from our resident 'paediatric' herbalist and cited sources. The table below was compiled together with our Dilston Physic Garden herbalist, Davina Hopkinson.

Condition	Medicinal plant
Bleeding, e.g. nosebleeds	capsaicin, yarrow
Bruises and burns	aloe, arnica, comfrey, calendula, cucumber
Calm, relaxation, sleep	catnip, chamomile, lavender, lemon balm, lime flower, passion flower
Colds, coughs, congestion	angelica (root), aniseed, blackberry, dog rose (hips), echinacea, elderberry, eucalyptus, garlic, ginger, lavender, lemon, liquorice, marshmallow, mullein, plantain, peppermint, thyme, wild cherry (bark), yarrow
Constipation	fennel (seed), ginger, liquorice, marshmallow , slippery elm
Diarrhoea	cardoon, ginger, fennel, marshmallow, meadowsweet, raspberry (leaves), rose
Earache	chamomile, elderflower, garlic, ground ivy, mullein, onion, plantain
Fever	catnip, chamomile, elderflower, lemon balm, lime flower, spearmint, yarrow
Hay fever	elderflower, nettle, plantain, yarrow
Headache	chamomile, lavender, valerian
Nappy rash	calendula, chamomile, chickweed, plantain leaf
Nausea	cardamom, ginger, slippery elm
Sore throat	blackcurrant, cleavers, elder, echinacea, garlic, ginger, liquorice, marshmallow, slippery elm, thyme
Stomach ache	chamomile, fennel, dill, ginger, lemon balm, peppermint
Swelling	aloe, cucumber
Toothache	cinnamon, cloves
Travel sickness	ginger
Worms	garlic

Unlike drugs such as aspirin, some of these plant remedies are safe for children under two years. Gripe water is given to babies aged one month; over-the-counter liquids containing herbs like dill, fennel or caraway are sold as gripe waters for winding and colic calm. These and other herbs like ginger, chamomile, cardamom, liquorice, cinnamon, clove, lemon balm and peppermint are used for colic as well as teething pain and hiccups. And you can make your own from fresh garden produce.

A little lavender oil (diluted at least 100-fold with a carrier oil like coconut or almond) is a popular massage remedy for calming babies and helping them to sleep. Clinical trial evidence supports reductions in young babies' crying times, though long-term use would not be advisable.

Rosehip and elderberry syrups.

Helping the medicine go down

Here are some preparations suitable for children, and which they usually like to take.

Teas, ices, infusions, decoctions

Most children enjoy tasty teas: lemon balm, chamomile, rose, elderberry and peppermint. You can also use teas to make ice pops/popsicles, which are especially good for children with sore throats. Infusions, which are steeped for longer than teas, are more concentrated. Decoctions – herbs simmered in boiling water – make great herbal syrups.

Herbal baths

A herbal bath before bedtime is a fun way of administering herbs. The skin absorbs the medicinal properties of the herb while the aroma can be clearing for colds and coughs or soothing and relaxing for restless or fractious children. Children can make their own herbal bath sachets (under supervision), using epsom salts or oats as a base and adding the appropriate dried herbs and safe essential oils.

Herbal syrups

Made from decoctions, adding honey or a natural sweetener (in 2:1 ratio, liquid to sweetener), syrups can be very soothing for colds, flu and coughs. Elderberry syrup is the one we hand out to our youngsters during cold seasons. Adding soda water to make a herbal fizzy 'pop' or pouring the syrup over pancakes is particularly popular.

Herbal honeys

You can make herbal honeys with either dry or fresh herbs. Mix the herb into the honey (preferably local and unprocessed) and leave to infuse for a few days – or longer for a stronger flavour. Honey is antiseptic, soothing and moistening, so good for sore throats and easing coughs. Adding yarrow, peppermint and elderflower to honey and then diluting with hot water makes a soothing drink for sore throats and colds. Chamomile-infused honey makes a relaxing hot drink before bedtime, or to help an upset tummy.

Herbal oils

Herbal oils are made by infusing the plant material into oils (olive, sweet almond or jojoba) for a relaxing massage before bedtime for children with sleep problems.

Salves for sores

For bumps and scrapes, bites, stings and skin-healing, and to soothe sore muscles, salves made with a combination of herbal-infused oil and beeswax are a great solution. Different combinations and recipes depend on the purpose of the salve. For children's skin lesions and stings, a good salve is made from calendula, St John's wort and lavender, with a little tea tree essential oil. You can add eucalyptus to make a menthol chest rub (essential oils at less than 1%).

Glycerite tinctures

Glycerites, like tinctures using vegetable glycerin instead of alcohol to extract the active ingredients from the plant, are suitable for children. They find them sweet and highly palatable (see previous chapter on preparations).

Traditional Chinese and Ayurveda herbs

In Traditional Chinese medicine (TCM), herbs with a long-standing and uninterrupted tradition of treating children are used, although a licensed professional is always consulted. TCM for children involves close attention to diet and a combination of plants tailored to the individual. In Ayurveda, again, a professional practitioner is enlisted. Ayurvedic remedies for children use medicinal fruits such as dates, mango and fig, as well as herbs like holy basil and turmeric for colds or colic.

Plant substitutes for sugar

The idea of plant food as medicine is particularly relevant for children, given the rise in obesity, diabetes and food allergies in both the developed and developing worlds. Instead of sugars like sucrose and fructose, you can use plants such as liquorice or sweet cicely (*Myrrhis odorata*) as sweeteners. Both plants have numerous health benefits, including soothing stomach pains and sore throats. Clinical and lab evidence indicates that liquorice also improves dental health: chewing the roots is one sweet way to stop decay. The fruit of the lucuma (*Pouteria lucuma*), 'gold of Incas', is used as a low glycaemic index sweetener (raising blood sugar slowly), as well as being nutritious, antioxidant and antihyperglycaemic.

Playing and learning

We love to see how children calm down after rolling about on our physic garden chamomile lawn, and how they seem more content after drinking lemon balm tea. Our herbalist, who hosts school visits, creates treasure and scavenger hunts and quiz trails. She finds that children enjoy the facts about the plants if they come with a good story, like the one about St John's wort chasing away ghosts and devils, or the angel who told a monk that angelica could cure the plague.

Youngsters can also learn a kind of bush craft that includes taking more control of their health. Of course, supervision is needed where potentially toxic plants grow, as in any garden.

However, when children reach their teens, ideas about herbs and drugs can veer off into recreational rather than medical directions – a perennial concern to parents and teachers.

An elf reminds children that elfwort (*elecampane*) protected against elfshot and now relieves painful conditions today.

Knowledge arms youngsters against the dangers, so we introduce a few safe, non-addictive 'feel good' plant species like catnip in Chapter 16.

Herbal help for ailing animals

We humans once watched and learned as birds and mammals selected plants to cure or prevent infections, relieve pain and remove worms or ticks as part of evolved, learned or instinctual behaviour.

According to Cindy Engel, author of *Wild Health*, monkeys and bears rub citrus oils and pungent resins into their coats as insecticides and as antiseptics for infected insect bites. We know that birds line their nests with leaves, particularly from aromatic plants with antibiotic properties to disinfect the nest and protect their chicks from blood-sucking mites and lice. In cities, birds even use cigarette ends, which contain insecticidal nicotine! In herb gardens there are reports of birds stripping leaves from lavender and tansy in spring time (as antiseptics or some other use we can only guess at). Both wild and domestic animals seek out plants that are not part of their normal diet (see Introduction), as anyone with a grass-chewing cat or dog will know. Grasses are laxative and help pass or vomit hairballs, or worms lodged in their intestines, and one of our animal herbalists tells us that sick dogs and horses show strong preferences if offered a choice of herbs such as your physic garden could provide.

The health of pets or domestic or farm animals, not free to roam in the wild, depends on us. Today, veterinary medicine has mostly abandoned herbal medicine in favour of chemical drugs. Intensive farming in crowded animal housing promotes the spread of diseases and prompts widespread antibiotic use. The immunity of free-grazing animals is boosted by

Caution: animals are different

Just as some things that are good for us are bad for animals – such as chocolate, which is toxic to dogs, and aspirin, which is fatal to cats – so some plants that are medicinal for us are poisonous to pets. One example is St John's wort, which is toxic for horses, goats and sheep. So it's just as important when treating animals to be well-informed on identification, preparation, dose and contraindications. If in doubt always consult a professional.

herbs they eat naturally. But modern pastures lack variety of species, and chemical soil-dressings deplete the mineral and nutrient content. Juliette de Baïracli Levy, the famous English herbalist, pioneered holistic veterinary medicine. She suggested such remedies as 'eating an abundance of turnip and garlic', which, she claimed, was 'a sound peasant remedy for the cure of tumours, superior to excising the tumour' (a bold statement lacking evidence for any animal as yet).

However, the law forbids the treatment of any animal by a non-veterinarian (in the UK; in the US, regulations are state-dependent, and they vary elsewhere). Few UK vets prescribe licensed herbal remedies or supplements. Chris Day, one of the few UK herbalist vets, confirms that most vets ignore plant medicines (although, when our rabbit-catcher cat went berserk after an anaesthetic, he was prescribed skullcap, which was effective in calming him down). Even so, nobody will prohibit garlic in your cat's bowl or dandelions in the horses' hay!

Oregano, proven to promote piglet survival.

Evidence-based and traditionally used medicinal plants for sick pets and farm animals

Plant	Animal	Health effect/condition treated
cascara (*Rhamnus purshiana*)	cats and dogs	laxative
catnip	cats and dogs	calming
cayenne	dogs	parasitic worms
chicory	deer and sheep	parasitic worms
chamomile	horses	calming
chrysanthemum (*Chrysanthemum cinerariifolium*)	poultry	insecticide
comfrey	cows	wounds
dandelion	horses	urinary retention
fenugreek	cats and dogs	minor infections
	horses	appetite
garlic	sheep, horses, poultry, dogs and cats	worms, fleas
	sheep	mastitis
	poultry	immunostimulant
	horses	bronchial infections
ginger	horses	colic
goosefoot (*Chenopodium ambrosioides*)	sheep and cattle	parasitic worms
lavender	dogs	pain
meadowsweet	horses	fever
mint	horses	colic
male fern (*Dryopteris filix-mas*)	most farm animals and pets	tapeworm
oregano	pigs	birthing, piglet survival
parsley	dogs	worms
raspberry	horses, cats and dogs	birthing, muscle toning
sage	sheep	coughs
senna (*Senna alexandrina*)	cats and dogs	laxative
skullcap	cats and dogs	nervousness, excitability, fears, phobias
sulla (*Hedysarum coronarium*)	sheep	parasitism
thyme	various farm animals (goats, sheep and poultry) as well as horses	antibiotic, improving gastric and respiratory functions
valerian	cats, dogs and horses	stress-relieving
witchazel	cows	postpartum bleeding
wormwood	poultry	worms

The evidence

Evidence for traditional remedies for animals, as for humans, is convincing where available as shown in the following round-up of scientific reports.

Pigs and chicks on oregano

Evidence on oregano fed to birthing sows is particularly impressive: lower annual sow mortality rate, lower sow culling rate during lactation, increased farrowing rate, increased number of live-born piglets per litter and decreased stillbirth rate. Multiparous sows (i.e. those producing more than one piglet) had higher daily voluntary feed intake compared to non-treated sows. For hens, adding oregano essential oil to the feed increases egg production. Oregano even helps reduce stress in transported animals.

Garlic and fenugreek against germs

Garlic's natural antibiotic, antiseptic and antiviral properties fight infections in many animals. Garlic is also proven to ward off fleas and other parasites, is a good digestive tonic and relieves common skin conditions such as eczema and dermatitis. Together with fenugreek, garlic is a veterinary-approved plant medicine for the symptomatic relief of skin conditions, arthritis, coughs and minor infections in dogs and cats. Fenugreek, given regularly, increases resistance to infections by stimulating the immune system. It is used by vets to treat minor infections such as interdigital cysts, eczema, pyoderma, cystitis, coughs, arthritis and skin complaints.

Calmer kittens and peaceful pups

Skullcap with valerian is a herbal combination that relieves anxiety, nervousness, excitability, apprehension, phobias, hyperactivity and travel sickness in dogs and cats. It is widely used for noise phobias, and doesn't cause drowsiness or impair normal behaviour or performance, making it suitable for shows, travelling and training. In cats, it is also effective in the control of territorial spraying by keeping the cat relaxed and so reducing the urge to mark territory. Supporting evidence for these claims comes from laboratory animal research.

Chicory helps control gastrointestinal worms in wild animals.

Grazing for goodness

Grazing herbs in natural pastures enhances animal health. Sheep consuming sulla (*Hedysarum coronarium*) maintain higher productivity (including more nutritious cheese) and have significantly fewer parasites. Greater bird's-foot trefoil (*Lotus pedunculatus*) reduces worms in grazing lambs by up to 50%. One of the most widely researched pasture herbs is chicory. Red deer and lambs grazing chicory have fewer lung and gastrointestinal worms, and productivity/growth is boosted. Other research supports its use for cattle. It is also renowned as an immunostimulant in humans.

Raspberry leaves, not just for helping human births, work for cats and dogs too.

Raspberry for cats and dogs?

Traditionally, raspberry leaf helps with giving birth. It tones and strengthens smooth muscle, such as the uterus, and helps to ensure easy and straightforward delivery. It is available commercially. Its toning effects are said to be helpful for bitches suffering from leaking bladders, which can occur with age or after spaying or other surgery. Supporting evidence is based on lab studies on muscle cells and models like guinea pigs.

Vet-approved plant medicines

Also available commercially and approved for veterinary use are senna, aloe, cascara, valerian and dandelion, providing symptomatic relief of constipation in dogs and cats. Cascara acts as a laxative, and sennas are established purgatives. Sennas share active ingredients with aloe and rhubarb (anthraquinone derivatives and their glucosides).

Oil of goosefoot (*Chenopodium ambrosioides*) is the most widespread and commonly used herbal antiparasitic. Archaeological and ethnological studies suggest that it has been used for many centuries. In the early eighteenth century, Peter Kalm, a Swedish botanist and traveller, reported that it was used by both indigenous inhabitants and European settlers in the American colonies for the treatment of worm infections. The active chemical, ascaridole, a volatile terpene, was isolated and eventually synthesised. Other plants – wormwood, mugwort, tansy, caraway, thyme or mint – added to feeds reduce roundworm in sheep.

So for animals, as for humans, herbal medicine is a viable alternative, increasingly backed by science. A responsible revival of medicinal herbs for animal health in the home or on the farm would surely be welcome.

Keeping your home healthy

You can extend physic garden benefits to keeping your home healthy by making room fresheners, pet deodorisers, antiseptics and disinfectants. Sweet-smelling 'strewing' herbs were scattered on unclean floors and disguised foul smells in times when many people slept on the floor. Concoctions included herbs with insecticidal and deodorant properties. Lady's bedstraw and pennyroyal kill fleas; lavender, rosemary, sweet woodruff, sage, tansy and thyme repel insects and are antimicrobial; sweet flag, rose, lavender and meadowsweet smell pleasant.

A medieval strewing recipe for purification/disinfection

'Sage, tansy, violets, roses, mints, pennyroyal, winter savory, marjoram, hops, germander, sweet fennel, cowslips, lady's mantle, balm, basil, costmary, lavender, juniper, rosemary, chamomile, daisies of all sorts, lavender cotton, and sweet woodruff.'

Over time, such freshly picked and strewn herbal mixes were replaced by chemical air fresheners and antiseptics. Synthetic disinfectants have long been considered non-toxic to humans, though some can cause pulmonary or skin reactions and there are concerns that they can poison cats grooming after contact with them. You can make effective botanical alternatives using plant extracts to create herbal air fresheners, antiseptics and insecticides (and other animal repellents) with scientific proof of aromatic or antibiotic potency.

Floor strewn with freshly picked fragrant and antimicrobial herbs from the physic garden.

Air fresheners and deodorants

In the past, windows were thrown open every morning, summer *and* winter. In colder climes today, rooms have become sealed heated containers, retaining smells and germs from the kitchen, the bathroom, pets and people.

You can send fresh botanic aromas around your house with reed diffuser bottles; lidless pans of water simmering with herbs for aromatic steam; electric or candlelit essential oil dispersers or diffusers; homemade plant extract sprays; drops of pure essential oil in specific areas; burning leaves, bark or resins (see Chapter 16); and pots and vases of scented plants.

Removing harmful molecules is just as important as disguising unpleasant aromas. Indoor pollution (toxins from paint, computer printers, furniture and even cleaning agents) are estimated by the UK Royal College of Physicians to contribute to up to 100,000 deaths per year in Europe, so prevention is important. Bring live plants into the house to absorb toxic chemicals: mother-in-law's tongue (*Sansevieria trifasciata*), the peace lily (*Spathiphyllum*) and scarlet star (*Guzmania lingulata*).

Air-freshening scented plants

green and woody	cedar, pine
florals	jasmine, hyacinth, lavender, narcissus
fruity	orange, lemon
spicy	cinnamon, cloves
to aid meditation	frankincense, sandalwood, vetiver

Disinfectants and antiseptics

Traditionally, garlic bulbs were hung in doorways to ward off evil spirits. We now know that garlic is one of the most effective plant antibiotics. Other more pleasantly scented plants with proven antibiotic and antifungal properties include basil, bay, cardamom, cinnamon, clove, eucalyptus, ginger, hyssop, lavender, lemongrass, oregano, peppermint, pine, rose geranium, rosemary, sage, spearmint, tea tree and thyme. They can be used in air sprays, floor washes, surface cleaners or furniture creams. The liquid base is water for freshly made sprays, to use at once; or vinegar or lemon juice with added solids like baking soda, soap or borax, together with drops of one or more of the essential oils to last a while.

Recipes for herbal home care on 'green cleaning' websites vary in amounts, and as long as you avoid skin contact, there are no set limits on essential oil concentration (20% makes for a more powerful effect).

You can also use plant extracts very simply. When someone is ill with cold or flu and probably infectious, place a few drops of antibiotic oils – pine, tea

A room spray

We often freshen and/or disinfect using an alcohol–water mix (10% alcohol) added to finely chopped leaves of pine, eucalyptus and lavender (proportions to suit). Mixed regularly over 3 to 4 weeks, strained and stored in a dark glass bottle spray (adding a few drops of the plant essential oils for more aroma, if needed), this is the kind of addition to your cleaning 'caddie' that the physic garden can provide.

tree, thyme or eucalyptus (containing natural antibiotics like cineole, carvacrol and geraniol) – around the house. The delightful, lemon-scented gum of eucalyptus (*Corymbia citriodora*), with its high content of citronellal (instead of cineole, common to most gums), is a proven antiseptic (the oil chemical disrupts the cell walls of bacteria).

We also have a stock of sprays made from single oils (pine, may chang, lemon, lavender from sustainable sources). Mix oils (1 or 2 per cent) with vodka; better for dispersing the oils is perfumer's (paraben-free) alcohol. Store in dark glass spray bottles because essential oils can be affected by light and 'eat' into plastic. Apart from the oils, all the antibiotic plants mentioned can be added, freshly picked, to the same liquid base, steeped, filtered and stored (the alcohol ensuring sterility).

Home care herbal products made from plants like lavender and pine.

Keeping insects and pests at bay

Even the best kept home has occasional unwelcome visitors like mosquitoes, midges, moths, even bed bugs and rodents.

Mosquito repellents include citronella (*Cymbopogon winterianus*), lemon balm (containing citronellal, the main ingredient of citronella), catnip, thyme and basil. Bog myrtle (*Myrica gale*), abundant in Scottish marshlands, conveniently keeps the local midge menace at bay. The use of these and many other plants as insecticides is backed by powerful scientific evidence, with over ten thousand papers on the subject published in the last twenty years.

Mouse repellents include oils of peppermint, spearmint, wormwood and catnip, currently based more on tradition than scientific evidence. Scientific reports on 'mint' and 'mice' are not about driving the mice away; one paper notes antimanic effects of a spearmint chemical (carvone)! To deter the mice, just put a few drops of the oil near the infestation (checking it does not damage any surface material like carpet).

Some plants are deodorant, disinfectant and repellent combined. Lavender – by now the certain winner of any physic garden all-rounder prize – is antibiotic, insect repellent, strongly scented and even said to repel mice.

Home-care plant products have a reassuring legacy of centuries of use compared to potentially toxic synthetic chemicals with relatively short histories. (Of course, 'green' doesn't necessarily mean risk-free: rhubarb leaves are a great stain remover due to their oxalic acid, but they can be toxic if inhaled or absorbed through the skin.)

Moving from home and family care to taking your plant medicine in one of the most natural and agreeable ways – eating and drinking it – the next chapter is about health foods and herbal teas (nutraceuticals).

14

Plant Health Foods and Herbal Teas

'Let food be your medicine and medicine your food.' (Hippocrates)

'Eat, drink and be healthy!' Of all the different ways of taking plants as medicines, food and drink has immense appeal.

Botanical nutraceuticals: plant food as medicine

The cardiac and anticancer benefits of everyday fruit and vegetables are widely advertised: cholesterol-lowering stanols or sterols in oils from nuts, grains and olives, and cancer-protective chemicals in everything from broccoli to berries. Online and university courses teach about medicinal plants and 'functional' foods – how chemicals like antioxidant flavonoids provide health benefits beyond food as fuel. Plant-based diets are more popular than ever in the West. Vegan milks and cheeses are increasingly available in supermarkets and veganism captures headlines with its eco, ethical and health benefits.

While the influence of diet on health preoccupies complementary practitioners, celebrities and consumers, the concept of food as a way of enjoyably dosing yourself with medicinal plants as preventative medicine is new to many of us – though not to Hippocrates! By providing a time-tested, safe alternative to long-term medical drug use and solving the problem of remembering to take medication on time, this is a valuable contribution to disease prevention. And scientific studies show how traditional health benefits are backed up by evidence today. So, looking beyond basic calorie, vitamin and mineral needs, how can you use food plants as medicine?

First, decide what you and your family's specific needs are (such as reducing blood pressure or cholesterol, stress relief, cutting cancer risks, countering cognitive decline). Then find out which medicinal plants are proven to have these effects, and seek or create inspiring recipes for a new kind of 'good life'.

Phytonutrients like polyphenols are star players in the health benefits of vegetables.

Good food news

The table focuses on health-enhancing vegetables, cereals, nuts and fruits from Dilston's culinary and orchard areas. Each is backed by scientific evidence, and their benefits often match the effect of chemical drugs for the same condition. There are, of course, hundreds more food plants with benefits you can find in online scientific papers (see Chapter 2) and probably few without health benefits beyond nutrition (polyphenols are common to most).

Evidence-based foods for general health conditions

Asparagus	Diuretic, laxative, cardiac tonic, sedative, antirheumatic. *In vivo* studies indicate oestrogenic and neuroprotective effects of *A. racemosus*.
Beetroot	Improves exercise performance in healthy individuals; increases life expectancy in prostate cancer patients; the nitrate in beetroot reduces blood pressure, heart disease and stroke, and beetroot's betaine component is calming and antidepressant.
Cabbage	Traditionally used for rheumatic and arthritic pain; clinically proven for lactation engorgement pain; contains lupeol, an anti-inflammatory and anticancer chemical.
Carrot	Reduces markers of oxidative stress and risk of breast cancer.
Chickpea	Clinically verified as the top cholesterol-reducing legume.
Hazelnuts	Reduce blood lipids and blood pressure.
Oats	Clinically proven to reduce weight and metabolism in diabetics; among different wholegrain cereals it is the best at lowering cholesterol; active chemical, beta-glucan, boosts the immune system.
Onion	Reduces blood sugar, blood pressure and lipids; organosulfide chemicals are antioxidant and anti-inflammatory.
Radish	Traditional remedy for stones (e.g. gall bladder); clinically proven to improve kidney function.
Tomato	Clinically proven to reduce blood pressure; reduce markers of cardiovascular disease risk in overweight, middle-aged adults; reduce risks of prostate, ovarian, gastric and pancreatic cancers.

These are tasters, gleaned from tens of thousands of published scientific studies, of the hundreds of plant food medicines (select papers are cited in the endnotes). The subject of plant food as medicine snowballed at the beginning of this century, with numbers of reports increasing five-fold in less than twenty years.

The scientific data on dose is not always straightforward. Epidemiological studies that follow long-term effects usually assume regular, normal consumption (weekly portions, for example). Dosage for long-term health or protection may be lower than for acute issues. But if you regularly use savoury or spicy plants in mouth-watering jams and jellies, salsas and soups, dips, stir-fries and breads you will most likely reap long-term health benefits.

Dilston Physic Garden volunteers enjoy lunch made from proven plant health foods (chickpea, chilli, beet and ginger).

Given our interest in medicinal plants for brain/mind health, here are some suggestions, backed by human and lab studies (2014–16) for 'brain foods'.

Foods and their ingredients that enhance mood and cognition

Asparagus	Relieves stress and improves sleep quality.
Beetroot	Improves cognitive performance.
Blueberry	Improves a range of cognitive functions, including in children.
Coconut	Enhances memory and cognitive function.
Coffee	Reduces the risk of depression.
Dark chocolate	Improves mood (induces calm, relieves depressive symptoms) and cognitive function.
Folic acid- and tryptophan-rich plants	Plants like spinach, asparagus and avocado (folic acid), and tryptophan-rich bananas, chickpeas, nuts, seeds and soy raise serotonin levels associated with improved mood.
Lettuce sap (latex)	Sedative, soporific, calming and relieves arthritic pains; active chemical in the milky sap is lactucarium.
Plants rich in omega 3 fatty acids	Flax, squash and mung beans, for example; omega 3 reduces inattention (in boys with and without attention deficit disorder) and also relieves depression.
Resveratrol supplements	Chemical found in peanuts, pistachios, grapes and blueberries, for example, improves memory performance and brain glucose metabolism in older adults.
Soy	Soy snacks (like spicy edamame beans) reduce tension anxiety in adolescents.
Walnut	Improves select aspects of cognition.

Your gut is said to be a 'second brain', with its own nerve cells (the enteric part of the autonomic nervous system) and nearly ten times more serotonin than the brain itself. So your digestive system is vital for well-being. Eating what makes you feel good could, within limits, be a marker for what will *do* you good.

Some diets for special medical needs may also help us all. The low sugar, diabetic diet benefits body weight, cardiovascular and cognitive functions. Clinical and lab studies show that ketogenic slimming diets (low carb, high fat in foods like nuts and coconut oil) have neuroprotective, antidepressant and cognitive-enhancing effects.

Choosing foods with active 'phytochemicals'

Instead of choosing foods according to their overall benefits, a different approach is to choose foods that contain specific disease-preventative active chemicals. These phytochemicals ('secondary metabolites'), which plants make for self-defence and protection, are common to many plants and can provide the same benefits for us, providing potent antioxidant or anti-inflammatory, cardioprotective, neuroprotective and immunostimulant actions (see Chapter 1).

Mixed salad of medicinal plant leaves (like wild garlic, dandelion and Good King Henry) growing in early spring.

Health-providing phytochemicals

Chemical	Plant source	Health benefits
Anthocyanin flavonoids	Blueberries, raspberries and other purple or red fruits and vegetables as well as cocoa	Immunostimulant (boosting cytokines), anticancer, anti-inflammatory, antioxidant, neuroprotective, enhance vision
Catechins	Tea	Antioxidant, protecting the cardiovascular system and reducing the risk of stroke
Carotenoids	Carrots, squash, sweet potatoes	Antioxidant, anticancer, eye and cardiovascular benefits
Coumarins	Citrus fruit	Blood-thinning, antimicrobial
Isoflavones	Soy	Oestrogenic, cholesterol-controlling, antioxidant
Resveratrol	Purple grapes	Cardioprotective, antioxidant

Our favourite 'free medicine' menus

Finally, here is our pick of favourite ingredients for exciting and healthy daily menus, sufficient to benefit bodily systems beyond nutrition. You could create a 'medicinal food' area in your physic garden to grow many of these, climate permitting.

Starters	Vegetable soups or pâtés, served with wholegrain bread (oat) and nuts (e.g. walnut, almond) butter.
Salads	Mixed green leaves. The spring salad illustrated includes Alexanders, chicory, dandelion, garlic, mustard, Good King Henry, lovage, sorrel and wild garlic, each with medical benefits. For dressings, olive or nut oils, lemon juice and pepper.
Mains	Curries, including the spices caraway, cumin, fenugreek, garlic, ginger, mustard and turmeric for potent health-giving properties. Or Mediterranean dishes, rich in vegetables, tomatoes and olive oil.
Desserts	Sweets made of chocolate and coconut (each with so many health benefits the lists run into double figures), berries, plant milks (soya or nut) thickened with arrowroot or rice flower and sweetened with stevia, sweet cicely or lucuma (*Pouteria lucuma*).
To drink	Aperitif or digestive herb spirit (our homemade absinthe is a favourite), ginger beer or elderflower champagne, followed by a choice of freshly picked and brewed herbal teas.

Plant health foods lead us on to the most popular way of taking herbs today. While your physic garden may not provide all the ingredients for your favourite plant food recipes, you can readily grow medicinal plants for a great choice of fresh herbal teas.

Spices, each with its own health benefits, for favourite fish or vegetable curries.

Brewing herbal teas

Herbal tea from freshly picked, health-enhancing leaves or flowers is one of the greatest delights of any physic garden – herbal medicine with the added pleasures of calming ritual, sensual stimulation and socialising.

Botanical teas played an important role in the recent revival of interest in herbal health benefits, and words like 'detox', 'digest', 'wake up', 'tonic', 'quality sleep' and 'love' appear on hundreds of commercial tea labels. Now, new controlled trials confirm that teas are as medicinally effective as other formulations like tablets or tinctures prepared from the same herbs (though the medicinal dose is often more than one cup a day). Fennel tea eases menstrual dysfunctions and marjoram tea improves female hormonal and metabolic markers. A combination of Chinese herbs (*Radix Astragali*, *Angelicae gigantis Radix*, *Zizyphi fructus*) relieves fatigue and insomnia. In these trials it's several cups a day for health benefits, so as you make tea from your physic garden (safety-assured) plants, think of one cup as a taster and more (advisedly) as medicine.

Trying teas for taste and mixing different herbs is great fun. We have learned more from visitors' reactions at our physic garden tea table than from any book! But some still insist on a caffeine fix and ask for traditional tea. Tonic or stimulating black and green teas get their kick from caffeine. There is more caffeine weight for weight in tea leaves (*Camellia sinensis*) than in coffee beans, though other chemicals in tea (especially green tea) like catechins are blood pressure- and cholesterol-lowering, weight-controlling, and reduce the risk of breast and prostate cancers. Interestingly, the dried spring leaves of our beautiful flowering garden camellia (*C. japonica*) finely ground make an interesting tea, tasting rather like Japanese

Fresh herbal infusions are high on the how-to-take-medicinal-plants list.

matcha – safe enough, but lacking any research record so far. Other beverage plants like cacao, Yerba mate (*Ilex paraguariensis*) and Guarana (*Paullinia cupana*) also contain caffeine. But caffeine at high doses can raise blood pressure, induce insomnia or cardiac arrhythmias and even heart attacks. The tea plants in your physic garden will be caffeine-free and you will want to know how to decide which plants to use, which brewing method, how much to drink, and how to get the best flavour with the biggest health boost.

Which plants to pick?

Any of the safe, effective medicinal plants you grow can be made into tea. The taste will vary, from the piquant flavour of peppermint or the sweet taste of woodruff to the extreme bitterness of wormwood. After serving 'bespoke' teas to visitors for many years, we favour flavour, freshly harvested and brewed: bergamot (*Monarda*) flowers (for relaxation), raspberry leaves (for near-term mums-to-be), thyme and sage sprigs (to clear coughs and catarrh), hawthorn and lime (linden) flowers (heart tonics), nettle (spring tonic) and catnip (for a gentle uplift). Lemon balm and lavender add favoured aromas and tranquillity.

Favourite brews, using aromatic medicinal plant leaves, fruit or flowers

Plant or blend	Evidence-based mind and body effects
Black peppermint leaves	Mentally stimulating and digestive (black peppermint is stronger then the common white variety).
Brain booster	Memory-enhancing leaves of sage, lemon balm, peppermint, rosemary and ginkgo with nigella seeds.
DPG House Tea	Lemon balm leaves, chamomile flowers, mint, fennel flowers or seeds, and lavender leaves or flowers for calm and cogntion.
Flower-power tea	Rose petals and elderflowers – uplifting and antibiotic.
Ginger, lemon, turmeric golden blend	Delicious and digestive for gardens in warmer areas.
Herbal-high tea	Catnip, mugwort, melissa and bay leaves with poppy seed and citrus peel for gentle uplift.
Lemon balm	Leaves from the plant that calms and gets its name from the honey bee, with honey optional.
Nettle tops	Young spring leaves and flowers make an unexpectedly delicious tea and wonderful tonic.
Sage leaves	Soothing sore throats, boosting memory and easing the menopause, with optional honey.
Summer fruit tea	Blackcurrant, bramble, elderberry and raspberry – cardioprotective.
Thyme tea	Leaves for coughs and catarrh.

Our 'house tea' blend is the most popular, combining both calming and mentally stimulating effects. You will find many other herbal teas to try on websites and in books like *Herbal Teas and Health Infusions*, by Jessica Houdret. Or just discover for yourself the finest physic garden brews for you, your family and friends. It could even be the start of something big: Celestial Seasonings, based in Colorado, was a company started in 1969 by a group of college students making teas from mountain plants they foraged. It sold to Kraft for $14 million in 1984.

How to harvest plants for teas

Tea-testing is a wonderful way to find out more about your physic garden plants. Aromatic herbs are strongest after some sunshine; pick leaves before flowering and flowers when just in full bloom. Avoid washing (except muddy roots) to keep all the goodness. Remove any yellowed or dead parts or insects. Use a small handful for each cup. Add boiling water (though some sources recommend slightly cooler than boiling, to avoid the bitterest elements). Then for the infusion, the pot or cup needs a lid on it to retain the aroma. The Chinese traditionally discard the first brewing, which may enhance the flavour, but probably not the health benefits. As with any form of herbal medicine, ensure correct identification, and if you're taking the tea at a higher medicinal dose, the usual cautions apply (especially if you're on medication, have a chronic health issue or are pregnant or nursing).

How to infuse your tea

Then there is the steeping (infusing) time. Our visitors usually opt for delicate, sweeter tastes gained from two- to three-minute infusions, though a medical herbalist at Dilston believes that herbs need to infuse for 15 to 20 minutes to be medicinal. What the flavour gains in bitterness, the tea gains in health benefits. Bitter can be good; teas that are 'astringent' – a common term in herbalism meaning it induces cells to contract – promotes digestive juices. We leave the pot with the tea drinker to decide how long to infuse. Adding sugar or milk may be appropriate for bitter or high tannin teas, but spoils the taste of aromatic herbal teas. Best to stick to honey. Many herbal teas can be refrigerated to drink cold later. Generally, for medicinal use, drink up to 1–2 cups twice daily.

Fresh flower tea from lavender, chamomile, fennel and mint flowers.

Taking time for tea

The Japanese tea ceremony, 'the Way of Tea', is about pleasure, sensuality and ritual: handmade or antique pots and cups, a carefully placed table with a calming or entrancing view, allowing yourself time to savour the brew. There is even a 'spiritual' side to herbal tea. Shamans believe they can contact the spirit of a plant by sitting beside it or by drinking the tea. It will, they say, give you guidance about whatever you need to know. So we do sometimes figuratively take off our science lab coats, sit, sip and dream a while.

Before favourite tea plants in your garden die back for the winter dry some for the winter months. Lemon balm or nettles leaves may lose some aroma if not properly dried, though drying can concentrate aromatics as for lavender flowers. Other evergreen plants, like rosemary, bay and sage, still make fine fresh infusions mid-winter, even if it's not high season for harvesting or the source of scientific testing.

Nettle, fresh or dried, makes a delicious mellow-flavoured tea.

Tempting as the way of eating and drinking is for taking in the health benefits of plants, equally delightful though rather more mysterious is the way of absorbing the volatile parts by inhaling or massaging plant essential oils.

15

Absorbing Aromatic Plant Volatiles

We now explain how to take plant medicines that depend on their aromatic volatile ingredients, beginning with pure plant essential oils and aromatherapy, moving on to incenses and essences, and ending with cosmetics.

Aromatic plants, essential oils and aromatherapy

Your physic garden will enhance your well-being without you realising it. Volatile chemicals (terpenoids) evaporate from tiny oil sacs in aromatic plant leaves and flowers. On hot humid days, their scent triggers emotions, moods and memories. These aromatic medicinal plant molecules pass through lungs or skin into the bloodstream to directly affect brain and body cells and systems. At Dilston, we have an 'aroma trail' through the garden, after which visitors give feedback on which plants induced what feelings. It's hard to put smells into words, but our aroma-trailers do end up smiling after their subliminal aromatherapy session.

The science of scents

During tests, essential oils deliberately released into the atmosphere measurably alter peoples' psychological and physical well-being: lavender reduces pain and induces sleep; rose promotes relaxation; rosemary enhances memory (see Chapter 9). The volatile chemicals (terpenoids) trigger responses in body tissues, digestive and respiratory, nerve and hormonal. They rapidly reach the brain, being lipophilic (fat-loving), and can attach themselves to the same receptor molecules that synthetic drugs and our own brain chemicals act on.

Essential oils or their ingredients are also laboratory-tested on molecules and mice, verifying healing herbs recorded for centuries. Lavender oil, in a classic 1991 study by a German team (led by Gerhard Buchbauer), calmed lab mice as the lavender ingredient linalool in their blood increased. This moved aromatherapy from 'alternative' medicine into pharmacological science.

Similar scientific testing now proves chamomile (Roman and German) and lemon balm are calming; thyme and tea tree are antimicrobial; sage (both *Salvia officinalis* and *lavandulaefolia*) and rosemary improve memory; peppermint and fennel relieve digestive discomforts; and lavender does it all!

Plants use their volatile essential oil ingredients as chemical weapons, deterring would-be grazers by disabling motor or nervous systems or obstructing digestion, making them disorientated or sick. They also use oils to attract pollinators of flowers and propagators of fruit and nuts, activating the brain's pleasure and arousal chemicals such as dopamine and noradrenaline. A favourite notion of ours, that attracter chemicals might be safer than deterrers for long-term use, is not proven.

A scented stroll

Walk around a virtual physic garden to help you plan what aromatics you might grow.

Starting in the woods, sniff pungent evergreen leaves – pine, spruce, juniper, cedar, or, in hotter climes, acacia, citrus and eucalyptus trees – all medicinal. The strong, balsamic, turpentine-like odour of pine decongests, disinfects and relaxes. The Christmassy smell of spruce soothes muscle discomfort. The mint-smelling pepper tree (*Schinus molle*) is antiseptic.

Then, stop by the pond or the river to savour water-loving mints. Pungent peppermint banishes mental fatigue and apathy; ginger in hotter areas relieves pain and nausea; bog myrtle in colder climes is antimicrobial.

Moving on to the kitchen herbs, inhale sage and rosemary, which aid cognitive functions. Strong, penetrating thyme oil disinfects and is said to abolish a hangover. Sweet spicy marjoram dulls pain. In the herbal tea borders, lemon balm essential oil enhances states of calm and alertness, especially in children. Citrus species like bergamot (*Citrus bergamia*) relieve anxiety. A bed of lavender, a chamomile lawn or a rose garden induce calm and serenity, all verified scientifically.

Next, we go from calming to exhilarating! In a secret 'what turns you or your partner on' area, there are herbal highs and aphrodisiacs. Clary (*Salvia sclarea*), neroli (from the flowers of the bitter orange tree (*Citrus x aurantium*) or, in colder climates, mock orange (*Philadelphus*)) stimulate with their heady scents. Spring daffodils may inspire more than Wordsworth's poetry: the Arabs considered them an aphrodisiac although human studies are lacking. But unromantically named black cohosh works in lab studies, strengthening male reproductive organs in rats, while nutmeg increases mating performance in male and female mice. Many of the essential oils we discuss here are also usefully antibiotic (bactericidal, virucidal, fungicidal, antiparasite and insecticidal). Safe-to-take herbal highs are covered in the next chapter.

Your body-boosting or mind-blowing aromatic stroll will linger on, as a whiff of rosemary, sage or melissa can press 'imprint' buttons in your brain, helping store memories that can be recalled later, like listening to music.

Water-loving mint, proven to aid digestion and memory..

Aromatics in therapy

While any of these aromatics can be part of a physic garden experience, essential oil therapy rarely relies on a walk round the garden. Essential oils, most often prepared by steam extraction or distillation, are used in vaporisers and lotions, or massaged into the skin by aromatherapists. As the oils are up to 1,000 times stronger than the herb or its extracts in water or alcohol, all (except lavender) have to be diluted at least a hundredfold using a 'carrier' oil. Some oils are never used in aromatherapy: wormwood, bitter almond, camphor, wintergreen or sage (*Salvia officinalis*, not the Spanish sage, *S. lavandulaefolia*) because they are high in thujone, a potentially convulsant and abortifacient chemical in large doses. Others, like verbena, bergamot and rue, can cause phototoxic skin reactions.

As for taking any essential oil internally, most medical herbalists in the UK and US do not generally prescribe essential oils internally, bearing in mind that healing requires the whole-plant extract. But in France, where pharmacists prescribe plant medicines, essential oils are often capsulated for oral and suppository use. In the UK aromatherapists do not recommend swallowing essential oils. And yet, paradoxically, one of the few plant medicines listed in the British National Formulary, the essential reference for mainstream medical practitioners, is oral peppermint oil (for gastrointestinal conditions – in capsules).

The safe essential oils currently do not come with any warnings to avoid them with medicinal drugs. As well as skin oils or lotions, you can add them to your bath or shower, inhale from pillows, vaporise in a room diffuser, or vape them; skin patches are increasingly popular as the dose can be easily regulated. Before our clinical trial of lemon balm in a care home, we applied the lotion to one of our lab team, a man not a mouse. His blood sample was sent to Kew laboratories where the chemicals (like geranial) were detected, showing the oils had been absorbed into his system.

Favourite oil blends of ours are: lavender and chamomile for relaxing (calming, pain-relieving and sleep-inducing); Spanish sage and rosemary for stimulating (arousal, attention and memory); rose and rose geranium for good mood (uplifting and cheering). All are 1% or less in sweet almond oil. Individual skin reactions, other health conditions, age and pregnancy also have to be taken into account. Beyond checking if an oil is safe for young children or pregnant mums, individual reactions are unknown so it's worth trying out just as few drops to start with.

Plant essential oils, safe as long as properly diluted.

Distilling plant essential oils

While the idea of home distillation from medical plants is appealing, the quantity of material required and the possible illegality of owning a still (even if not for alcohol) are less so. It may take a mere 100kg of lavender to make 1kg of oil (100lbs for 1lb), but it takes more than 5,000kg (5 tons!) of damask rose petals or lemon balm leaves for the same amount.

To obtain essential oils from your physic garden plants, your options are:

- steam distillation, which involves passing steam through plant material and collecting the oil as it condenses while the vapour is cooled;
- cold pressing (e.g. citrus fruit peel), where the oil is squeezed out without applying heat;
- solvent extraction (ether or methanol), where the herb is soaked in the solvent;
- enfleurage, a method still used by French perfumeries in Grasse. It involves putting fat on the leaves and allowing the perfume to be absorbed into it; this method is better for delicate flowers.

But steam distillation is the usual method, practised since ancient times. A still can be purchased or put together from everyday items of equipment and running water. Detailed instructions on websites include using simple attachments to a kettle so that the steam generated from the heated herb inside can be collected through a stopper into copper pipe connections that lead to a cooled collecting vessel. It's well worth trying if you have large quantities of your favourite aromatic herb – and if you succeed in obtaining a sweet-scented oil you could save yourself a fortune!

Making perfume from your own essential oils is yet another benefit bestowed by a physic garden. Almost all today's commercial perfumes are synthetic. The perfume industry is not externally regulated. Some added chemicals are toxic: parabens are synthetic preservatives that interfere with hormone production; phthalates are carcinogenic and linked to reproductive effects (decreased sperm counts and even birth defects); and synthetic musks are linked to hormone disruption.

From the pleasures of using pure essential oils we now move on to other ways to enjoy plant volatiles.

The apothecary rose (*R. gallica*) is not so aromatic but was hybridised to produce the perfectly scented damask rose.

Essences and incenses

The new physic garden provides simple mood-enhancing delights like flower essences and incenses, opportunities for fun activities like herbal flower arranging, and confetti-making for a fragrant 'green' wedding. Here we deviate from the evidence-based path as we explore ways of using physic garden products grounded more in joy than science.

The inspirational beauty of flowers, from the most dramatic cultivars to the most delicate wild species, has a single evolutionary purpose. Sights and scents that evoke intuitive responses reflect a biological imperative – to attract pollinators to propagate the species. Our sensory and nervous systems are biologically close enough to those of the bees for us to fall for these highly successful botanical adverts. Colour and scent chemicals demand attention and stimulate positive reactions in the brain.

Essential essences?

From ancient Egypt to modern Tibet, the 'essence' of the flower has been used for its 'magical' healing qualities. Flower essences are made from the flowering part of the plant. They differ from the herbal infusions or decoctions used by herbalists because the water-based extract is diluted many times, similar to the preparation of homeopathic medicines. Flower essences are not about extracting aromatic chemicals. But we slip them in here as they are considered to be unique, working at the 'energetic' rather than material level. Taking just a few drops of the essence is said to address specific aspects of emotional and mental well-being.

Best known are Bach flower remedies; others are the Australian bush flower and Findhorn remedies. Dr Edward Bach viewed emotional balance as essential for physical health because stress is associated with many disorders. Each of his thirty-eight flower essences relates to one specific negative emotion and is intended to induce the corresponding positive quality.

Their actions may ring bells with psychologists; for example:

- Agrimony (*Agrimonia eupatoria*) for outwardly cheerful people who hide their troubles and inner torment;

- Elm (*Ulmus procera*) for people who are usually very confident and capable, but at times become overwhelmed by work or other responsibilities;

- Rockrose (*Helianthemum nummularium*) to help with panic, terror and despair that can grip people in an emergency.

We make a flower essence from black cohosh (also called fairy candle, on account of its delicate white flower fronds). Its delightful beauty and scent is said to be uplifting, invigorating and mood balancing. Leave one whole flower in sunlight in a large glass bowl of spring water for 5 hours, adding alcohol (vodka or cognac to 10% final alcohol content) to preserve this 'mother' liquor for further dilution. While herbal flower extracts contain active chemicals, dilution renders them below any effective dose recognised by herbal medicine. But this is different from plant medicines made from flowers – saffron is as effective as antidepressants for mild to moderate depression.

Black cohosh (*Actaea racemosa*) used to make a favourite Dilston flower essence.

There is currently little scientific evidence to support the health benefits of flower essences; almost all placebo-controlled trials have been negative. As with homeopathy, opinions vary. 'Just placebo,' say some, while others insist that conventional science can't prove effects not yet understood.

For many, the fact that an essence or homeopathic remedy works – 'subjective evidence' – is enough. Science is starting to take subjectivity seriously; conscious awareness sits at the heart of all observation. One scientific finding that might validate flower-essence effects is that flowers emit electrical signals to tell bees whether they have already been pollinated, and something similar might be at work in flower essences.

You can decide for yourself, but here are a couple of quotes from scientific journals. The first is from a review in a medical journal: 'In 1930, Dr Edward Bach developed flower essences … they are becoming more and more popular and are used by many practitioners, despite a total lack of scientific support for their use.' An Australian nursing journal carried an article stating that 'these essences … can be used without any interference with medical procedures … and there are over 16 hospitals which are currently offering these treatments to their patients.'

Unlike twentieth-century Bach and Bush flower essences, incense has been used for thousands of years. Its effect on mind and body is backed up by more scientific evidence.

Incenses

You might wonder if church incense is merely a psychological stimulus, the familiar smell signalling spirituality. But then think of tobacco and how inhaling it allows the volatile chemical nicotine to affect the brain directly (relaxing and alerting). Verified volatile chemicals are released by burning plant products in churches or in shamanic smudging rituals or pipes of peace. Incense can induce calm, stimulate, promote meditative mental states or purify atmospheres by obscuring unpleasant smells (and by being antimicrobial). Once believed to join heaven and earth, allowing people to connect with their deities in prayer, incense directly affects mind and body functions.

Best-known incense ingredients are gums or spices like myrrh, frankincense, amber, sandalwood and cloves, though common healing herbs like sage, bay and lavender are also often used.

Juniper, used in incense-making.

Effects of incense plants

(First line: *Subjective evidence*; second line: scientific evidence)

Plant	Effect
Cedar	*removes negative energy* cannabinoid system implicated in analgesic effects
Frankincense	*cleanses, protects, promotes transcendental states, enhances intuition* antimicrobial, anticancer, analgesic, antidepressant, improves cognitive function
Juniper	*invigorating* analgesic and anxiolytic
Lavender	*removes negative feelings, promotes peacefulness* calming and sedative
Myrrh	*aids meditation* improves circulation, antimicrobial
Mugwort	*removes obstructions and negativity, promotes lucid dreaming* heat effects on acupuncture points, sedative
Rose	*promotes peacefulness and love (including spiritual)* calming and mood uplifting

Science explains how plants such as frankincense (*Boswellia* plant resin) promote spiritual states. One of its fragrant ingredients reduces signs of anxiety and depression in mouse models and affects an unusual receptor in the brain. The chemical, appropriately named incensole, activates molecules (vanilloid or capsaicin receptors, associated with pain) in our brains, especially the cerebral cortex (associated with cognitive function). Not just a holy incense, frankincense was used to combat the plague, and today it's used to support cancer therapy (see Chapter 4). The antimicrobial effects of many incense plants may be incidentally relevant to protecting health in group gatherings.

Smudging using Dilston aromatic herbs.

In our physic garden, inspired by these ritualistic plants and the new research, we decided to try all the safe aromatic plants. We dried and burned the collected plants (mainly leaves), most not burning long. But one determined volunteer bound together what seems to be a magic mix of fresh mugwort, lavender, sagebrush (*Artemisia heterophylla*) and rosemary which, when dried, burns well.

You can prepare incense sticks or cones from any other herb you like, adding incendiary ingredients like charcoal, gums or resins. The traditional indigenous American equipment for 'smudging' is an abalone shell with a charcoal disc or tablet placed on a little sand and a feather to waft the smoke from the burning herb around the people gathered for a ceremony.

Smoking herbs

For a more personal and direct experience there is always the cigarette or pipe. Some herbs are used ritualistically in smoking ceremonies involving inhaling smoke directly from a pipe, such as the highly decorated Native American peace pipes. As well as tobacco, cannabis and opium, other herbs like dyer's greenweed (*Genista tinctoria*), lobelia, mugwort and wild lettuce (*Lactuca virosa*) are smoked ritualistically and contain neuroactive chemicals like lobeline (related to nicotine and producing similar effects) and a latex (lactucarium) that is sedative (see the next chapter).

Mapacho (tobacco, *Nicotiana*) is considered particularly sacred by Amazonian shamans, used on its own, or combined with other plants to promote visions. It is traditionally used as a medicine with dozens of *Nicotiana* species native to North and South America, especially in the Andes. The commercial exploitation of tobacco, taking its use out of its original context and adding chemical ingredients, has had dire consequences. But using other safer aromatic herbs, you could explore smoking physic garden plants for subtle states of well-being. However, there is the added health warning that tar and carbon monoxide from any burning plant material means inhalation should be restricted.

While using plants as essences or incenses may be more for fun than for getting a medicinal plant dose, the next way of 'delivering the dose' is ever more popular and may strike you as quite surprising!

Cosmeceuticals: herbal cosmetics for health

Cosmetics with health benefits (beyond skin) are increasingly pursued by commercial companies. Most cosmeceuticals contain essential oils that promote well-being, relaxation, serenity, peaceful sleep or improved mood (as in aromatherapy). Here we discuss how cosmeceuticals have craftily slipped past regulations for medicines, and how to make your own safe versions to improve well-being and immunity.

How do cosmeceuticals work? They contain potent essential oils that confer a secondary biological property. The unique feature of essential oils is that they easily cross our skin and

Selection of bioactive, healing lotions made by medical herbalist Ross Menzies.

brain 'barriers'. When applied to the skin or inhaled, their bioactive ingredients are rapidly absorbed into your bloodstream to interact with tissues. Each oil may contain several potentially 'bioactive' ingredients.

Traditional lavender in bath oil has been clinically proven to enter our bloodstream and reach our brain to have relaxant effects on the central nervous system. It may also be inhaled because the volatiles easily enter the bloodstream.

Regulations for naming and production of cosmetics

By definition **cosmetics** are allowed to clean, perfume, protect and correct body odour, but not act as drugs. Traditionally, cosmetics combine synthetic and natural chemicals to enhance skin or hair texture, or tooth whiteness. Whether antioxidant or allegedly anti-ageing, effects are literally (only) skin deep. Some companies brand anti-ageing products as cosmeceuticals, but they don't have secondary or 'systemic' effects because most can't cross the skin barrier, although they may have a medicinal effect on the skin.

Cosmeceuticals combine cosmetic *and* pharmaceutical effects. Creams, oils, bath and shower foams, shampoos, toothpastes, roll-ons and sprays have, or claim to have, a secondary biological property such as lavender in bath oils for relaxation or aloe in creams for skin-healing. Claims for mood come with the relaxing bath foam, the zinging shower gel, the calming body lotion. Rosemary traditionally added to hair products has been shown by recent clinical evidence to improve hair growth, so it works superficially, but it also reaches the brain to boost memory.

Bath products are cosmeceutical as well as aromatherapeutic.

Cosmeceutical regulation is a relatively new and hazy area. Currently the FDA doesn't recognise the term: in the US, most cosmeceuticals are considered to be cosmetics. In Europe a cosmetic 'may have a secondary preventative, but not a curative, purpose'. Regulatory bodies have problems classifying products that blur the boundaries between cosmetics, aromatherapy products and even foodstuffs flavoured by essential oils. Thus many cosmeceuticals and traditional herbal medicines are legally unable to claim a medicinal effect.

We mention this confusing situation because visitors to our physic garden have asked about making skin lotions to sell.

Making your own cosmeceuticals

To make a natural and effective skin cream, ointment or spray directly from physic garden plants, the principles are simple and recipes abundant online.

Choose your fresh herbs and prepare an extract in water, oil (heated or not) or alcohol, straining off the solids and adding beeswax or base creams for ointments or lotions. Then add a few drops of essential oil to enhance the aroma and act as a preservative. For us, these oils are the essential ingredients for additional systemic, health-enhancing effects but always within safe limits – officially no more than 1% of the final product, though aromatherapists do raise this limit. We always ensure the oil is sustainably produced, natural and pure (some commercial sources are adulterated).

Our choice of cosmeceuticals

Peppermint and sage mouthwash: prepare fresh peppermint and sage leaves as for a strong tea, strain, add the appropriate amount of the same plants' essential oils, plus perhaps tea tree as an option. The result is refreshing and antibiotic, and slows plaque formation on teeth.

Citrus uplift spray: extract lemon balm and lemon peel in alcohol with drops of citrus oils like lemon and may chang. The resulting spray is skin-toning, refreshing, mood-boosting and insect-repelling, but should not be used in sunlight.

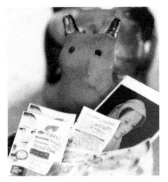

Not just plants, snail slime for human skin is backed by lab findings. It keeps cells healthy.

Comfrey and calendula ointment: boil comfrey leaves and marigold flowers in an oil such as sunflower. Strain, add beeswax and a drop of tea tree oil. The ointment is skin-smoothing and helps heal lesions.

Regenerative face oil: frankincense, patchouli, rose and mandarin essential oils are blended, with sweet almond oil as a carrier. The oil smoothes and moisturises ageing skin.

In passing, there's a new trend in skin gels derived from snail slime in case you (unlike us) feel inclined to use one of the pests in your garden as a source of health and beauty …

Boosting commercial beautifiers with essential oils

Add an enlivening drop of rosemary, sage and peppermint to your commercial face cream to boost attention and memory. Just one drop of rose, lavender, lemon balm or chamomile (Roman or German) in your bath or body oil before you sleep will calm, relax and sedate you. Or why not pop drops in a roller ball in sweet almond oil for when you need to be alert or de-stress at work? When we add lavender to our bath salts or rosemary to our hair products we know there is science behind the calming, attention-boosting and hair-growth effects.

So while science is gathering evidence for agents that cross the skin barrier, we can enjoy watching the children at our Potion Club delight in herb gathering, grinding, mixing, making and applying their own safe skin lotions.

To end this section of the book on using your physic garden plants we move back to an area that was the reason for establishing our physic garden in the first place – plants in mind.

16

Plants in Mind

And now an admission of bias: using plants in the physic garden for the mind and brain. This is what our research is about (for one of us, it goes back forty years!) and what our physic garden specialises in. It also fits with growing mental health awareness.

We introduce plants that enhance your mood and mind (briefly, as it's all in our *Botanical Brain Balms* book) and add a few favourite recipes. Then we offer you a choice of plants that could be called 'herbal highs' – not hazardous psychedelics but safe herbs used by medical herbalists that enhance our conscious states, like attentiveness and mood.

Botanic brain boosters

Maintaining or restoring well-being is more than ever a subject about needs. Stress, dementia and depression are all on the increase and are not yet (or, at least, not for all people) treated safely and effectively by synthetic chemical drugs. Talks on plants for brain/mind are popular at Dilston: 'memory and mood'; 'calm and sleep'; 'plants of the gods'.

Our selection of plants has evidence from human and lab tests that back up traditional use. Most work by affecting our brain signals. Their chemicals attach to receptors ('docking stations') where they are mistaken for the brain's own chemical signals. These brain signals include serotonin (positive mood and well-being); dopamine (drive and pleasure); acetylcholine (attention and learning); noradrenaline (arousal); encephalins (pain); our own cannabinoids (an expanding list of actions, including sleep and pain); GABA (relaxation, sedation, switching off); glutamate (overall activation); and oxytocin (socialising).

We won't dig deeper into the science now, but instead offer suggestions for symptoms and a few tried and tested recipes or ways of taking the plants. And these are medicinal plants, good for the brain, that grow in our physic garden.

Plants in the Dilston memory area.

Improving memory

Evidence-based memory enhancers include ginkgo, lemon balm, sage (*S. officinalis* and *lavandulaefolia*), rosemary, saffron, peppermint and black cumin (*Nigella sativa*).

Fry sage leaves in oil or butter and add a little salt and sugar to make delicious crisps/chips. Ginkgo nuts roasted or cooked in soups and stews are highly prized by the Chinese, though there is a caution on consuming too many as they contain a toxin (methylpyridoxine). 'Lemonbalmade', our popular cold summer drink is chilled, strong melissa tea with added honey and lemon juice.

Anxiety and stress relief

The evidence for reducing anxiety and stress effects in clinical trials is overwhelming for lavender and chamomile (both Roman and German), which is often taken in teas or as lotions.

Other plants with ingredients that disguise themselves as the brain's calming GABA chemical are lemon balm, valerian, hemp, passion flower, skullcap and oat. The fruits of passion flower are as active as its leaves and stems but are much tastier. Hemp, grown from healthfood hemp seed, is the chemical type of cannabis plant with only a trace of the psychoactive (THC) chemical, but rich in the one that lowers pain and anxiety (CBD, cannabidiol). Buds and leaves make delicious tea and the CBD oil is added to snacks, beverages and vapes.

Improving mood/antidepressants

Apart from the renowned antidepressive St John's wort, other clinically verified mood-lifting herbs include saffron, valerian and rhodiola. Those with less evidence are: rose and, particularly for women, black cohosh and clary sage. These all affect serotonin (among other) signals.

The somewhat bitter taste of St John's wort tea made from leaves or flowers is improved with added lemon balm (also a mood booster). But for sensual delight, little competes with the scent of damask roses or, if you can afford it, pure rose essential oil. Mood-enhancing effects can be enjoyed in pillows, baths, lotions or diffusers.

Sleep-promoters

Passion flower and hops increase sleep length and quality. Plants proven to promote sleep are often anti-anxiety too: lavender, lemon balm, chamomile and valerian. Pillows with added lavender oil or filled with hops are excellent options, and hop flowers infused in alcohol (hops schnapps) make a fine nightcap.

Pain relief

Among many clinically verified analgesics are capsicum (also used in mainstream medicine as capsaicin), dill, feverfew, ginger, nigella, peppermint, willow (bark), as well as our old friends lavender and lemon balm. Then there is, of course, cannabis (if legal in your area), which is proven to reduce pain. The much cited cannabidiol ingredient of hemp (see above) is being explored for pain as well as its many other benefits. Whether our addiction to fresh chilli oil, added to soups and pastas, prevents pain when taken internally is not clear, but we do find that a few drops of lavender oil rubbed on the forehead helps to relieve headaches.

Neuroprotective

For more long-term effects, we have already featured anti-inflammatory and antioxidant fruits, nuts and spices which, to judge by population studies (epidemiology), protect against degenerative brain conditions like Alzheimer's. The same applies to curry (with spices like turmeric) and Mediterranean dishes (rich in olive oil and vegetables). Ginkgo and garlic protect against ischaemic strokes. Many plants that help maintain heart and metabolic function (see the charts in Chapter 8) have the knock-on effect of keeping the brain in working order.

These brain-boosting plants, safe at the right dose, would benefit from further research to determine exact effects. But we have provided you with ideas on how to enjoy some. For the more conventional, brain-boosting medicinal tinctures and tablets consult recommended sources for dosage, especially if you are taking other medications (St John's wort, for example, can affect the action of a number of drugs).

Beyond the these mainly European species, there is a host of traditional Chinese plants being tested for all these actions. Given the resources now being invested in Chinese plant medicine research, we will soon be familiar with oriental herbs and formulations like the Xiaoyao Kangai Jieyu Fang formula for depression or Suanzaoren (*Ziziphus spinosa*) decoction for insomnia.

Herbal highs: psychedelic plants for ritual, recreation and remedy

When our university research moved into the direction of hallucinations in people with brain diseases, we created new areas in the garden for plants of the gods and herbal highs! Studying hallucinations in a disease called 'dementia with Lewy bodies' (closely related to Parkinson's disease), we discovered the brain system affected in patients who experienced visual hallucinations. It is the same system (cholinergic) that belladonna's active chemical (atropine) can disrupt, bringing about the same kind of visions in healthy people.

Ritualistic use of such plants is evident in ancient burial sites and cave art, and may even have influenced the development of creative consciousness. With our growing interest came a collection of safe (legal) psychoactive plants that alter consciousness (change visual perception, induce enlightenment or euphoria). Such plants are now widely used for recreation, but they are also moving into the realms of therapy, relieving anxiety and depression, for example. So they deserve a place in an 'enlightened' physic garden.

For growing (legal) species in the physic garden, you can divide psychoactive plants into three classes, with common-sense safety precautions:

Hallucinations in brain diseases can resemble the effects of belladonna berries.

Toxic

Never use potent, potentially toxic species, even if you grow them for their beauty and intriguing history. These include plants in the Solanaceae family (mandrake, belladonna, datura, scopolia). Used traditionally by shamans and witches for spiritual rather than recreational use, they can induce vivid, often frightening, hallucinations of animals and people. And the difference between an effective and a fatal dose is very small, so they are exceptionally dangerous. Youngsters seeking herbal highs have been hospitalised and even died of datura (*Datura stramonium*, also called devil's trumpet) poisoning.

Despite its name, Angel's trumpet (*Brugmansia*) is, like datura, a poisonous plant.

Divine sage (*Salvia divinorum*).

Use with caution

For species that are much less toxic but still potentially hazardous, check whether they are legal to grow in your country for personal use. And bear in mind that they are best used under the supervision of a reputable shaman or trained psychotherapist, as they carry possible risks of uncontrollable behaviour, psychosis or addiction.

Plants in this category that can be grown in some countries (as long as not supplied to others) include the peyote cactus (source of mescaline), kava (at doses above the calming range), cannabis, opium poppies and divine sage (*Salvia divinorum*). In our Dilston 'plants of the gods' workshops, the leader demonstrates effects by chewing a couple of divine sage leaves (the recommended dose) and describing his visions. He 'saw' one of us turn into a witch with a long protruding chin and blue hair. But this is still the safest mind-altering plant used by shamans (the same does not apply to using its active chemical, salvinorin A).

Can be used safely

In this category are medicinal plants that can be used safely as a mild means of reaching happy or enhanced states of mind and mood. We take a closer look at this third group of plants for subtle altered states of consciousness. As usual, correct identification, preparation and dose are essential, and they may need to be avoided if pregnant or on medication.

Panel of safe mild herbal highs

Wild wormwood or mugwort

The common European mugwort (*Artemisia vulgaris*) is less aromatic than the Chinese mugwort (*A. argyi*) used in 'moxibustion' (where cups of burning herb are placed on acupuncture points). Wild wormwood is perennial, and thrives and spreads in our cold northern climate. It is a Dilston potted-plant bestseller: no customer has ever complained of adverse effects, and some report having cathartic dream experiences and return for more.

Mugwort (*Artemisia vulgaris*), also known as the witches herb.

Medically, mugwort is analgesic, sedative, hypnotic and anticonvulsant. Its chemicals, like cineole and thujone, act on the inhibitory brain signal (GABA), attention signal (acetylcholine) and on the cannabinoid receptor.

Originally used by Druids and witches to sharpen awareness and promote visions, it is used today to induce lucid dreaming (being aware of and controlling dreams). Leaves smoked with, or instead of, cannabis evoke dreamy states of consciousness. Leaves or roots can also be made into tea, used in stir-fries or extracted in alcohol – we make a mean mugwort spirit using rum with brown sugar. Users often report cannabis-like effects, altered colour perception, improved sleep and pleasant dreams.

Broom (*Cytisus scoparius*)

Smoking dried broom flowers is said to be mentally stimulating, enhancing colour appreciation and inducing mild euphoria. Its active chemicals (cytisine and sparteine, also an anti-arrhythmic drug) act on brain nicotinic receptors (as nicotine does), which keep the mind alert. In traditional herbal medicine it has been used as a diuretic and for gout and arthritis. The plant must not be confused with the similar yellow-flowering Spanish gorse (*Genista hispanica*) which is toxic.

Catnip

Cat owners will know how the mint-like catnip (*Nepeta cataria*) got its name. Cats love it so much they roll in and destroy it, though its use as a human herbal high similar to cannabis is less well known. The main chemical is a terpene (nepetalactone), which acts on our opioid receptors, accounting for its medicinal effects – inducing mild euphoria, relaxation and sleep, and alleviating pain.

Catnip (*Nepeta cataria*).

Hop (*Humulus lupulus*)

Hop belongs to the Cannabaceae or hemp family. Most familiar for flavouring beer, this vigorous vine smothers plants as wolves do sheep, hence the Latin name meaning 'little wolf'. Female hops contain more volatile terpenes (humulene and lupulin) than the male; these components affect the brain by raising the action of our inhibition signal GABA. Although related to cannabis, hop contains none of the cannabis chemical THC but does contain humulene (as does cannabis). Smoking the resin is said to be like opium, but not addictive. However it is taken, the dose is one or two grams. Hop pillows promote sleep and pleasant dreams, and are said to prevent nightmares.

Hop flowers, decorative and sleep-inducing.

Skullcap (*Scutellaria*)

Also known as Quaker bonnet, helmet flower and mad dog weed tobacco. The seedpods look like tiny skulls. It is used by herbalists to benefit the nervous system, being sedative, antidepressant and anti-anxiety. Smoked like tobacco, it is said to induce visions and was used by witches to produce the sensation of flying. It works by its flavone chemicals (baicalin and baicalein) acting on the calming brain signal (GABA), the same system affected by benzodiazepines (tranquillising drugs).

Wild lettuce (*Lactuca virosa*)

Wild, or opium lettuce, is the species our salad lettuce derives from. (The stem and bolted parts of salad lettuce have similar mind-altering effects to the wild form.) The 'high' is described as euphoric, mildly sedative, dreamy and happy. It is tranquillising and pain-relieving. Sedative effects are attributed to two non-addictive chemicals (lactucopicrin and lactucin), which explains the 'soporific' effects of garden lettuce on Beatrix Potter's Flopsy Bunnies!

Wild lettuce (*Lactuca virosa*).

Wormwood and absinthe

Wormwood (*Artemisia absinthium*) produces absinthe, the powerful liqueur notoriously used by writers and artists such as Oscar Wilde, Hemingway, Picasso and Van Gogh. Euphoria was frequently followed by misery and addiction, though wormwood was unfairly blamed. In the 1850s, the French wine crop failed and absinthe took over, with absurd quantities – up to ten glasses of 70–90% alcohol – downed daily. By the end of the century, half the patients in French mental hospitals were absinthe-abusers, but their hallucinations and sleeplessness, tremors, paralysis and convulsions are also symptoms of alcoholism. Wormwood's chemical, thujone, can be toxic in high doses, but disrepute resulted from a 'smear' campaign by a failing French wine industry, which needed to recapture its market.

Wormwood (*Artemisia absinthium*).

Whether wormwood itself has psychedelic properties is not clear, but absinthe today is said to have mind-altering effects. And there is a certain magic in a spirit that emits a green light when burned, the reason absinthe was known as 'the green fairy'.

Citrus fruits

Common members of the citrus family contain DMT (dimethyltryptamine), the active psychoactive chemical in the plant mix ayahuasca: bergamot (*Citrus bergamia*), and even lemons, limes and oranges. However, for DMT (referred to by some as the 'spirit molecule') to affect the brain for more than a split second it has to be prevented from being broken down by adding another ingredient that blocks the enzyme monoamine oxidase. So any exhilarating effects of your Christmas clementine will be fleeting unless you add in one of a growing list of plants reported to block the enzyme (examples are ingredients in bacopa, damiana, and the flavonoid quercetin found in vegetables like broccoli).

Some of these plants have calming and mood-enhancing (antidepressant) effects, in keeping with new findings that stronger psychedelics relieve symptoms of depression, addiction or anxiety: ayahuasca (the mix of plants that allows the DMT molecule to linger longer) or 'magic mushrooms' (*Psilocybe*). Other species used spiritually or ritualistically (as well as medicinally) remain to be explored scientifically: bay (*Laurus nobilis*) for clairvoyance and wisdom, and Balsam of Peru (*Myroxylon balsamum*) for peace and love.

We could have ended this part of our book about using your physic garden plants on this 'high note'. But there is one other way you can use your physic garden as a whole that goes beyond effects of individual plants. It relates to complementary or alternative medicines.

17

Bringing Back the Magic?

'Nature itself is the best physician.' Hippocrates

From how to use individual plants to how to use the whole garden, we look at how your physic garden could be a haven for people interested in complementary and alternative therapies. Such treatments don't all have a firm footing in evidence-based science (herbal medicine, as you will know by now, is an exception!). Some think alternative therapies may work by magic and, indeed, what was once regarded as magic (St John's wort chasing away demons, for example) can turn out to have a rational basis in modern medicine (see the Introduction).

We finish with what *seems to us* to be magic. We tell you about our epiphany – how, as we wrote this book, we developed a new sense of wonder at the way medicinal plants help keep us healthy. Add to this remarkable evidence the notion that plants have many senses not unlike our own and the idea that not only are we plant-watching in the physic garden but the plants themselves are 'watching' us and there's magic in the air!

Alternative therapies in physic gardens

The physic garden is a perfect setting for mind, body and spirit alternatives, from meditation to yoga. To follow up ways of using medicinal plants, we share a wider vision of how to use the whole physic garden as a healer. Our vision was inspired by the alternative therapists (aromatherapists, reiki masters, shamans) who came to share our physic garden. They tell us that being surrounded by medicinal plants enhances their healings or teaching.

This applies to evidence-based complementary therapies, like herbal medicine and aromatherapy. Aromatherapists massage clients with essential oils while surrounded by living aromatic plants; yoga postures practised on a chamomile lawn benefit from the calming aroma; qigong or tai chi movements are relished in the open space of a wild meadow of healing plants; mindfulness meditation walks along paths through therapeutic trees have a soothing soundtrack of wind-waved branches.

People consulting medical herbalist Davina Hopkinson at Dilston love being in a garden where the medicines grow.

Mindfulness brain aids

Walking mindfully leads to intense awareness of the present and letting go of intrusive thoughts. For inclement weather, there can be sheltered patios or gazebos, colonnades, or frames laden with climbing herb vines like hops and honeysuckle. So your physic garden can host therapies in the setting of its nurturing plants.

Controlled clinical trials of mindfulness meditation repeatedly prove reductions in depression or anxiety. Brain scans of people practising the technique show activity in cortical areas involved in cognition and pain perception. Scans even show that the actual thickness of the cerebral cortex increases in some areas, which fits with other findings that it helps to counter age-related cognitive decline. The evidence of benefits for people with mood-related mental health issues is so overwhelming that the UK MHRA (Medicines and Healthcare Products Regulatory Agency) has approved including mindfulness meditation in mainstream medicine.

Yoga postures in the open

In its country of origin, yoga always took place outside. Studies of yoga have identified all kinds of bodily benefits, from reducing blood pressure and cardiovascular risk, to improving the quality of life in cancer patients. The challenge of providing a suitable placebo may mean the controlled trial 'stamp of approval' is harder to obtain. But you or your garden visitors will enjoy yoga postures in the open air.

Energy flows among flowers

Qigong is an ancient Chinese therapy closely related to tai chi. It integrates physical postures, breathing techniques and mental concentration. Many trials suggest it helps with pain, cardiovascular dysfunction and chronic fatigue. Qigong is energy-based and, intriguingly, qigong masters have been able to control energy flow to influence results in laboratory tests: enhanced immune function of white blood cells, survival of brain cells and genetic changes.

Yoga on the chamomile lawn.

Chinese mugwort (*Artemisia argyi*) used in acupuncture to warm meridian points.

Other alternative therapies actually enlist the support of medicinal plants. Acupuncture uses mugwort for a warming procedure known as moxibustion that has proven health outcomes (more than a placebo effect). Both reiki and reflexology often add in healing herbs. Though these practices still lack scientific support, it was traditional health practices that paved the way to many of today's medicinal drugs and helped biologists discover how our bodies work, so we should not be surprised if they lead to new medical discoveries in the future.

The garden as physician?

Therapeutic gardens are officially described as 'meeting people's physical, psychological or spiritual needs'. There are hundreds of studies on the benefits of being in a garden. By landscaping your physic garden with medicinal plants to create aromatic and calming or stimulating areas for different moods, and nurturing habitats for wildlife as pollinators or propagators, you can effectively and simply enhance well-being. So add a seat under an arch of passion flower in a quiet corner and surround it in blue flowers like rosemary, violets and periwinkle for contemplative enjoyment.

Physic gardens can enhance hospices, care homes, special schools, prisons and city deadlands. Increasingly, healing gardens feature in mainstream healthcare, attached to general hospitals as well as care centres for dementia, rehabilitation and cancer. A few are devoted to complementary therapies, such as The Therapy Centre in rural Worcestershire (UK) where you walk through a garden haven to reach your treatment room. Communities are establishing gardens too, often in inner cities, such as the one near us in Scotswood, an area of Newcastle once the centre of mining and military engineering.

As we write, gardening itself hits the headlines for all kinds of proven health benefits, even prompting demands for it to be on prescription! So enjoy growing and using herbal remedies in your garden and keep an eye on colours, shapes, textures, tastes and smells through the changing seasons. See spring leaves used to make mucilage-rich comfrey lotions or agrimony's astringent tinctures; absorb the scents of fresh clary, myrtle or lavender as you prepare a body spray; watch aspen leaves tremble in the wind to see why its Bach flower remedy is said to ease anxiety. The magic and folklore of your herbs lives on through you as you work in harmony with nature's healing powers.

Stone seat and surrounding aromatic plants that warm up in the midday sun.

Discovering the powers of plants

Back to the future, plant medicine is newly emerging from books by ancient herbalists and from grandmother's remembered remedies into realms of modern science and medicine. The idea of creating your own physic garden will hopefully be inspiring you to find out more about medicinal plants. Your can start your physic garden with just a few plants in pots, or mark off an area in the garden where medicinal plants already grow, or follow a grand plan for a whole physic garden. All it takes is a passion for plants that have a proven place in medicine today and enough enthusiasm to get to know, grow and use them.

Aspen (*Populus tremuloides*) leaves trembling in the breeze inspired the Bach flower remedy for stress.

For us, writing this book led to an epiphany. About half way through it dawned on us that it's the plants' own amazing survival strategies that we can use to heal and keep healthy as if by magic. We found ourselves in awe of the plant kingdom with something akin to religious fervour. After all, the Druids worshipped trees and the Hindus revere plants like holy basil. Our new admiration extends across the medicinal plant kingdom, from the tallest tree to the humblest herb or weed, and is informed by new scientific research. At Dilston, tallest is the silver birch with its diuretic chemicals and humblest has to be Robert Burns 'wee, modest' daisy with its insulin-like ingredients.

Based on just some of the wonderful health-giving properties of plants we have referred to throughout the book, here is our Scientist's Ode to Medicinal Plants

Your siren-song in scent and savour brings you pollinators and propagators.
With those same signals you seduce our senses and stimulate pleasure pathways of our brain.
Cells die as if by design. It's called 'apoptosis', programmed cell death.
For cells that divide and grow too fast in us, your chemical controls for apoptosis give us drugs to slow or stop the growth of tumours.
You keep tabs on fats and sugars, rule their rise and fall within your cells,
As you can and do for our cholesterol-clogged or over-sweet blood.
Creating anti-inflammation, antioxidation chemicals to protect yourself,
You free us from pain, protect our brain and fend off our diseases.
Seeking to confuse or distract a nibbling predator, you cook up more chemicals to muddle their minds, sicken stomachs.
We turn the tables, use them to correct our bowels and brains.
You create or alter yet more chemicals to ward off germ and worm, fungus and virus,
Antibiotics and antivirals to kill our own unseen invaders.
As you control the ebb and flow of water, moving ions, washing out your waste,
This gives us diuretics and strengthens the muscle of our hearts.

Some remarkable plant survival strategies are still being discovered, and who knows what the implications will be for human health. Plants can communicate with each other, signalling danger when attacked by insect predators so the other plants can raise their production of protective anti-pest chemicals. Birch tree roots produce chemicals that travel through the soil into nearby saplings of the same species, helping them to survive. Other discoveries of plant senses (similar to seeing, hearing, smelling, feeling physical contact and memory) inspire us with the idea of plants as alert, aware and responsive beings. Who would have guessed that plants can sweeten their nectar in response to the buzzing of a bee?

As you come to regard your medicinal plants as sentient, communicative and even altruistic, new doors will open. The chances are that growing your own physic garden will be life-changing, a more exciting adventure than you could have imagined. That's what it was and still is for us! And you will play your role in keeping the idea of plant medicine alive and maintaining natural biodiversity.

Words chosen to reflect the relation between us and medicinal plants float in the Dilston tranquillity pool.

To complement our scientific ode, here, finally, is a 'quantum haiku' by Valerie. The nine words, which normally float separately on the Dilston tranquillity pool, randomly rewriting themselves into new poems with the aid of wind and water, are arranged here to reflect that special relationship between ourselves and plants.

Herbal healing haiku
Plants mirror minds;
Healing, calming powers
Growing green thoughts.

Touching wood (in this instance all from medicinal trees) is not proven to affect one's health and safety – but the belief that it could just might!

As Plato wrote: 'I said the cure itself is in a certain leaf, but in addition to the drug there is a certain charm ... without the charm there is no profit from the leaf.' In Ancient Greece, words spoken as the patient received the medicine were considered an essential part of the therapy. It took another two thousand years for the power of the placebo to be discovered! So as you nurture your medicinal plants there could be a double blessing, from the plant itself and your knowledge of it. An open mind is said to lie at the heart of discovery.

As we said at the beginning of the book, the magic of plant medicines is often the forerunner of the science. Appealing as this is, we offer as an afterword a vision of future physic gardens and their health-giving plants – firmly grounded in science.

Afterthoughts

If our book helps you to grow and use plants for health and well-being, one of our dreams will have come true. In the meantime, here's our wishlist for the future – a full renaissance for the physic garden grounded in science and medicine with:

- physic gardens springing up on wastelands in every city;
- more medicinal plant research, allowing the science to be fully established;
- professional medical herbalists officially ratified to practise alongside doctors;
- the efficacy of plant medicine being taught in medical schools;
- growing and using plants for health taught in schools, along with the benefits of being outdoors;
- governments setting guidelines for school meals using herbs for health;
- more and more people, like those we meet at Dilston Physic Garden, enjoying and using medicinal plants.

Meanwhile as and when you set up your own physic garden, we at Dilston would love to hear from you. Email us at info@dilstonphysicgarden.com.

Notes, Resources and Further Reading

Throughout the book, the Latin names of plants are provided at, or near to, the first mention of the medicinal plant, but for the sake of brevity, common names are mostly used thereafter.

Introduction | Plant Medicine: Ancient to Modern

Our introduction is largely based on histories of medicinal plants and ancient herbals such as:

Coles, William. *Adam in Eden, or Nature's Paradise: The History of Plants, Herbs, Flowers* (London, 1657).

Culpepper, N. *Culpepper's Complete Herbal* (first published 1653) (Wordsworth Editions, 2007).

Dioscorides de Materia Medica. Written in Greek in the first century AD. A New Indexed Version in Modern English by Tess Anne Osbaldeston & R.P.A. Wood (Johannesburg, SA: Ibidis Press, 2010). https://archive.org/details/Dioscorides_Materia_Medica/.

Gerard, J. *Gerard's Herbal* (first published 1597; Bracken Books, 1985). Some of the tet is also available at http://exhibits.hsl.virginia.edu/herbs/herball/.

Ghazanfar, S.A. *Handbook of Arabian Medicinal Plants* (CRC Press, 1994) includes historical uses of Arabian medicinal plants.

Great Master S. *The Divine Husbandman's Materia Medica* (c. 2700 BC; also called *The Divine Farmer's Materia Medica*), is the classic text on ancient Chinese medicines. It is available as *The Divine Farmer's Materia Medica: A Translation of the 'Shen Nong Ben Cao Jing'*, by Yang Xhou-Zhong (Blue Poppy Press, 1998).

Hippocrates, *The Writings of Hippocrates and Galen. Epitomised from the Original Latin translations*, by John Redman Coxe (Philadelphia: Lindsay and Blakiston, 1846). https://oll.libertyfund.org/titles/hippocrates-the-writings-of-hippocrates-and-galen/simple.

Khalsa, K.P.S. and M. Tierra, *The Way of Ayurvedic Herbs: The Most Complete Guide to Natural Healing and Health with Traditional Ayurvedic Herbalism* (Lotus Press, 2008) includes a discussion of the historical practice of ancient Ayurvedic medicine.

Moore, Michael, Southwest School of Botanical Medicine (Arizona) contains references to many 'historical' herbals. http://www.swsbm.com/HOMEPAGE/HomePage.html.3.

Parkinson, John. *Theatrum Botanicum* (first published in 1640). See *The Herbalist's Bible: John Parkinson's Lost Classic Rediscovered*, by Julie Bruton-Seal and Matthew Seal (Merlin Unwin, 2014).

The Red Book of Hergest, a large vellum manuscript written in the Welsh language, which has survived from the late 14th century and can be found in Jesus College, Oxford. Translated into English. https://en.wikisource.org/wiki/Welsh_Triads/Red_Book_of_Hergest.

Turner, William. *A New Herball* (first published in 1551). 2 vols (Cambridge University Press, 1996).

There are numerous sources on the folklore of medicinal plants, folklore that is often specific to each country. For example, a useful site about Scottish herbs can be found at Wilderness Scotland: https://www.wildernessscotland.com/blog/folklore-scotlands-plantlife-scottish-medicinal-plants/, and a good book to consult on English and Irish medicinal plants is *Medicinal Plants in Folk Tradition: An Ethnobotany of Britain & Ireland*, by D.E. Allen and G. Hatfield (Timber Press, 2004).

The 'Magic to Medicine' theme is also explored with some of our favourite plants in Chapter 9. Other topics discussed in the introduction are covered in later chapters (especially concerning modern, science-based evidence). Chapters 8 and 9, on choosing and using medicinal plants, list modern sources on medicinal plants and herbalist practices.

Chapter 1 | Plant Chemistry

To explore the vast domain of plant chemicals further we recommend the following books and websites:

American Botanical Council. *The Commission E Monographs*. An English translation of all 380 monographs on medicinal herbs published by the German Commission E, an expert group within the German federal health agency charged with evaluating the safety and efficacy of herbal medications. http://cms.herbalgram.org/commissione/index.html.

American Botanical Council. *Healthy Ingredients*. Information on over 100 ingredients found in self-care products. http://cms.herbalgram.org/healthyingredients/index.html.

American Botanical Council. *Herbal Medicine: Expanded Commission E Monographs Online* Provides 101 expanded monographs from the German Commission E and six new ones. http://cms.herbalgram.org/expandedE/.

Chemspider, a free chemical structure database: http://www.chemspider.com/.

Chem-TCM: Chemical Database of Traditional Chinese Medicine is a database of individual molecules, constituents of plants used in Chinese herbal medicine. http://www.chemtcm.com/.

Duke, James A. *Dr. Duke's Phytochemical and Ethnobotanical Databases*. A useful starting point to find out what constituents are found in specific plants. https://phytochem.nal.usda.gov/phytochem/search.

Evans, W.C. *Trease and Evans' Pharmacognosy*, 16th ed. (Saunders Ltd, 2009). A classic textbook on natural drugs with plant chemicals at the core.

List of Medicines Made from Plants is a website about medical drugs derived from plants. http://chemistry.about.com/library/weekly/aa061403a.htm.

Pengelly, A. *The Constituents of Medicinal Plants*. (CABI Publishing, 2004). An easy-ish introduction to plant constituents and their actions.

US National Library of Medicine, *PubChem* is a database of chemical molecules and their activities against biological assays, maintained by the National Center for Biotechnology Information. https://pubchem.ncbi.nlm.nih.gov/.

Wichtl, M. ed. *Herbal Drugs and Phytopharmaceuticals*. 3rd ed. (Medpharm, 2004). Comprehensive information on the origins, constituents, effects, indications and dosage of herbal drugs and phytopharmaceuticals.

Chapter 2 | Testing and Approving Herbal Medicines

Americans For Medical Progress: https://www.amprogress.org.

British Library: https://www.bl.uk/.

Cochrane Library: https://www.cochranelibrary.com/.

Linde, K., et al. 'St John's wort for depression: an overview and meta-analysis of randomised clinical trials', *British Medical Journal*, 313 (August 1996), pp. 253–8. This was the first report on a clinical trial of a medicinal plant in a high-profile medical journal. https://www.ncbi.nlm.nih.gov/pubmed/8704532.

Miyasaka, T., C. Xie, et al. 'Curcumin improves tau-induced neuronal dysfunction of nematodes', *Neurobiology of Aging*, 39 (March 2016), pp. 69–81. Lab research on turmeric improving function in ageing nematode worms. https://www.ncbi.nlm.nih.gov/pubmed/26923403.

PubMed: https://www.ncbi.nlm.nih.gov/pubmed/. PubMed is our gold standard. Skip to the last line of the report's conclusion for a less technical 'bottom line' to help you decide whether to read the full abstract or paper.

Chapter 3 | Herbalism as Complementary Medicine

Zhang, Y., et al, 'Cognitive Improvement during Treatment for Mild Alzheimer's Disease with a Chinese Herbal Formula: A Randomized Controlled Trial', *PLoS One* (June 2015). A key research paper on Chinese medicine for dementia. https://www.ncbi.nlm.nih.gov/pubmed/26076022.

Regulatory guidelines for herbal products have varied in the past and no doubt will continue to do so in the future. Websites include:

Report on the Regulation of Herbal medicines and Practitioners (March 2015): https://www.gov.uk/government/uploads/system/uploads/attachment_data/file/417768/Report_on_Regulation_of_Herbal_Medicines_and_Practitioners.pdf.

'Do herbal supplements contain what they say on the label' (*Trust me, I'm a doctor*, BBC): http://www.bbc.co.uk/programmes/articles/4hX30rMYkMv9YjMTH38MY6/do-herbalsupplements.

'Legal Status of Traditional Medicine and Complementary/Alternative Medicine: A Worldwide View': http://apps.who.int/medicinedocs/en/d/Jh2943e/7.5.html.

More on the regulation of medicinal plants/ herbal medicines/ dietary supplements can be found in Chapter 11.

Chapter 4 | Plant Medicines for the Future

Selection of reports referred to in this chapter:

Kon, K.V., Rai, M.K., 'Plant essential oils treat drug-resistant bacteria: Plant essential oils and their constituents in coping with multidrug-resistant bacteria', *Expert Review of Anti-infective Therapy*, 10 (2012), pp. 775–90.

Miladinović, D.L., Ilić, B.S., et al, 'Antibiotic activity of thyme and sage essential oil: Antibacterial Investigation of Thyme Essential Oil and Its Main Constituents in Combination with Tetracycline', *Journal of Medicinal Food*, 18 (2015), pp. 935–7.

Sienkiewicz, M., Głowacka, A., et al, 'The effect of clary sage oil on staphylococci responsible for wound infections', *Advances in Dermatology and Allergology*, 32 (2015), pp. 21–6.

Medicinal plants for dementia:

Akram, M., Nawaz, A. 'Effects of medicinal plants on Alzheimer's disease and memory deficits', *Neural Regeneration Research*, 12 (2017), pp. 660–70;

Johannessen, B., 'Nurses experience of aromatherapy use with dementia patients experiencing disturbed sleep patterns. An action research project', *Complementary Therapies in Clinical Practice*, 19 (2013), pp. 209–13.

Perry, E., Howes, M.J. 'Medicinal plants and dementia therapy: herbal hopes for brain aging?', *CNS Neuroscience & Therapeutics*, 17 (2011), pp. 683–98

There is more on sage and lemon balm in Chapter 9.

Medicinal plants for cancer and palliative care:

Agar, M. 'Cannabinoids for palliative care: Medicinal cannabinoids in palliative care', *Br J Clin Pharmacol*. 84 (2018), pp. 2491–4.

Bhalla, Y., Gupta, V.K., Jaitak, V. 'Essential oils and cancer therapy: Anticancer activity of essential oils: a review', *Journal of the Science of Food and Agriculture*, 93 (2013), pp. 3643–53.

Boehm, K., Büssing, A., Ostermann, T. 'Aromatherapy for cancer patients: Aromatherapy as an adjuvant treatment in cancer care—a descriptive systematic review', *African Journal of Traditional Complementary and Alternative Medicines*, 9 (2012), pp. 503–18.

Chung, V.C., Wu, X., et al, 'Chinese herbal medicine benefits cancer patients in palliative care: Chinese Herbal Medicine for Symptom Management in Cancer Palliative Care: Systematic Review And Meta-analysis', *Medicine (Baltimore)*, (2016); 95:e2793. doi: 10.1097/MD

D'Alessandro, A., De Pergola, G., Silvestris, F. 'Polyphenolic chemicals in Mediterranean diet prevent cancer spread: Mediterranean Diet and cancer risk: an open issue', *International Journal of Food Sciences and Nutrition*, 67 (2016), pp. 593–605.

Plants for cancer: http://www.ncbi.nlm.nih.gov/pmc/articles/PMC3314490/.

Wu, T.H., Chiu, T.Y., et al, 'Taiwanese diet controls pain in cancer patients: Effectiveness of Taiwanese traditional herbal diet for pain management in terminal cancer patients', *Asia Pacific Journal of Clin Nutrition*, 17 (2008), pp. 17–22.

Zuzak, T.J., Wasmuth, A., et al, 'Mistletoe for cancer therapy: Safety of high-dose intravenous mistletoe therapy in pediatric cancer patients: A case series', *Complementary Therapies Medicine*, 40 (2018), pp. 198–202.

Many more papers on this chapter's 'hot' topics for the future of medicinal plants will be appearing as you read this book. Do use the PubMed library to find out more!

Chapter 5 | Physic Gardens, Then and Now

For more information on the modern physic or medicinal plant gardens mentioned here, this summary table includes websites, up to date at the time of writing.

We've selected examples from countries across the globe on the basis of their unique features and their being open to the public.

Locations of physic and medicinal plant gardens today

Information correct to 2020

EUROPE		
Biohorma, Netherlands	Physic garden belonging to the Dutch company Biohorma, selling A. Vogel and therapeutic products.	http://www.biohorma.nl/van-plant-tot-klant/avogel-tuinen.php and http://www.avogel.nl/tuinen/kwekerij.php
Chelsea Physic Garden, London	Oldest physic garden still in existence, founded by the Worshipful Society of Apothecaries; established 1673.	https://www.chelseaphysicgarden.co.uk/
Cowbridge Physic Garden, Wales	Small, tranquil space for medicinal plants and herbs; established 2004.	http://www.cowbridgephysicgarden.org.uk/
Dals Rostock Herb Garden, Sweden	Established by leading expert on Swedish medicinal plants.	https://rostock.se/home/the-herb-garden/
Dilston Physic Garden, Northumberland	Established in 2005 as a consequence of neuroscience research, with continuing research into plants for the brain.	https://dilstonphysicgarden.com/

Le Jardin Camifolia, France	Collection of aromatic, cosmetic and medicinal plants.	http://www.parcsetjardins.fr/pays_de_la_loire/maine_et_loire/camifolia_jardin_des_plantes_medicinales_et_aromatiques-1003.html
John Wesley Physic Garden, Westhill, Birmingham	Celebrates the contribution of John Wesley to the well-being of the poor who were unable to pay for a physician; established 2006.	http://www.westhillendowment.org/John-Wesley-Physic-Garden
Petersfield Physic Garden, Hampshire	A peaceful garden in the town centre; highly rated by visitors.	http://petersfieldphysicgarden.org.uk/
RCP Garden of Medicinal Plants, London	Attached to historic building, reflecting the college's 500 year history (redesigned 2005).	https://garden.rcplondon.ac.uk/
Sibbald Physic Garden, Royal College of Physicians, Edinburgh	Laid out according to medicinal plants across the centuries; redeveloped in the college garden in 1990.	https://www.rcpe.ac.uk/heritage/botany-and-physic-garden
Trinity College Dublin Physic Garden, Ireland	Opened in 2011 to celebrate three centuries of botany, chemistry and medicine at the university.	https://www.tcd.ie/Botany/botanic-garden/
Urban Physic Garden, London	Design based on the hospital and pharmacy; establshed 2011.	http://www.physicgarden.org.uk/
WALA Medicinal Herb Garden, Germany	Organic garden established in 1835 by Dr Hauschka in the Swabian Mountains; is run biodynamically; produces cosmetics.	https://www.dr.hauschka.com/en_GB/knowledge-base/raw-materials/the-wala-herb-garden/
FAR EAST		
Akatsuka Botanical Garden: Garden of Man'yō and Medicinal Plants, Tokyo, Japan	Plants from marshland, plains and mountains that are of medicinal and artistic significance provide welcome refuge in the heart of the city.	http://www.wakapoetry.net/waka-tourism/manyo-botanical-gardens/akatsuka-botanical-garden-garden-of-manyo-and-medicinal-plants/
Healing Garden, Singapore	Part of the Singapore Botanic Garden, laid out in the shape of the human body.	https://www.nparks.gov.sg/sbg/our-gardens/nassim-entrance/healing-garden
Kyoto Takeda Garden, Japan	Focus on medicinal plant conservation.	http://www.bgci.org/garden.php?id=509
Medicinal Plant Garden, Meiji Pharmaceutical University, Japan	Gives students with knowledge of plants that have provided medical drugs.	https://u-lab.my-pharm.ac.jp/~koho/English/yakusoen/index.html
Nanjing Botanical Garden of Medicinal Plants, China	Part of China's Pharmaceutical University, College of Traditional Chinese Pharmacy.	https://www.bgci.org/garden.php?id=1341
INDIA		
Arya Vaidya Pharmacy	Garden that educates students in awareness of herbs for health.	https://www.avpayurveda.com/

Rishi Valley Herbal Garden	Specialising in Ayurvedic medicinal plants; educating local children to take care of their own health.	https://www.rishivalley.org/
	See also National Medicinal Plants Board.	https://www.nmpb.nic.in/
MEXICO		
Jardin Botanico del Instituto de Biologia, Mexico City	Established 1959.	https://www.bgci.org/garden.php?id=166
NEW ZEALAND		
Phytofarm, Banks Peninsula, South Island	Garden in Okuti Valley devoted to medicinal plant growing, using and learning.	http://www.phytofarm.co.nz/
SOUTH AMERICA		
Medicinal Plant Garden, Guatemala	Maya traditional medicinal plants for local community education.	https://www.mayatraditions.org/community-programs/health-program/
USA		
Atkins Medicinal Garden, Chicago	Established as part of the University of Illinois College of Pharmacy in memory of local pharmacist; provides research and education facilities.	https://pharmacy.uic.edu/research/botanical-dietary-supplements/atkins-medicinal-garden
Maynard W. Quimby Medicinal Plant Garden, Mississippi	Part of the National Center for Natural Products Research at the University of Mississippi (resited in 2013).	http://pharmacy.olemiss.edu/ncnpr/the-maynard-w-quimby-medicinal-plant-garden/
Medicinal Plant Garden, Indiana Medical History Museum	Features Native American plants.	http://www.imhm.org/garden
Piedmont Physic Garden, South Carolina	Plants with historical medicinal uses; also runs education programmes; established 2014.	https://www.piedmontphysicgarden.org/

Numerous national and university botanic gardens now have a medicinal plant or apothecary area. Here are some examples:

Acorn Bank National Trust Garden, UK.

Botanic Gardens of the Democratic People's Republic of Korea.

Botanical Garden of Medicinal Plants 'Fran Kusan', Faculty of Pharmacy and Biochemistry, University of Zagreb, Croatia.

Chinese Medicinal Herb Garden, University of Bristol, UK.

Dunedin Botanic Garden, Herb Garden, Dunedin, New Zealand.

Faculties of Pharmacy in Lille, Lyon and Paris, France.

Hortus Botanical Garden, Amsterdam, Netherlands.

Kaunas Botanic Garden, Lithuania.

Kraidergaart Commune de Wanseler Jardin des Plantes Médicinale, Luxembourg.

Lowveld National Botanical Garden, South Africa.

Medicinal Plant Garden, Southern Cross University, Australia.

Moscow Botanical Garden of Academy of Sciences, Russia.

National Botanic Garden of Latvia, Salaspils, Latvia.

National Botanic Garden of Wales.

Prague Botanical Garden, Czech Republic.

Saint Petersburg Botanical Garden, Russia.

Seoul Botanical Garden, Korea.

University of British Columbia Botanical Garden, Canada.

University of Ljubljana Botanical Garden, Slovenia.

University of Rhode Island Botanical Gardden, USA.

Chapter 6 | Reasons to Grow Your Own

Cambridge University Botanic Garden where genetic research was first fostered: https://www. botanic.cam.ac.uk/.

Kew Gardens, London, which offers many educational courses: https://www.kew.org/learning.

Physic Garden Café, Chelsea Physic Garden: https://www.chelseaphysicgarden.co.uk/the-physic-garden-café.

For ideas on plants as spices, go to the Geographic Spice Index (http://gernot-katzers-spice-pages.com/engl/index.html) as well as the many books, ranging from the popular, such as L. E. Dobbins, *Healing Herbs & Spices: Health Benefits of Popular Herbs & Spices Plus Over 70 Recipes To Use Them In* (2012) to textbooks such as Eberhard Teuscher, ed. *Medicinal Spices* (2005).

A topic not covered in detail in this book is herbal wines and spirits. You could consult:

Mother Earth Living: http://www.motherearthliving.com/cooking-methods/a-worty-wine-is-a-worthy-wine.aspx.

Weyn's Honey wine: http://weynshoning.be/en/products/honey-beverages/herbal-wine/?id=255.

Wikipedia gives an A–Z list of worldwide herbal liqueurs: https://en.wikipedia.org/wiki/Category:Herbal_liqueurs.

Chapter 7 | Planning Your Physic Garden

The Chelsea Physic Garden website includes a description of its world medicine garden: https://www.chelseaphysicgarden.co.uk/the-garden-of-medicinal-plants. Websites for the other physic gardens referred to here are listed in the resources section at the end of the book.

Giacosa, A. et al., 'The Effect of Ginger (*Zingiber officinalis*) and Artichoke (*Cynara cardunculus*) Extract Supplementation on Functional Dyspepsia: A Randomised, Double-Blind, and Placebo-Controlled Clinical Trial', *Evidence-Based Complementary Alternative Medicine*, (Apr. 2015): 915087. doi: 10.1155/2015/915087. Cardoon for digestion.

Kılıç, S. et al., 'Efficacy of two plant extracts against acne vulgaris: Initial results of microbiological tests and cell culture studies', *Journal of Cosmetic Dermatology* 18.4 (Nov. 2018), pp. 1061–5. Myrtle for treating acne.

Panahi, Y. et al., 'Comparative trial of Aloe vera/olive oil combination cream versus phenytoin cream in the treatment of chronic wounds', *Journal of Wound Care*, 24 (Oct. 2015), pp. 459–60, 462–5. Aloe heals chronic wounds.

Wu, A.L. et al., 'Effect of topographical factors on podophyllotoxin content in Sinopodophyllum hexandrum and study on ecological suitability', *China Journal of Chinese Materia Medica*, 40 (June 2015), pp. 2299–303 (abstract only in English). Growing conditions affecting plant chemicals.

For optimising growth of stevia (candyleaf; *Stevia rebaudiana*) to produce maximum levels of sweet glycosides, see: http://www.stevia.net/growingstevia.htm.

Chapter 8 | Deciding Which Plants to Grow

Charts were composed mainly on the basis of information contained in standard herbal medicine text books (particularly the ones by Bone and Mills, and by Hoffman). Each plant has been subjected to a comprehensive search on PubMed to ascertain if the traditional use is backed up by scientific evidence (see Chapter 2).

Authoritative books on medicinal plants

Bartrum, T., *Bartram's Encyclopedia of Herbal Medicine* (Grace Publishers, 1995).

Bonar, A., *Herbs: A Complete Guide to their Cultivation and Use* (Littlehampton Book Services Ltd., 1985).

Bone, K. and S. Mills, *Principles and Practice of Phytotherapy: Modern Herbal Medicine* (Elsevier, 2013).

Green, J., *The Herbal Medicine Makers Handbook* (The Crossing Press, 2000).

Hemphill, R., *Herbs for All Seasons* (Penguin Books, 1975).

Hoffman, D., *Holistic Herbal: A Sage and Practical Guide to Making and Using Traditional Medicine & Remedies*. new. ed. (Thorsons, 1990). The book we recommend for our Foundation in Plant Medicine course.

Kowalchik, C. and W.H. Hylton, *Rodale's Encyclopedia of Herbs* (Rodale Press, 1998).

McIntyre, A., *The Apothecary's Garden: How to Grow and Use Your Own Herbal Medicines* (Piatkus Books, 1997).

Perry, N. and E. Perry, *Botanical Brain Balms* (Filbert Press, 2018). Our book on plants for the brain.

Wichtl, Max (ed.), *Herbal Drugs and Phytopharmaceuticals* (CRC Press, 2004). It might break the bank but this reference book offers comprehensive information about the origins, constituents, effects, indications and dosage of herbal drugs and phytopharmaceuticals.

Williamson, E., *Potter's Herbal Cyclopaedia* (Random House, 2003).

Authoritative online information on medicinal plants

Dr Christopher's Herbal Legacy: http://www.herballegacy.com/index.html. Contains general, historical and modern uses backed up by science.

European Medicines Agency: https://www.ema.europa.eu/en/human-regulatory/herbal-medicinal-products. Scientific evaluations of medicines developed by pharmaceutical companies for use in the European Union. The site provides summaries of traditional medicinal plant use, including scientific research.

Hedgerow Medicine: www.hedgerowmedicine.com. Lists commonly used UK herbs with botany, uses and folkloric descriptions.

Henriette's Herbal Homepage: http://www.henriettesherbal.com/. Henriette, a Finnish herbalist who trained in the US, provides a wealth of up-to-date information.

The Herb Society of America: http://www.herbsociety.org/. Contains lots of information on growing and using herbs.

The Herb Society UK: http://www.herbsociety.org.uk/. It's well worth subscribing to their quarterly magazine with its interesting, up-to-date articles on medicinal plants.

Herbalgram: http://abc.herbalgram.org/site/PageServer. The American Botanical Council site containing a huge amount of interesting herb-specific data and commentaries on clinical trials.

The Herbarium: http://theherbarium.wordpress.com/. A blog full of interesting and practical information written by medical herbalists.

A Modern Herbal by Mrs M. Grieve (http://botanical.com/). Although not so modern (1931), it's still one of the best.

Natural Medicines: http://info.therapeuticresearch.com/natural-medicines-learn-more. Authoritative subscription-based resource.

Purple Sage Medicinal Herbs: http://www.purplesage.org.uk/. The site of Christine Haughton, medical herbalist, containing useful herb monographs.

The WHO Monographs: http://apps.who.int/medicinedocs/en/d/Js2200e/. Series on selected medicinal plants aiming to provide scientific information on the safety, efficacy and quality control of widely used medicinal plants.

Selection of scientific papers and websites specifically cited in this chapter:

American Pain Foundation (a non-profit organisation): their website has been shut down since this chapter was first written because of concerns about links to the pharmaceutical industry and the use of prescription painkillers. The information cited here is, however, still valid.

Bach, H., et al., 'Efficacy of Ginseng Supplements on Fatigue and Physical Performance: a Meta-analysis', *Journal of Korean Medical Science*, 31 (2016), pp. 1879–86.

Biswal, B.M., et al., 'Effect of *Withania somnifera* (Ashwagandha) on the development of chemotherapy-induced fatigue and quality of life in breast cancer patients', *Integrative Cancer Therapies*, 12(4), (July 2013), pp. 312–22.

Cai, H., et al., 'Practical Application of Antidiabetic Efficacy of *Lycium barbarum* [goji berry] Polysaccharide in Patients with Type 2 Diabetes', *Journal of Medical Chemistry*, 11 (2015), pp. 383–90.

Yu, X.N. et al. '"Yellow-dragon Wonderful-seed Formula" for hyperuricemia in gout patients with dampness-heat pouring downward pattern: a pilot randomized controlled trial', Trials, 19(1) (October 2018), p. 551. doi: 10.1186/s13063-018-2917-8.

Zahn, R., N. Perry, E. Perry, E.B. Mukaetova-Ladinska, 'Use of herbal medicines: Pilot survey of UK users' views', *Complementary Therapies in Medicine*, 44 (June 2019), pp. 83–90. Our survey on the used of herbal medicines in the UK.

Herbal medicines during pregnancy

While controlled trials on the safety of herbal medicines in pregnancy is lacking, information about any herbal medicines usually includes advice on use in pregnancy (see, for example, Chapter 9).

Aviva Romm's *Botanical Medicine for Women's Health* (Elsevier, 2017) makes these important points:

- natural is not synonymous with safety
- many botanical meds contain potent pharmacological constituents
- many constituents consumed by the mother can pass through the placenta and reach the foetus
- physiologic and metabolic changes during pregnancy may influence the pharmacokinetics of the herbs, thus changing expected actions or safety
- herbs with known mutagenic, teratogenic or abortifacient properties should be avoided.

See also Babycentre: https://www.babycentre.co.uk/a536346/herbal-remedies-in-pregnancy.

Chapter 9 | Favourite Medicinal Plants

Historical and folklore sources are listed in the Introduction; for modern herbalist uses (including formulations, dose and safety) see sources in Chapter 8. The science is based on literature searches on testing and lab studies (see Chapter 2). From numerous research reports just two citations for each plant are provided below.

Angelica

Rajtar B et al. 'Antiviral effect of compounds derived from *Angelica archangelica* L. on Herpes simplex virus-1 and Coxsackievirus B3 infections', *Food and Chemical Toxicology*, 109 (2017), pp. 1026–31.

Wei, W.L. et al. 'Angelica sinensis in China – A review of botanical profile, ethnopharmacology, phytochemistry and chemical analysis', *Journal of Ethnopharmacology*, 190 (2016), pp. 116–41.

Arnica

Cameron, M. and Chrubasik, S. 'Topical herbal therapies for treating osteoarthritis', *Cochrane Database Systematic Reviews* (31 May 2013): CD010538. doi: 10.1002/14651858. CD010538.

Oltean, H. et al. 'Herbal medicine for low-back pain', *Cochrane Database Systematic Reviews* (23 Dec. 2014): CD004504. doi: 10.1002/14651858. CD004504.

Black cohosh

Bai, W. et al. 'Efficacy and tolerability of a medicinal product containing an isopropanolic black cohosh extract in Chinese women with menopausal symptoms: a randomized, double-blind, parallel-controlled study versus tibolone', *Maturitas* 58(1) (Sept. 2007), pp. 31–41.

Shams, T. et al. 'Efficacy of black cohosh-containing preparations on menopausal symptoms: a meta-analysis', *Alternative Therapies in Health and Medicine*, 16(1) (Jan.–Feb. 2010), pp. 36–44.

Calendula

Andersen, F.A. et al. 'Final report of the Cosmetic Ingredient Review Expert Panel amended safety assessment of *Calendula officinalis*-derived cosmetic ingredients', *International Journal of Toxicology*, 29(6 Suppl), (Nov.–Dec. 2010), pp. 221S–43.

Efstratiou, E. et al. 'Antimicrobial activity of *Calendula officinalis* petal extracts against fungi, as well as Gram-negative and Gram-positive clinical pathogens', *Complementary Therapies in Clinical Practice*, 18(3), (Aug. 2012), pp. 173–6.

Chamomile

Howrey, B.T. et al. 'Chamomile Consumption and Mortality: A Prospective Study of Mexican Origin Older Adults', *Gerontologist*, 56 (2016), pp. 1146–52.

Zargaran, A. et al. 'Evaluation of the effect of topical chamomile (*Matricaria chamomilla L.*) oleogel as pain relief in migraine without aura: a randomized, double-blind, placebo-controlled, crossover study', *Neurological Sciences*, 39 (2018), pp. 1345–53.

Cranberry

Blumberg, J.B. et al. 'Impact of Cranberries on Gut Microbiota and Cardiometabolic Health', *Advances in Nutrition*, 7(4) (July 2016), pp. 759S–770S.

Luís, Â, et al. 'Can Cranberries Contribute to Reduce the Incidence of Urinary Tract Infections? A Systematic Review with Meta-Analysis and Trial Sequential Analysis of Clinical Trials', *Journal of Urology*, 198(3) (Sept. 2017), pp. 614–21.

Dandelion

Clare, B.A. et al. 'The diuretic effect in human subjects of an extract of Taraxacum officinale folium over a single day', *Journal of Alternative Complementary Medicine*, 15 (2009), pp. 929–34.

González-Castejón, M. et al. 'Diverse biological activities of dandelion', *Nutrition Reviews*, 70 (2012), pp. 534–47.

Echinacea

Rauš, K. et al. 'Effect of an Echinacea-Based Hot Drink Versus Oseltamivir in Influenza Treatment: A Randomized, Double-Blind, Double-Dummy, Multicenter, Noninferiority Clinical Trial', *Current Therapeutic Research, Clinical and Experimental*, 77 (2015), pp. 66–72.

Schapowal, A. et al. 'Echinacea reduces the risk of recurrent respiratory tract infections and complications: a meta-analysis of randomized controlled trials', *Advances in Therapy*, 32 (2015), pp. 187–200.

Elder

Barak, V. et al. 'The effect of Sambucol, a black elderberry-based, natural product, on the production of human cytokines', *European Cytokine Network*. 12 (2001), pp. 290–6.

Tiralongo, E., Wee, S.S., Lea, R.A. 'Elderberry Supplementation Reduces Cold Duration and Symptoms in Air-Travellers: A Randomized, Double-Blind Placebo-Controlled Clinical Trial', *Nutrients*, 8(4) (Mar. 2016), p. 182. doi:10.3390/nu8040182.

Fennel

Ostad, S.N. and Soodi, M. 'The effect of fennel essential oil on uterine contraction as a model for dysmenorrhea, pharmacology and toxicology study', *Journal of Ethnopharmacology*, 76 (2001), pp. 299–304.

Rahimikian, F. et al. 'Effect of *Foeniculum vulgare Mill*. (fennel) on menopausal symptoms in postmenopausal women: a randomized, triple-blind, placebo-controlled trial', *Menopause*, 24 (2017), pp. 1017–21.

Garlic

Percival, S.S. 'Aged Garlic Extract Modifies Human Immunity', *Journal of Nutrition*, 146 (2016), pp. 433S–436S.

Schwingshackl, L. et al. 'An umbrella review of garlic intake and risk of cardiovascular disease', *Phytomedicine*, 23 (2016), pp. 1127–33.

Ginger

Ghayur, M.N. et al. 'Pharmacological basis for the medicinal use of ginger in gastrointestinal disorders', *Digestive Diseases and Sciences*, 50 (2005), pp. 1889–97.

Marx, W. et al. 'Is ginger beneficial for nausea and vomiting? An update of the literature', *Current Opinion in Supportive and Palliative Care*, 9 (2015), pp. 189–95.

Ginkgo

Nabavi, S.M. et al. 'Neuroprotective Effects of Ginkgolide B Against Ischemic Stroke: A Review of Current Literature', *Current Topics in Medicinal Chemistry*, 15 (2015), pp. 2222–32.

Zhang, H.F. et al. 'An Overview of Systematic Reviews of *Ginkgo biloba* Extracts for Mild Cognitive Impairment and Dementia', *Frontiers in Aging Neuroscience*, 8 (2016), p. 276.

Hawthorn

Jayachandran, K.S. et al. 'Crataegus oxycantha extract attenuates apoptotic incidence in myocardial ischemia-reperfusion injury by regulating Akt and HIF-1 signaling pathways', *Journal of Cardiovascular Pharmacology*, 56 (2010), pp. 526–31.

Pittler, M.H., Guo, R. and Ernst, E. 'Hawthorn extract for treating chronic heart failure', *Cochrane Database Systematic Reviews* (23 Jan. 2008): CD005312. doi: 10.1002/ 14651858.CD005312.

Lavender
Farshbaf-Khalili, A. et al. 'Comparison of the effect of lavender and bitter orange on anxiety in postmenopausal women: A triple-blind, randomized, controlled clinical trial', *Complementary Therapies in Clinical Practice*, 31 (2018), pp. 132–8.

Woelk, H. and Schläfke, S. 'A multi-center, double-blind, randomised study of the Lavender oil preparation Silexan in comparison to Lorazepam for generalized anxiety disorder', *Phytomedicine*, 17 (2010), pp. 94–9.

Lemon balm (papers co-written by Dilston Physic Garden authors)
Abuhamdah, J. et al. 'Pharmacological profile of an essential oil derived from *Melissa officinalis* with anti-agitation properties: focus on ligand-gated channels', *Journal of Pharmacy and Pharmacology*, 60(3), (Mar. 2008), pp. 377–84.

Scholey, A., et al. 'Anti-stress effects of lemon balm-containing foods', *Nutrients*, 6 (2014), pp. 4805–21.

Milk thistle
Abenavoli, L. et al. 'Milk thistle (*Silybum marianum*): A concise overview on its chemistry, pharmacological, and nutraceutical uses in liver diseases', *Phytotherapy Research*, 32 (2018), pp. 2202–13.

Zhong, S. et al. 'The therapeutic effect of silymarin in the treatment of nonalcoholic fatty disease: A meta-analysis (PRISMA) of randomized control trials', *Medicine (Baltimore)*, 96(49), (Dec. 2017): e9061. doi: 10.1097/MD.0000000000009061.

Nettle
Amiri Behzadi, A. et al. 'Effects of Urtica dioica supplementation on blood lipids, hepatic enzymes and nitric oxide levels in type 2 diabetic patients: A double-blind, randomized clinical trial', *Avicenna Journal of Phytomedicine*, 6 (2016), pp. 686–95.

Patel, S.S. et al. 'Urtica dioica extract attenuates depressive like behavior and associative memory dysfunction in dexamethasone induced diabetic mice', *Metabolic Brain Disease*, 29 (2014), pp. 121–30.

Nigella/black cumin
Bin Sayeed, M.S. et al. '*Nigella sativa L.* seeds modulate mood, anxiety and cognition in healthy adolescent males', *Journal of Ethnopharmacology*, 152(1) (27 Feb. 2014), pp. 156–62.

Heshmati, J., Namazi, N. 'Effects of black seed (*Nigella sativa*) on metabolic parameters in diabetes mellitus: a systematic review', *Complementary Therapies in Medicine*, 23(2) (Apr. 2015), pp. 275–82.

Peppermint
Kennedy, D. et al. 'Volatile Terpenes and Brain Function: Investigation of the Cognitive and Mood Effects of *Mentha × Piperita L.* Essential Oil with In Vitro Properties Relevant to Central Nervous System Function', *Nutrients*, 10(8) (Aug. 2018). pii: E1029. doi: 10.3390/nu10081029.

Khanna, R. et al. 'Peppermint oil for the treatment of irritable bowel syndrome: a systematic review and meta-analysis', *Journal of Clinical Gastroenterology*, 48 (2014), pp. 505–12.

Rhubarb

<u>Chinese rhubarb</u>

Yang, Y. et al. 'Effects of adding Rheum officinale to angiotensin-converting enzyme inhibitors or angiotensin receptor blockers on renal function in patients with chronic renal failure: A meta-analysis of randomized controlled trials', *Clinical Nephrology*, 89 (2018), pp. 445–54.

<u>English rhubarb</u>

Dören, M. 'The special extract Err 731 of the roots of *Rheum rhaponticum* decreases anxiety and improves health state and general well-being in perimenopausal women', *Menopause*, 14 (2007), pp. 809–10.

Rosemary

Moss, M. et al. 'Aromas of rosemary and lavender essential oils differentially affect cognition and mood in healthy adults', *International Journal of Neuroscience*, 113 (2003), pp. 15–38.

Moss, M. et al. 'Acute ingestion of rosemary water: Evidence of cognitive and cerebrovascular effects in healthy adults', *Journal of Psychopharmacology*, 32 (2018), pp. 1319–29.

Roseroot

Ishaque, S.I. et al. '*Rhodiola rosea* for physical and mental fatigue: a systematic review', *BMC Complementary and Alternative Medicine*, 2 (2012), p. 70. doi: 10.1186/1472-6882-12-70.

Kasper, S. and Dienel, A. 'Multicenter, open-label, exploratory clinical trial with *Rhodiola rosea* extract in patients suffering from burnout symptoms', *Neuropsychiatric Disease and Treatment*, 13 (22 Mar. 2017), pp. 889–98.

Sage (papers co-written by Dilston Physic Garden authors)

Perry, N.S. et al. 'In-vitro activity of S. lavandulaefolia (Spanish sage) relevant to treatment of Alzheimer's disease', *Journal of Pharmacy and Pharmacology*, 53 (2001), pp. 1347–56.

Scholey, A.B. et al. 'An extract of Salvia (sage) with anticholinesterase properties improves memory and attention in healthy older volunteers', *Psychopharmacology (Berlin)*. 198(1) (May 2008), pp. 127–39.

Saw palmetto

Giulianelli, R. et al. 'Multicentre study on the efficacy and tolerability of an extract of Serenoa repens in patients with chronic benign prostate conditions associated with inflammation', *Archivio Italiano di Urologia e Andrologia*, 84 (2012), pp. 94–8.

Latil, A. et al. 'Effects of hexanic extract of Serenoa repens (Permixon® 160 mg) on inflammation biomarkers in the treatment of lower urinary tract symptoms related to benign prostatic hyperplasia', *The Prostate*, 75 (2015), pp. 1857–67.

St John's wort

Ng, Q.X. et al. 'Clinical use of *Hypericum perforatum* (St John's wort) in depression: A meta-analysis', *Journal of Affective Disorders*, 210 (Mar 2017), pp. 211–21.

Samadi, S. et al. 'The effect of *Hypericum perforatum* on the wound healing and scar of cesarean', *Journal of Alternative and Complementary Medicine*, 6 (2010), pp. 113–17.

Thyme

Hashemian, F. et al. 'The effect of thyme honey nasal spray on chronic rhinosinusitis: a double-blind randomized controlled clinical trial', *European Archives of Oto-Rhino-Laryngology*, 272 (2015), pp. 1429–35.

Saidi, M. et al. 'Ex Vivo Evaluation of Thymus daenensis as an Antioxidant and Antibacterial Medicinal Herb', *Drug Research (Stuttgart)*, 66 (2016), pp. 657–9.

Valerian

Fernandez-San-Martin, M.I. et al. 'Effectiveness of Valerian on insomnia: a meta-analysis of randomized placebo-controlled trials', *Sleep Medicine*, 11 (Jun. 2010), pp. 505–11.

Poyares, D.R. et al. 'Can valerian improve the sleep of insomniacs after benzodiazepine withdrawal?' *Progress in Neuro-Psychopharmacology & Biological Psychiatry*, 26(3) (Apr. 2002), pp. 539–45.

White willow

Bonaterra, G.A. et al. 'In vitro anti-proliferative effects of the willow bark extract STW 33-I', *Arzneimittelforschung* [Drug Research], 60(6) (2010), pp. 330–5.

Gagnier, J.J. et al. 'Herbal Medicine for Low Back Pain: A Cochrane Review', *Spine (Phil. PA, 1976)*, 41(2) (Jan 2016), pp. 116–33. doi:10.1097/BRS.0000000000001310

Note that there are only a few hundred papers on willow bark compared to over 60,000 for aspirin since the 1960s.

Chapter 10 | Cultivating Medicinal Plants

Much of this chapter is generic. Specific instructions on planting, growing and maintaining will depend on which plants you choose from over tens of thousands, if you venture beyond the few hundred mentioned in this book! You can find useful instructions for cultivating many medicinal plants in the sources provided in the Introduction and Chapter 8.

Others sources we find useful (many old texts are as valuable as modern):

Bonar, Ann, *Herbs, A Complete Guide to their Cultivation and Use* (Hamlyn, 1985).

BritishFlora: http://www.britishflora.co.uk/.

Herbert, Christine, Herbalist and Natural Healer: http://hedgerow.joeherbert.co.uk.

Hewer, Dorothy, *Practical Herb Growing* (Bell & Sons, 1942).

Houdret, Jessica, *Growing Herbs: Design, Planting, Harvesting, Using* (Southwater, 2003).

Iona Herbal, blog about herbal medicine: http://www.ionaherbal.ie/posts.

Loewenfeld, Claire, *Herb Gardening* (Faber & Faber, 1964).

McVicar, Jekka, *Grow Herbs: An Inspiring Guide to Growing and Using Herbs* (Dorling Kindersley, 2013).

Murdoch Books, *Growing herbs* (Murdoch Books, 2006).

North Carolina University, *Growing Herbs for the Home Gardener* (PDF; 1998): https://content.ces. ncsu.edu/growing-herbs-for-the-home-gardener.

Rohde, Eleanor Sinclair, *Herbs and Herb Gardening* (The Medici Society, 1936).

Royal Horticultrural Society UK (RHS), Herbs: growing: https://www.rhs.org.uk/advice/ profile?PID=679.

_____, Herbs: propogating: https://www.rhs.org.uk/advice/profile?PID=639.

Segall, Barbara, *Your Herb Garden Month-By-Month* (David & Charles, 2011).

Simmonds, Monique, Melanie-Jayne Howes and J. Irving, *The Gardener's Companion to Medicinal Plants: An A-Z of Healing Plants and Home Remedies* (Published for Royal Botanic Gardens Kew by Francis Lincoln, 2017).

Identifying your plant is key and you will need to find a guide to your area (having more than one is useful). For Britain try these:

Sutton, David, *Field Guide to the Wild Flowers of Britain and Northern Europe* (Editions Larrouse, 1993). Essential for identification of your medicinal plants.

Barker, Julian, *The Medicinal Flora of Britain and Northwestern Europe* (Winter Press, 2001).

Grey-Wilson, Christopher, *Wild Flowers of Britain & Northwest Europe* (Dorling Kindersley, 1997).

Hickey, Michael, and Clive King, *Common Families of Flowering Plants* (Cambridge University Press, 1997).

Hazards

Cornell University, Department of Animal Science, Plants Poisonous to Livestock http:// poisonousplants.ansci.cornell.edu/php/plants.php?action=display&ispecies=horse.

DermNet NZ, Plants that cause skin problems: http://www.dermnetnz.org/dermatitis/plants/.

Earth Clinic, List of Poisonous Plants for Cats and Dogs: http://www.earthclinic.com/pets/ poisonous_plants.html.

Wikipedia, List of herbs with known adverse effects: https://en.wikipedia.org/wiki/List_of_herbs_ with_known_adverse_effects.

Sourcing medicinal plants

We only list a few sites here, as nurseries come and go. The Herb Society magazine lists current suppliers in the UK. Trade in live plants within the EU is not restricted and we include a couple of non-EU nurseries to broaden perspective:

Groves Nurseries & Garden Centre: https://grovesnurseries.co.uk/herbs.

Norfolk Herbs: https://www.norfolkherbs.co.uk/.

Poyntzfield Herb Nursery: http://www.poyntzfieldherbs.co.uk/cataloguemed1.asp.

Victoriana Nursery Gardens: https://www.victoriananursery.co.uk/Healing_Herb_Seeds/.

Native plant centres:

Nielson's Native Nursery, Australia: http://www.nielsensnativenursery.com.au/ (specialise in Australian native plants).

Crimson Sage Medicinal Plants Nursery, USA: https://www.crimson-sage.com (specialise in rare and endangered medicinal plants).

Chapter 11 | Safety First

Plant identification

Sources on identification are provided in Chapter 11, plant parts to use and dosage is in Chapter 9. Other sources referred to here include:

European Medicines Agency: https://www.ema.europa.eu/en. This agency is responsible for scientific evaluation of medicines developed by pharmaceutical companies for use in the European Union and provides summaries of traditional plant medicinal use including scientific research.

GOV.UK, 'Advice on regulating herbal medicines and practitioners', independent report published 26 Mar 2015: https://www.gov.uk/government/publications/advice-on-regulating-herbal-medicines-and-practitioners. Current UK Government position on herbal medicines: 'Having taken into account the evidence available and the views of representatives of the sector, I consider that despite strong calls by many for statutory regulation, there is not yet a credible scientific evidence-base to demonstrate risk from both products and practitioners which would support this step.'

Musgrave, Ian, 'Herbal medicines Adulterated, Contaminated or just plain Missing. It's an International Scandal', *The Conversation*, 13 November 2013. http://theconversation.com/herbal-medicines-adulterated-contaminated-or-just-plain-missing-its-an-international-scandal-6060.

Waite, Arthur Edward (ed.), *The Hermetic and Alchemical writings of Aureolus Philippus Theophrastus Bombast, of Hohenheim, called Paracelsus the Great* (full text, 1894). https://archive.org/stream/cu31924092287113/cu31924092287113_djvu.txt.

World Health Organisation Monographs on Selected Medicinal Plants (Vol. 4; 2009), table of contents: http://apps.who.int/medicinedocs/en/m/abstract/Js16713e/.

Buying medicinal plant products

Here is a selection of reputable quality companies that that offer mail order and smaller quantities. Most have organic herbs available too. Others, such as Herbal Apothecary, are practitioner only and would be available through your local affiliated medical herbalist.

Amphora Aromatics: http://www.amphora-retail.com.

G Baldwin & Co. (London): https://www.baldwins.co.uk.

Just Ingredients (Monmouthshire): http://www.justingredients.co.uk.

Naturally Thinking: https://www.naturallythinking.com.

Rutland Biodynamics (Leicestershire). Larger quantities only: https://www.rutlandbio.com.

Statfold Seed Oils (carrier oils and essential oils): http://www.statfold-oils.co.uk.

Woodland Herbs (Glasgow): http://www.woodlandherbs.co.uk.

Professional associations for medical herbalist registration and information

American Botanical Council: www.herbalgram.org.

American Herbalists Guild: http://www.americanherbalistsguild.com.

British Herbal Medicine Association: http://bhma.info.

Canadian Herbalist Association of British Columbia: http://www.chaofbc.ca.

College of Practitioners of Phytotherapy: http://www.phytotherapists.org.

European Scientific Cooperative on Phytotherapy: http://escop.com.

National Institute of Medical Herbalists: http://www.nimh.org.uk.

Naturopaths & Herbalists Association of Australia: http://www.nhaa.org.au.

New Zealand Association of Medical Herbalists: http://nzamh.org.nz.

Scientific journals specialising in herbal medicine and medicinal plants (access via PubMed)

Herbal Medicine

International Journal of Herbal Medicine

Journal of Ethnopharmcology

Journal of Medicinal Plants

Phytotherapy Research

Courses on medicinal plants range from full degree programmes, qualifications to practice, such as at the National Institute of Medical Herbalism (see https://www.nimh.org.uk/becoming-a-herbalist/ and https://heartwood-uk.net/home/team) to short introductory courses such as our Foundation in Plant Medicine Course at Dilston Physic Garden (https://dilstonphysicgarden.com/foundation-courses/).

New courses appear all the time, so we haven't listed them all here.

Chapter 12 | Making Medicine: Formulating Your Physic Garden Plants

You will find information on making many of these formulations in the herbal textbooks and websites listed for Chapter 8.

Easley, T., and S. Horne, *The Modern Herbal Dispensatory: A Medicine-Making Guide* (North Atlantic Books, 2016) is indispensable.

Mother Earth News, 'Make Your Own Herbal Medicines'. https://www.motherearthnews.com/natural-health/make-your-own-herbal-medicines-zmaz04jjzsel.

Walker, K., and V. Chown, *The Handmade Apothecary: Healing Herbal Recipes* (Octopus, 2017).

Wong, J., *Grow Your Own Drugs: Fantastically Easy Recipes for Natural Remedies and Beauty* (Harper Collins, 2009) is a popular book with fun recipes like bath bombs.

Recipes for making herbal medicines or preparations at home pop up instantly on Google and it pays (as with cooking recipes) to compare a few to find common methods and ingredients.

For tinctures and glycerites, the volume of liquid to herb varies, so record your proportion to get the dose right. And there is variation in the percentage alcohol to best prepare a tincture; see Rutland Biodynamic catalogue (https://www.rutlandbio.com) for guidance. And don't forget to make and store in dark containers or bottles to stop light damage.

Chapter 13 | Caring for Your Family, Animals and Home

First aid

There's more information on the individual plants mentioned here in charts in Chapter 8.

Aggarwal, P.K. et al. 'Effect of *Rumex nepalensis* extracts on histamine, acetylcholine, carbachol, bradykinin, and PGs evoked skin reactions in rabbits', *Annals of Allergy, Asthma & Immunology*, 56 (1986), pp. 177–82. Report on dock leaves for skin reactions.

Briggs, R., *Herbal First Aid: Assembling a Natural First-Aid Kit* (Microcosm Publishing, 2011).

Christensen, K.D., *Herbal First Aid and Health Care: Medicine for a New Millennium* (Amberwood Publishing, 2000).

Feldt, Linda Diane, 'Seven first-aid plants you can forage', *The Ann Arbor News*, 26 April 2012. http://www.annarbor.com/entertainment/food-drink/seven-first-aid-plants-you-can-forage/.

Kidman, D., *Nature to the Rescue: How to Build Your Own Herbal First-Aid Kit* (CreateSpace, 2013).

Vukovic, Laurel, 'Make Your Own Natural First-Aid Kit', *Mother Earth Living*, July/August 2004. http://www.motherearthliving.com/health-and-wellness/make-your-own-natural-first-aid-kit.aspx.

Children

Baziar, S., et al. '*Crocus sativus L.* Versus Methylphenidate in Treatment of Children with Attention-Deficit/Hyperactivity Disorder: A Randomized, Double-Blind Pilot Study', *Journal of Child and Adolescent Psychopharmacology*, 29(3), (Apr. 2019), pp. 205–12.

Becker, B. et al. 'Double-blind, randomized evaluation of clinical efficacy and tolerability of an apple pectin-chamomile extract in children with unspecific diarrhea', *Arzneimittelforschung* [Drug Research], 56 (2006), pp. 387–93.

Gladstar, Rosemary, *Rosemary Gladstar's Herbal Remedies for Children's Health* (Storey Books, 1999).

Helmer, Robert, 'TCM for Children', *Vitality*, 1 Sept. 2015. http://vitalitymagazine.com/article/tcm-for-children/.

Herbal Academy (https://theherbalacademy.com) is a good resource for general herbal medicine, with information for children in their 'kid's cupboard'.

Małachowska, B., et al. 'Essential oils reduce autonomous response to pain sensation during self-monitoring of blood glucose among children with diabetes', *Journal of Pediatric Endocrinology and Metabolism*, 29(1), (2016), pp. 47–53.

Mcintyre, A. *Herbal Treatment of Children: Western and Ayurvedic Perspectives* (Butterworth-Heinemann, 2005).

Pacific College of Oriental Medicine, 'The Benefits of Traditional Chinese Medicine for Children'. https://www.pacificcollege.edu/news/press-releases/2015/05/14/benefits-traditional-chinese-medicine-children.

Romm, Aviva J., *Naturally Healthy Babies and Children: A Commonsense Guide to Herbal Remedies, Nutrition, and Health* (Celestial Arts, 2003).

Ross, S.M., 'Valerian Root and Lemon Balm Extracts: A Phytomedicine Compound Improves Symptoms of Hyperactivity, Attention Deficits, and Impulsivity in Children', *Holistic Nursing Practice*, 29(6), (2015), pp. 391–5.

Rugino, T., 'A review of modafinil film-coated tablets for attention-deficit/hyperactivity disorder in children and adolescents', *Neuropsychiatric Disease and Treatment*, 3 (2007), pp. 293–301. Drugs for ADHD.

Soltani, R., et al. 'Evaluation of the effect of aromatherapy with lavender essential oil on post-tonsillectomy pain in pediatric patients: a randomized controlled trial', *International Journal of Pediatric Otorhinolaryngology*, 77(9), (Sep 2013), pp. 1579–81.

Tierra, Lesley, *A Kids Herb Book: For Children of All Ages* (Reed Publishers, 2000). This is a wonderful book full of enticing recipes and stories to inspire youngsters. Her recipe for 'snappy cider' made from onion, garlic, mustard, horseradish, pepper, cayenne is a hot contender for the best cold and flu remedy.

Animals

Alternative Veterinarian, 'Herbal Medicine for Animals'. http://www.alternativevet.org/herbs.htm.

Baïracli Levy, Juliette de, *The Complete Herbal Handbook for Farm and Stable* (first pub. 1952; 4th rev. ed. Faber & Faber, 1991).

Engel, Cindy, *Wild Health: How animals keep themselves well and what we can learn from them* (Houghton Mifflin, 2003).

The Herbal Encyclopedia, 'Herbal Healing for Pets'. http://www.naturalark.com/herbpet.html.

Morgan, Jenny, *Herbs for Horses* (Kennilworth Press, 1996).

Natural Animal Health, 'Animal Treatment Laws'. http://www.natural-animal-health.co.uk/animal-treatment-laws.php.

Wulff, Mary, and Greg L. Tilford, *Herbs for Pets: The Natural Way to Enhance Your Pet's Life* (2nd ed. Companion House Books, 2009).

Selected recent papers on plant research

Oregano

Forte, C., et al. 'Dietary integration with oregano (*Origanum vulgare L.*) essential oil improves growth rate and oxidative status in outdoor-reared, but not indoor-reared, pigs', *Journal of Animal Physiology and Animal Nutrition (Berlin)*, 101(5) (Oct. 2017): e352–e361. doi: 10.1111/jpn.12612.

Zou, Y., et al. 'Effects of dietary oregano essential oil and vitamin E supplementation on meat quality, stress response and intestinal morphology in pigs following transport stress', *Journal of Veterinary Medical Science*, 79(2), (Feb. 2017), pp. 328–35.

Raspberry

Rojas-Vera, J. et al. 'Relaxant activity of raspberry (*Rubus idaeus*) leaf extract in guinea-pig ileum in vitro', *Phytotherapy Research*, 16 (2002), pp. 665–8.

Garlic

Varmaghany, S. et al. 'The effects of increasing levels of dietary garlic bulb on growth performance, systolic blood pressure, hematology, and ascites syndrome in broiler chickens', *Poultry Science*, 94 (2015), pp. 1812–20.

Fenugreek

Zentek, J. et al. 'Fenugreek seed affects intestinal microbiota and immunological variables in piglets after weaning', *British Journal of Nutrition*, 109(5), (2013), pp. 859–66.

Skullcap

Liu, X. and Liu, C. 'Baicalin ameliorates chronic unpredictable mild stress-induced depressive behavior: Involving the inhibition of NLRP3 inflammasome activation in rat prefrontal cortex', *International Immunopharmacology*, 48 (2017), pp. 30–4.

Valerian

Jung, H.Y. et al. '*Valeriana officinalis* root extract suppresses physical stress by electric shock and psychological stress by nociceptive stimulation-evoked responses by decreasing the ratio of monoamine neurotransmitters to their metabolites', *BMC Complementary and Alternative Medicine*, 14 (2014): 476. doi: 10.1186/1472-6882-14-476.

Chicory

Peña-Espinoza, M. et al. 'Antiparasitic activity of chicory (Cichorium intybus) and its natural bioactive compounds in livestock: a review', *Parasites & Vectors*, 11(1), (2018), p. 475. doi: 10.1186/s13071-018-3012-4.

Home care

Royal College of Physicans, 'Every breath we take: the lifelong impact of air pollution (report)'. https://www.rcplondon.ac.uk/projects/outputs/every-breath-we-take-lifelong-impact-air-pollution.

A Shakespeare Garden, 'Strewing Herbs'. https://bardgarden.blogspot.com/2014/06/strewing-herbs.html.

'Green cleaning' sites

Cleansmart, 'Green Cleaning'. www.ukcpi.org/green-cleaning.

El-Helaly, M. et al. 'Respiratory symptoms and ventilatory function among healthcare workers exposed to cleaning and disinfectant chemicals, a 2-year follow-up study', *Toxicology and Industrial Health*, 32 (2016), pp. 2002–8.

Treehugger, 'How to green your cleaning routine'. www.treehugger.com/htgg/how-to-go-green-cleaning.html.

Chapter 14 | Plant Health Foods and Herbal Teas

Plant healthfoods

Caldecot, T. *Food as Medicine* (Lightning Source, 2014).

Colbert, D. *Let Food Be Your Medicine* (Worthy Media, 2016).

Ewin, J. *The Plants We Need to Eat* (Thorsons, 1997).

Graedon, J. and T. *Spice up Your life* (People's Pharmacy Press, 2016).

Have A Plant, 'What Are Phytonutrients?'. http://www.fruitsandveggiesmorematters.org/what-are-phytochemicals. A useful website on the relevant plant chemicals (see also Chapter 1).

Leaf, C. *Think and Eat Yourself Smart* (Baker Books, 2016).

Wenk, G. L. *Your Brain on Food: How Chemicals Control Your Thoughts and Feelings* (Oxford University Press, 2015).

Select scientific papers on the general health benefits of plants as food

Chen, H. et al. 'Association between dietary carrot intake and breast cancer: A meta-analysis', *Medicine (Baltimore)*. 97(37) (Sep 2018): e12164. doi: 10.1097/MD.0000000000012164.

Krasinska, B. et al. 'Standardised tomato extract as an alternative to acetylsalicylic acid in patients with primary hypertension and high cardiovascular risk – a randomised, controlled trial', *Archives of Medical Science*, 14 (2018), pp. 773–80.

Li, X. et al. 'Short- and long-term effects of wholegrain oat intake on weight management and glucolipid metabolism in overweight type-2 diabetics: a randomized controlled trial', *Nutrients*, 8(9) (2016), pii: E549. doi: 10.3390/nu8090549.

Pittaway, J.K. et al. 'Effects of a controlled diet supplemented with chickpeas on serum lipids, glucose tolerance, satiety and bowel function', *Journal of the American College of Nutrition*, 26 (2007), pp. 334–40.

Razani, Z. et al. 'Cardioprotective effects of pomegranate (Punica granatum) juice in patients with ischemic heart disease', *Phytotherapy Research*, 31 (2017), pp. 1731–8.

Waldron, M. et al. 'Beetroot supplementation improves the physiological responses to incline walking', *European Journal of Applied Physiology*, 118 (2018), pp. 1131–41.

Brain benefits of plants as food

Crews, W.D. Jr, et al. 'A double-blind, placebo-controlled, randomized trial of the effects of dark chocolate and cocoa on variables associated with neuropsychological functioning and cardiovascular health: clinical findings from a sample of healthy, cognitively intact older adults', *Journal of the American College of Nutrition*, 67 (2008), pp. 872–80.

Pour, Z.S. et al. 'Double-blind randomized placebo-controlled trial on efficacy and safety of Lactuca sativa L. seeds on pregnancy-related insomnia', *Journal of Ethnopharmacology*, 227 (2018), pp. 176–80.

Pribis, P. et al. 'Effects of walnut consumption on cognitive performance in young adults', *British Journal of Nutrition*, 107 (2012), pp. 1393–401.

Whyte, A.R. et al. 'A randomized, double-blinded, placebo-controlled study to compare the safety and efficacy of low dose enhanced wild blueberry powder and wild blueberry extract (ThinkBlue™) in maintenance of episodic and working memory in older adults', *Nutrients*, 10(6) (2018), pii: E660. doi: 10.3390/nu10060660.

See also Chapter 16, and our book, *Botanical Brain Balms*.

Herbal teas

Just a few of many books and websites we like (many sites are commercial but the label on the packet indicates what the herb is generally used for):

Codekas, C. *Healing Herbal Infusions* (Page Street Publishing Co., 2018).

Esplan, C. *The Healing Power of Herbal Teas* (Thorsons, 1981).

Houdret, J. *Herbal Teas and Health Infusions* (Anness Publishing, 2012).

Indigo Herbs, 'How to make herbal tea'. https://www.indigo-herbs.co.uk/natural-health-guide/how-to-make-herbal-tea.

Mother Earth News, 'How to Make Herbal Teas, Herbal Infusions and Herbal Tinctures'. http://www.motherearthnews.com/natural-health/herbal-remedies/how-to-make-herbal-teas-infusions-tinctures-ze0z1202zhir.aspx.

For scientific evidence of the efficacy and safety of the medicinal plants included here (not specifically taken as tea) refer to Chapters 8 and 9.

Just a few of increasing numbers of reports on controlled trials of herbal tea

Baek, Y. et al. 'Three-component herbal tea alleviates prolonged fatigue and improves sleep quality: a randomized controlled pilot study', *Explore (NY)*, 14(6) (2018): 420–23. doi: 10.1016/j.explore.2018.05.001.

Falahat, F. et al. 'Efficacy of a herbal formulation based on Foeniculum vulgare in pligo/amenorrhea: a randomized clinical trial', *Current Drug Discovery Technologies*, 29 Oct. 2018. doi: 10.2174/157 0163815666181029120512.

Haj-Husein, I. et al. 'The effect of marjoram (Origanum majorana) tea on the hormonal profile of women with polycystic ovary syndrome: a randomised controlled pilot study', *Journal of Human Nutrition and Dietetics*, 29(1) (Feb. 2016), pp. 105–11.

Tea company started by students

Celestial Seasonings, 'Our History'. http://www.celestialseasonings.com/learn-about-us/our-history.

Chapter 15 | Absorbing Aromatic Plant Volatiles
Aromatherapy / Essential oils

Bowles, E. J. *The Chemistry of Aromatherapeutic Oils* (Allen and Unwin, 2003).

Davis, P. *Aromatherapy: An A–Z* (rev. ed. Vermilion, 2005). This is recommended as the best book on aromatherapy in the *International Journal of Aromatherapy*.

Essential Oil Safety (Churchill Livingstone, 2013).

Instructibles Living, 'Build Your Own Essential Oil Extractor Distiller'. https://www.instructables.com/id/Build-Your-Own-Essential-Oil-Extractor-Distiller/.

Lawless, J. *The Aromatherapy Garden* (Kyle Cathie, 2001).

Mamavation, 'Deadly Scent: Toxic Perfume Chemicals'. https://www.mamavation.com/featured/toxic-perfume-chemicals.html.

Tisserand, R. and Young, R. wikiHow, 'How to Make Essential Oils'. http://www.wikihow.com/Make-Essential-Oils.

Wildwood, C. *Create Your Own Aromatherapy Perfumes* (Piatkus Books, 1994).

Worwood, V. A. *The Fragrant Mind* (Doubleday, 1996).

The science behind specific essential oil effects described is this chapter is backed by information on plants extracts in Chapters 8 and 9. Here are a few more:

Buchbauer, G. et al. 'Aromatherapy: evidence for sedative effects of the essential oil of lavender after inhalation', *Zeitschrift für Naturforschung C* [Journal of Biosciences], 46 (1991), pp. 1067–72. Mouse experiment on lavender oil that revolutionised thinking about aromatherapy.

Guimarães, A. G. et al. 'Encapsulation of carvacrol, a monoterpene present in the essential oil of oregano, with β-cyclodextrin, improves the pharmacological response on cancer pain experimental protocols', *Chemico-Biological Interactions*, 227 (Feb. 2015), pp. 69–76. About pain-relieving oregano essential oil.

Leandro, L. F. et al. 'Antibacterial activity of *Pinus elliottii* and its major compound, dehydroabietic acid, against multidrug-resistant strains', *Journal of Medical Microbiology*, 63 (2014), pp. 1649–53. Antibiotic effects of pine (*Pinus*) essential oil on drug-resistant bacteria.

Oliva, A. et al. 'High Potency of *Melaleuca alternifolia* Essential Oil against Multi-Drug-Resistant Gram-Negative Bacteria and Methicillin-Resistant Staphylococcus aureus', *Molecules*, 23 (2018). pii: E2584. doi: 10.3390/molecules 23102584. Antibiotic effects of tea tree essential oil on drug-resistant bacteria.

Essences and incenses

Bach Centre, 'All about Bach remedies': https://www.bachcentre.com/centre/firstpag.htm.

Balinski, A. A. 'Use of Western Australian flower essences in the management of pain and stress in the hospital setting', *Complementary Therapies in Nursing and Midwifery*, 4 (1998), pp. 111–17.

Emer, A. A. 'The role of the endocannabinoid system in the antihyperalgesic effect of *Cedrus atlantica* essential oil inhalation in a mouse model of postoperative pain', *Journal of Ethnopharmacology*, 210 (2018), pp. 477–84. On pain-relieving cedar.

Harvey, C. *The New Encyclopedia of Flower Remedies: A Practical Guide to Making and Using Flower Remedies* (Watkins Publishing, 2007).

Lechien, J. et al. 'Treatment by Bach flowers: magical potion or factual medicine? A review of the literature', *Revue Médicale de Bruxelles*, 33 (2012), pp. 105–10.

Moussaieff. A. et al. 'Frankincense chemical action on brain receptor Incensole acetate, an incense component, elicits psychoactivity by activating TRPV3 channels in the brain', *FASEB Journal*, 22 (2008), pp. 3024–34.

PallasDowney, R. *The Complete Book of Flower Essences: 48 Natural and Beautiful Ways to Heal Yourself and Your Life* (New World Library, 2002). Based on the Bach flower remedies.

Siddiqui, M. J. et al. 'Moxibustion (*Artemisia* Plant at Acupuncture Point) as alternative therapy in hypertension: a promising approach', *Journal of Pharmacy and Bioallied Sciences*, 9 (2017), pp. 279–81. Sedative effects of mugwort smoke.

Taghizadeh, M. et al. 'The effect of tablet containing *Boswellia serrata* and *Melissa officinalis* extract on older adults' memory: A randomized controlled trial', *Archives of Gerontology and Geriatrics*, 75 (2018), pp. 146–50. Frankincense improves memory.

Zhang, K. and Yao, L. 'The anxiolytic effect of *Juniperus virginiana L.* essential oil and determination of its active constituents', *Physiology & Behavior*, 189 (2018), pp. 50–8. Juniper relieves anxiety.

Zhao, J. et al. 'Evaluation on Analgesic and Anti-Inflammatory Activities of Total Flavonoids from *Juniperus sabina*', *Evidence-Based Complementary and Alternative Medicine*, 5 Jul 2018: 7965306. doi: 10.1155/2018/7965306. On pain-relieving juniper.

See Chapters 8 and 9 for evidence on lavender and rose effects.

Smudging

Alexander, J. *The Smudging and Blessings Book: Inspirational Rituals to Cleanse and Heal* (Sterling, 2009).

Encyclopaedia Britannica, 'Sacred pipe: American Indian Culture'. https://www.britannica.com/topic/Sacred-Pipe. About smoking pipes of peace.

Grove and Grotto, 'The no-nonsense smudging giude: Easy tips and tricks for clearing your space'. https://www.groveandgrotto.com/blogs/articles/the-no-nonsense-smudging-guide.

Cosmeceuticals

Baumann, L. *Cosmeceuticals and Cosmetic Ingredients* (McGraw Hill, 2014).

Curtis, S., Johnson, J. and Thomas, P. *Essential Oils: All-Natural Remedies and Recipes for your Mind, Body and Home* (DK Publishing, 2016).

Little, K. *Kitty Little's Book of Herbal Beauty* (Penguin Books, 1980).

There are numerous reports on Chinese herbal combinations; a few plants are not known to us Westerners, others are familiar:

Graziano, A.C. et al. 'Protective effects of an extract from Citrus bergamia against inflammatory injury in interferon-γ and histamine exposed human keratinocytes', *Life Sciences*, 90 (2012), pp. 968–74. Lemon protects skin cells from injury.

Pazyar, N. et al. 'Skin wound healing and phytomedicine: a review', *Skin Pharmacology and Physiology*, 27 (2014), pp. 303–10. A review of the action of plants for skin health, including aloe, comfrey and chamomile.

Chapter 16 | Plants in Mind

Brain boosters

Godfrey, H. D. *Essential Oils for Mindfulness and Meditation: Relax, Replenish, and Rejuvenate* (North Atlantic Books, 2018) .

Kennedy, D. O. *Plants and the Human Brain* (Oxford University Press, 2014).

Perry, N. and Perry, E. *Botanical brain balms: medicinal plants for memory, mood and mind* (Filbert Press, 2018). Our own book about the folklore, herbal medicine and science of plants for the brain. It is also published as *Les plantes pour l'esprit* in France and *Heilpflanzen für kopft und seele* in Germany.

Perry, N. and Perry, E. *Your Brain on Plants: Improve the Way You Think and Feel with Safe and Proven Medicinal Plants and Herbs* (Experiment (US), 2018).

Pursuit of Mindfulness, 'Achieving Mindful Awareness with Aromatherapy', 1 Dec. 2017. http://pursuitofmindfulness.com/mindful-awareness-aromatherapy/.

Wenk, G. L. *Your Brain on Food: How Chemicals Control Your Thoughts and Feelings* (Oxford University Press, 2010).

Herbal highs

Collerton, D., Mosimann, U. and Perry, E. (eds), *The Neuroscience of Hallucinations* (Wiley, 2015).

Devereux, P. *The Long Trip. A Prehistory of Psychedelia* (Arkana, 1997).

Furst, P. T. *Flesh of the Gods* (Waveland Press, 1972).

McKenna, T. *Food of the Gods* (Rider, 1992)

Perry, E.K., Perry R.H. 'Acetylcholine and hallucinations: disease-related compared to drug-induced alterations in human consciousness', *Brain and Cognition*, 28 (1995), pp. 240–58. Our paper on hallucinations, disease and drugs.

Schultes, R.E., Hofmann, A. and Ratsch, C. *The Plants of the Gods*. (Healing Arts Press, 1996, updated version). Our all time favourite book.

An invaluable, managed resource on the effects of psychedelics on humans is Erowid (https://www.erowid.org/), with fascinating reports of subjective experiences of people using chemicals and plants, including many plants mentioned in our panel here.

Scientific reports on consciousness-changing plants is confined to stronger, toxic species, and for the mild ones we advocate here, scientific reports relate to more general effects on mood or sleep. For example:

Catnip (*Napeta*) improves mood
Firoozabadi, A. et al. 'Efficacy of Nepeta Menthoides Boiss and Buhse Freeze-Dried Aqueous Extract on Anxiety of Patients with Depression: A Double-Blind Randomized Controlled Clinical Trial', *Iranian Journal of Medical Sciences*, 41(3 Suppl) (May 2016), p. S4.

Hop (*Humulus*) improves mood
Kyrou, I. et al. 'Effects of a hops (*Humulus lupulus L.*) dry extract supplement on self-reported depression, anxiety and stress levels in apparently healthy young adults: a randomized, placebo-controlled, double-blind, crossover pilot study', *Hormones (Athens)*. 16 (2017), pp. 171–80.

Skullcap (*Scutellaria*) improves cognition
Yimam, M. et al. 'Clinical and Preclinical Cognitive Function Improvement after Oral Treatment of a Botanical Composition Composed of Extracts from *Scutellaria baicalensis* and *Acacia catechu*', *Behavioural Neurology*, (2016): 7240802. doi: 10.1155/2016/7240802.

Citrus fruits
Servillo, L. et al. 'Psychoactive DMT chemical in citrus fruits: DMT Citrus genus plants contain N-methylated tryptamine derivatives and their 5-hydroxylated forms', *Journal of Agricultural and Food Chemistry*, 61 (2013), pp. 5156–62.

Psychedelics treat mood disorders
Dos Santos, R.G. et al. 'Efficacy, tolerability, and safety of serotonergic psychedelics for the management of mood, anxiety, and substance-use disorders: a systematic review of systematic reviews', *Expert Review of Clinical Pharmacology*, 11 (2018), pp. 889–902.

Chapter 17 | Bringing Back the Magic?

Complementary therapies
Fox, K.C. et al. 'Is meditation associated with altered brain structure? A systematic review and meta-analysis of morphometric neuroimaging in meditation practitioners', *Neuroscience & Biobehavioral Reviews*, 43 (2014), pp. 48–73. A review of how meditation alters brain imaging.

Kongkaew, C. et al. 'The effects of Thai yoga on physical fitness: a meta-analysis of randomized control trials', *Journal of Alternative and Complementary Medicine*, 24 (2018), pp. 541–51. A study of how yoga improves physical fitness.

Scotswood Community Natural Garden: https://sncg.org.uk/.

The Therapy Centre: https://www.thefold.org.uk/natural-therapy-centre/.

Yount, G. et al. 'In vitro test of external Qigong', *BMC Complementary and Alternative Medicine*, 15 Mar 2004, p. 5. The effects of qigong on cell division in lab tests.

Plant powers

Chamovitz, D. *What The Plant Knows* (Scientific American, 2017).

Donahue, M. Z. 'Flowers can hear buzzing bees – and it makes their nectar sweeter', *National Geographic*: https://www.nationalgeographic.com/science/2019/01/flowers-can-hear-bees-and-make-their-nectar-sweeter/.

Mancuso, S. *Brilliant Green: The Surprising History and Science of Plant Intelligence* (Island Press, 2015).

Wohlleben, P. *The Hidden Life of Trees* (William Collins, 2017).

Acknowledgements

First and foremost, we would like to thank David Taylor, award-winning professional photographer, for his own inspiring photographs from the physic garden and for his indispensable help in sourcing other images for the book; and Averill Buchanan, editing and publishing consultant, for editing, cover and book design, and her invaluable advice and support throughout the project.

We greatly appreciate all the invaluable information provided by the following friends and colleagues: Anne Pickering on cultivation; Cathy Skipper on French gardens; Cathy White-Webster on mindfulness meditation; Davina Hopkinson, medical herbalist, on first aid, herbs for children and the choosing charts advice; Deborah Donnelly on the Wala garden; Denise Wilson on UK dementia research; Heather Ring on the Urban Physic Garden; Iain Milne on the Edinburgh Royal College of Physicians; Francis Parsons on smudging; Jonathan Perry, General Practitioner, on choosing charts; Liz Marshall on physic gardens, old and new, and garden signage; Marie Addyman on plant folklore and the history of physic gardens; Richard Barling on the Singapore botanic garden; Ross Menzies, medical herbalist, on his professional experiences and the choosing charts; and all our wonderful volunteers who supported us through the hard as well as good times of book writing.

Image Credits

We have made every effort to identify the copyright holders of all images. If you feel that we've got it wrong or omitted you, please contact us (info@dilstonphysicgarden.com) and we will endeavour to correct it in the next edition.

All photographs are credited to David Taylor, apart from the following:

Cover image: Andrey Danilovich | iStock.com

p. 6 Hippocrates
Wellcome Collection. CC BY

p. 7 Dioscorides
Wellcome Collection. CC BY

p. 11 Snowdrops
Pauline Aitken

p. 11 Sweet wormwood
Rowan McOnegal. CC BY-NC

p. 18 Growing sage
Colin Cuthbert

p. 23 Pepper plant
Tookapic | pexels.com

p. 26 Maple leaves
ID 135171054 © Pipa100 | dreamstime.com

p. 40 Chinese medicine jars
Freestocks.org | pexels.com

p. 44 Asian farming
Hari Mahidhar | shutterstock.com

p. 45 Mayfield Lavender Farm
ID 55957729 © Irishka777 | dreamstime.com

p. 55 Frankincense resin
Madeleine Steinbach | shutterstock.com

p. 64 Oxford Physic Garden
Wellcome Collection. CC BY

p. 65 Yarrow
Sonia Tully

p. 66 Chelsea Physic Garden
Eugene Regis | shutterstock.com

p. 66 Urban Physic Garden
Mike Massaro

p. 68 The Wala Garden, Germany
© WALA Heilmittel GmbH

p. 69 Botanic Garden, Grasse, France
Dennis Jarvis

p. 69 A. Vogel Tuinen Garden, Netherlands
A Vogel Tuinen Garden

p. 70 Indiana Medical History Museum
© Justin C. Lane

p. 71 Maya Traditions Medicinal Garden
Maya Traditions Medicinal Garden

p. 71 Medicinal Garden, South Africa
© Lowveld NBG

p. 72 Healing Garden, Singapore
Singapore Botanical Garden

p. 81 Fenugreek
Rowan McOnegal. CC BY-NC

p. 82 Rainbow lorrikeet
Pixabay | pexels.com

p. 86 Holy basil.jpg
Quality Stock Arts | shutterstock.com

p. 89 Chamomile lawn at Dilston
Terence Walsh

p. 90 Padua Physic Garden, Italy
Wikimedia Commons | commons.wikimedia.org

p. 90 Cowbridge Physic Garden, Wales
ID 119236496 © Mark95m | dreamstime.com

p. 91 Piedmont Physic Garden, US
Piedmont Physic Garden

p. 92 Nairobi Physic Garden
Deborah Coulson

p. 93 Dilston henge
Sonia Tully

p. 115 Chaste tree
Simona Pavan | shutterstock.com

p. 122 Saffron sign
Dilston Physic Garden

p. 124 Chinese angelica
Doikanoy | shutterstock.com

p. 126 Arnica montana
Rowan McOnegal. CC BY-NC

p. 134 Cranberry
garmoncheg | shutterstock.com

p. 144 Garlic bulbs
Rowan McOnegal. CC BY-NC

p. 146 Ginger
ID 114644492 © Sarot Chamnankit | dreamstime.com

p. 164 Chinese rhubarb
ID 50238610 © Westhimal | dreamstime.com

p. 184 Tidying chamomile lawn
Anne Leuchars

p. 186 Teasel in frost
Maren Winter | shutterstock.com

p. 196 Foxglove and leaf
ID 43053747 © Emberiza | dreamstime.com

p. 197 Wolfsbane
ID 76859934 © Johannes Hansen | dreamstime.com

p. 202 Sagepills
Colin Cuthbert

p. 215 Butterfly on elf at Dilston
Sonia Tully

p. 238 Essential oils
Dilston Physic Garden

p. 263 Touching wood at Dilston
Sonia Tully

Index

The main pages about a favourite plant are in **bold**.

Recent books, chapters and scientific articles by the authors

Botanical Brain Balms. Nicolette Perry and Elaine Perry. Filbert Press, 2018. Also published in the US by The Experiment, in France (Editions de Rouergue, 2019) and in Germany (Haupt Verlag, 2019).

The Cambridge Handbook of the Imagination. Daniel Collerton, Elaine Perry and Alan Robert Bowman, 'Hallucinations and Imagination'. (Cambridge University Press, 2020), pp. 728–59.

'Role of phytochemicals as nutraceuticals for cognitive functions affected in ageing.' Howes, M.R., Perry, N.S.L., Vásquez-Londoño, C., Perry, E.K. *Br J Pharmacol*. 25 Oct 2019. doi: 10.1111/bph.14898.

'Use of herbal medicines: Pilot survey of UK users' views.' Zahn, R., Perry, N., Perry, E., Mukaetova-Ladinska, E.B. *Complement Ther Med*. Jun 2019, 44: 83–90. doi: 10.1016/j.ctim.2019.02.007. Epub: 16 Feb 2019.

'Want to boost your memory.' Perry, N. 2019. *Journal of the Herb Society*. 44.2, p. 15.

'A randomised double-blind placebo-controlled pilot trial of a combined extract of sage, rosemary and melissa, traditional herbal medicines, on the enhancement of memory in normal healthy subjects, including influence of age.' Perry, N.S.L., Menzies, R., Hodgson, F., Wedgewood, P., Howes, M.R., Brooker, H.J., Wesnes, K.A., Perry, E.K. *Phytomedicine*. 15 Jan 2018, 39: 42–48. doi: 10.1016/j.phymed.2017.08.015. Epub: 18 Aug 2017.

Changing Age, Changing Minds. Valerie Laws. University of Newcastle upon Tyne, 2011.

All That Lives. Valerie Laws. Red Squirrel Press, 2011; ebook 2013.